HOT CLIMATES, MAN AND HIS HEART

Frontispiece: Trading on the Congo.

HOT CLIMATES, MAN AND HIS HEART

By

GEORGE E. BURCH, M.D.

Henderson Professor of Medicine
Tulane University School of Medicine
Physician-in-Chief in Medicine
Tulane Unit of the Charity Hospital of New Orleans
Consultant in Medicine and Cardiology
Veterans Administration Hospital
Touro Infirmary, Hotel Dieu Hospital
Mercy Hospital, and Ochsner Foundation Hospital

and

NICHOLAS P. DePASQUALE, M.D.

Instructor in Medicine
Tulane University School of Medicine
Visiting Physician
Tulane Unit of the Charity Hospital of New Orleans
New Orleans, Louisiana

CHARLES C THOMAS • PUBLISHER
Springfield • Illinois • U.S.A.

CHARLES C THOMAS • PUBLISHER
BANNERSTONE HOUSE
301-327 East Lawrence Avenue, Springfield, Illinois, U.S.A.

Library of Congress Catalog Card Number: 61-17608

Printed in the United States of America

to

our wives, Vivian Gerard Burch and Judith Magner DePasquale in appreciation of their constant support and assistance in all of our work

PREFACE

THIS monograph is a brief summary of studies of the influence of tropical and subtropical environments on the normal and diseased cardiovascular system of man conducted over a period of more than twenty years in the Cardiovascular Laboratories of the Tulane University School of Medicine. The results of these studies have been published in many papers scattered throughout the literature. The data were presented in part as an exhibit at the meeting of the American Medical Association in Miami, June, 1960.

The studies were designed to learn the responses of the normal and diseased cardiovascular system to a hot and humid environment and were performed in specially constructed climatic rooms and in the wards of the Charity Hospital. All of the studies presented in this monograph were conducted on man. Studies of the influence of a hot and humid environment on normal man have been few, and investigations of the influence of such environments on man with heart disease are almost nonexistent.

This monograph summarizes selected aspects of our studies in a single volume for the convenience and interest of medical students, clinicians, physiologists and all those concerned with man subjected to hot and humid environments, including those who deal with heating and ventilation engineering, tropical health, industrial, architectural, agricultural, military, space and medicolegal problems. Because of the studies of skin, sweat, and sweating, dermatologists and dermal physiologists should find this monograph interesting. The studies of heat and water loss and respiratory ventilation should be of interest to pulmonary physiologists. It is not intended to review the literature, but selected studies of others are included for proper orientation of our data with those from other laboratories. Obviously, the reader must study the entire literature for a comprehensive review of the problem.

The importance of the influence of climate and weather on normal and diseased man needs no emphasis. Most of the inhabited areas of the world are hot for many weeks or months of the year. Man may escape disease, but he cannot entirely escape climate. Normal man is able to adapt to the most rigorous environmental conditions; however, aged or diseased man does not tolerate hot and humid environments and may even be killed by climatic stress. Because life expectancy and the incidence of heart disease are increasing pari passu, the physician should be aware of the deleterious effect of climatic stress on patients with heart disease. The importance of relieving the diseased cardiovascular system of the burden of thermal regulation is emphasized throughout the monograph.

Pathophysiologic and clinical implications of the studies are presented at the end of most chapters. Although they are incomplete, these discussions are added to indicate the relationship of the data to abnormal states and to point out possible clinical applications. Consideration of the many other applications is left to the reader since the primary purpose of this monograph is to summarize our experimental findings. The final chapter deals with the clinical states resulting from exposure to hot and humid environments. Essential aspects of technique and methods are presented in a concise manner, and a bibliography is presented at the end of each chapter for the benefit of those interested in more detailed information concerning experimental design and findings.

It is hoped that this monograph will be a source of useful information, that it will stimulate interest in clinical and physiologic climatology and that it will help the physician to bring comfort to the sick. May this monograph help to make clinicians and others more aware of the importance of weather and climate on the health and happiness of normal as well as diseased man. If this monograph improves to some extent the management of normal, diseased and old people in tropical and subtropical environments, the many years of research and this compendium will have served a purpose.

It is with great appreciation that the excellent assistance of Miss Ruth Ziifle, Miss Laura Holland, Miss Juanita Arbour, and of the publisher, Charles C Thomas, in the preparation of this monograph is acknowledged.

G. E. Burch, M.D.
N. P. DePasquale, M.D.

New Orleans

CONTENTS

Page

Preface vii

Chapter 1. INTRODUCTION 3
Climatology and Medicine 3
Bioclimatology 3
Medical Bioclimatology 3
Climatology and Man 4
The Adaptation of Man to Climate 4
Physical Anthropology and Climate 6
The "Ideal" Climate 7
Clothing and Climate 7

Chapter 2. THE ROLE OF THE SKIN IN THERMAL REGULATION 9
The Integument as a Thermal Barrier 9
The Integument as a Water Barrier 10

Chapter 3. METHODS OF MEASURING SENSIBLE AND INSENSIBLE WATER LOSS FROM THE SURFACE OF THE BODY 12
The Measurement of the Rate of Total Water Loss from the Body . . . 12
The Photographic and Recording Portions of the Balance 12
Method of Use of the Balance 14
Calibration of the Balance 15
The Measurement of Rate of Water Loss through the Skin and/or the Lungs 15
Insensible Water Loss from the Skin 16
Insensible Water Loss from the Lungs 16
The Measurement of the Rate of Water Loss from Isolated Areas of Skin 17
Intact Living Skin 17
Intact Dead Skin 18

Chapter 4. SENSIBLE AND INSENSIBLE WATER LOSS 22
The Rate of Total Insensible Water Loss 22
Rate of Insensible Water Loss from the Skin and Lungs with Loss from the Lungs Controlled 22
Rate of Insensible Water Loss from the Skin and Lungs with Loss from the Skin Controlled 22

Page

The Rates of Insensible Water Loss in Whites and Negroes 23
The Rate of Water Loss through the Skin of Cadavers 24
The Rates of Water Loss from Various Areas of Skin 25
The Rate of Water Loss through Isolated Dead Skin 27
The Rate of Water Loss through Isolated Living Skin 28
Definition of Sensible Perspiration, Insensible Perspiration and Occult Sweating 30
Pathophysiologic Interpretations 31
The Rate of Water Loss for Various Pathologic States 33
Hypothyroidism 34
Heat Intolerance 34
Nervous Sweating 34
Scleroderma 35
Acromegaly 35
Occlusive Vascular Disease 35
Congestive Heart Failure 36
Clinical Applications 37

Chapter 5. THE CUTANEOUS WATER AND ELECTROLYTE BARRIER 39
The Role of the Various Layers of the Human Skin in Limiting Water Loss from the Body 39
Formation of the Cantharides Blister 41
Water Loss through Skin Denuded by Vesication 41
Water Loss through the Blister Top 42
Water Loss through Skin Denuded by Abrasion 44
Nature of the Water Barrier 44
Removal of Lipids from the Epidermis 44
Removal of Keratin from the Epidermis 45
The Influence of Various Physical Factors on Diffusion of Water through Isolated Human Skin 46
The Transfer of Electrolytes across the Denuded Surface of the Human Skin 49
Method of Study 49
Transfer of Rb^{86}, Na^{22}, Cl^{36} and K^{42} 50
Influence of Histamine on Transfer of Rb^{86} 53
Rate of Entry of Na^{23} into Extracorporeal Compartment 53
Rate of Entry of Cl^{35} into Extracorporeal Compartment 54
Influence of Norepinephrine on the Rate of Transfer of Na^{22} and Rb^{86} across the Blister Surface 55
Pathophysiologic Interpretations 56
Clinical Applications 56

Page

Chapter 6. The Electrolyte Content of Sweat and the Kinetics of Electrolyte Excretion by the Sweat Glands 58
The Human Apocrine and Eccrine Sweat Glands 58
Method of Collection of Sweat 59
Concentration Time Courses of Na^{23}, K^{39} and Cl^{35} in Sweat 60
The Effect of Intense Thermal Stimulation on the Concentration-Time Courses of Na^{23}, K^{39} and Cl^{35} in Sweat 60
The Effect of Prolonged Thermal Stimulation on the Concentration-Time Courses of Na^{23}, K^{39} and Cl^{35} in Sweat 61
Relation of Site of the Sweat Glands to the Rate of Sweating 62
The Electrolyte Concentration of Normal Sweat 63
The Influence of Diet on the Composition of Sweat 64
The Influence of Climate on the Composition of Sweat 65
The Influence of Ischemia on the Composition of Sweat 65
The Kinetics of Electrolyte Excretion by the Sweat Glands 67
Rate of Excretion of Rb^{86} and K^{42} 67
Rate of Excretion of Na^{24} 69
Pathophysiologic Interpretations 69
Hyperhidrosis 69
Hypohidrosis 69
Ectodermal Dysplasia 69
Miliaria 70
Fibrocystic Disease (Mucoviscoidosis) 70
Ischemia 71
Acclimatization 71
Heat Cramps, Heat Exhaustion and Heat Stroke 72
The Role of the Sweat Glands in Acclimatization to Heat 72
Clinical Applications 73
The Sweat Retention Syndrome 74

Chapter 7. Peripheral Circulation 76
The Rheoplethysmographic Method 77
The Rheoplethysmograph 77
The Rheoplethysmographic Cup and Collecting Cuff 78
The Rheoplethysmographic Concept 80
Basal and Complemental Pulsatile Flow 83
The Rheoplethysmogram 83
Correction for Size of Part 83
Calibration of the Rheoplethysmograph 85
Conversion Factor in Plethysmography 85

Page

The Normal Peripheral Blood Flow 85
The Five Spontaneous Digital Volume Deflections 85
Environmental Temperatures and Digital Blood Flow 87
The Influence of a Hot and Humid Environment on Digital Blood Flow 87
The Influence of a Hot and Humid Environment on the Digital Veins 91
The Influence of a Cold Environment on Peripheral Blood Flow . . . 91
The Influence of a Cold Environment on the Digital Veins 92
The Influence of Environmental Temperature on Skin Temperature . . 92
Pathophysiologic Interpretations 96
The "Hunting Phenomenon" 96
Thermal Countercurrent Flow 96
Tissue Injury Due to Cold 98
Selectivity of Dermal Blood Flow 98
Dermal Blood Flow in Diseased States 98
Clinical Applications 99

Chapter 8. Water and Heat Loss from the Lungs: Methods and Theoretic Considerations 102
A Gravimetric Method for the Measurement of Expired Water 103
Method of Testing and Calibrating the Apparatus 106
A Method for Measuring the Rate of Heat Loss from the Respiratory Tract 108
Mathematic Consideration of Heat Loss from the Respiratory Tract . . 110

Chapter 9. Rates of Water and Heat Loss from the Lungs 112
The Rate of Water Loss from the Respiratory Tract 112
Influence of Environment on the Rate of Water Loss from the Respiratory Tract 112
Rate of Water Loss from the Respiratory Tract in Congestive Heart Failure 114
Rate of Irrigation of the Respiratory Tract with Air 115
Temperature of the Expired Air 116
Relative Humidity of the Expired Air 119
The Rate of Heat Loss from the Respiratory Tract 120
Heat Loss by Evaporation of Water (h_E) 120
Heat Loss by Convection (h_C) 122
Heat Loss by Decomposition of H_2CO_3 (h_{CO_2}) 122
Total Heat Loss (H) 124
Total Body Heat Production 124
Pathophysiologic Interpretations 124
Clinical Applications 127

Page

Chapter 10. THE EFFECT OF THERMAL STRESS ON THE CARDIOVASCULAR SYSTEM OF MAN: THEORETIC CONSIDERATIONS OF THE ESTIMATION OF CARDIAC WORK 130

Chapter 11. THE EFFECT OF THERMAL STRESS ON THE NORMAL AND DISEASED CARDIOVASCULAR SYSTEMS OF MAN 133
Observations on Patients in Air-Conditioned and Non-Air-Conditioned Hospital Wards 133
Clinical Observations on Patients with a Normal Cardiovascular System 133
Clinical Observations on Patients with Cardiovascular Disease . . . 134
Observations on Patients in the Climatic Room 136
Effect of Thermal Stress on Normal Subjects 136
Effect of Thermal Stress on Patients with Congestive Heart Failure 138
Cardiac Output, Work and Power in Subjects with Normal and Diseased Hearts Exposed to a Hot and Humid Environment 140
Cardiac Output and Stroke Volume 142
Time-Course Curves of Volume and Pressure 142
Pressure-Volume Diagrams 145
Accumulated Mechanical Work 145
Alterations in Myocardial Tension 146
Cardiac Output, Work and Power in Subjects Exposed to Warm and Humid Summer Weather 147
Pathophysiologic Interpretations 153
Clinical Applications 155

Chapter 12. THE EFFECT OF THERMAL STRESS ON RENAL FUNCTION . . . 158
Urinary Clearance Rates 158
Urinary Clearance of Rb^{86} and K^{39} 159
Urinary Clearance of Tritium 159
Urinary Clearance of Cl^{36}, Cl^{35} and Na^{23} 162
Urinary Excretion of Cl^{35} and K^{39} as Percent of Calculated Mass . . . 162
Osmolar Excretion and Glomerular Filtration 165
Osmolar Excretion 165
Rate of Glomerular Filtration 166
Pathophysiologic Interpretations 166
Clinical Applications 168

Chapter 13. GENERAL PHYSIOLOGIC RESPONSES TO THERMAL STIMULATION 169
The Initiation of Sweating 170
The Sweating Threshold 171
Cyclic Sweating 171

Page

Regional Variations in the Rates of Sweating 171
Regional Variations in a Comfortable Environment 171
Regional Variations in a Hot and Humid Environment 172
Physiologic Responses to Thermal Stimulation 172
Effect of Cooling Localized Areas of Body Surface on the Physiologic Responses to Thermal Stimulation 172
Method of Study 172
Effect of Cooling a Small Area of Body Surface 174
Effect of Cooling a Large Area of Body Surface 176
Pathophysiologic Interpretations 178
Clinical Applications 178

Chapter 14. CLINICAL SYNDROMES DUE TO EXCESSIVE EXPOSURE TO A HOT AND HUMID CLIMATE 179
Heat Asthenia (Calasthenia) 179
Heat Cramps 180
Incidence 180
Pathogenesis 181
Clinical Observations 181
Laboratory Data 182
Pathology 182
Differential Diagnosis 182
Treatment 183
Heat Exhaustion 183
Incidence 183
Pathogenesis 184
Clinical Observations 184
Laboratory Data 184
Pathology 185
Differential Diagnosis 185
Treatment 185
Heat Stroke 185
Incidence 185
Pathogenesis 185
Clinical Observations 186
Laboratory Data 187
Pathology 187
Differential Diagnosis 188
Treatment 188
Differentiating Characteristics of Heat Cramps, Heat Exhaustion and Heat Stroke 189

Index 193

HOT CLIMATES, MAN AND HIS HEART

I

INTRODUCTION

CLIMATOLOGY AND MEDICINE

Bioclimatology. Bioclimatology is the study of the relationship of all living things to climate and weather. The importance of climatic influences on man was recognized in ancient times. Hippocrates frequently referred to seasonal variations in disease. The general problem of the interaction between man and climate was stated clearly by Hippocrates (1) when he advised: "Whoever wishes to pursue properly the science of medicine must proceed thus. First, he ought to consider what effects each season of the year can produce, for the seasons are not alike, but differ widely both in themselves and at their changes. For with the seasons men's diseases, like their digestive organs, suffer change." Nevertheless, in medical practice the science of bioclimatology has been neglected. It is probable that the majority of practicing physicians are not fully aware of the influence of weather on normal physiologic processes and on disease. Furthermore, it is rare for a medical school to include even a single lecture on bioclimatology in its curriculum. Yet, it is well known that man is affected mentally and physically by climate and weather and that some diseases are almost totally under the influence of the weather.

Bioclimatology is a diversified science encompassing many aspects of human growth, including historic, economic, religious and biologic development. Paleoclimatologists, aided by many new developments including radioisotopic analysis for the determination of ancient temperatures, have recently made important contributions to the understanding of the effect of climate on the prehistory of earth and man. Geologists, archaeologists and historians have advanced theories by which the rise and fall of civilizations, the energy of nations, mass migrations, religious activity, customs and mores have been largely influenced by climate.

Medical Bioclimatology. Medical climatology is that aspect of bioclimatology which deals with the effect of climate and weather on the physical and mental health of man. It includes the study of the influence of climate and weather upon normal man as well as upon diseased man. It is concerned with man's vitality and efficiency and those climatic and meteorologic conditions which are ideally suited for his best physical and mental performance. It considers the effect of tropical and subtropical climates on man, particularly with respect to problems of infection, nutrition, parasitism, work efficiency and mental health. It also involves the study of adaptation to cold and the problems of human survival in arctic temperatures. Besides the adverse influences of climate on disease, medical climatology includes a study of climates which are most favorable for patients with particular diseases.

Many aspects of these problems affect our everyday lives. For example, most men recognize that when the air is cool and crisp they are vigorous, active and alert, whereas on hot and humid days they are listless, depressed and inactive. A sudden fall in barometric pressure tends to be associated with mental depression. Crimes of violence, traffic and industrial accidents, suicides and certain diseases seem to occur most often after a decline in barometric pressure (2, 3, 4). Hot and humid weather is also associated with depression and lassitude. Crime rates are highest in the summer. Most revolutions occur during the summer, as is evidenced by the fact that Independence Day and Bastille Day are both in July. Of course, military operations are conducted less effectively in cold weather.

Many diseases are more common in specific climatic zones. For example, malaria is a disease of tropical and subtropical areas, whereas rheumatic fever is a disease primarily of the temperate zones. In the tropics poor nutrition and parasitism have combined to produce diseases associated with impairment of physical and mental function. In the temperate zone chronic sinusitis, bronchitis and otitis affect a large portion of the population. Furthermore, within a given climatic area, certain diseases are more prevalent during one season than during another. For example, in the temperate zone upper respiratory tract infections are most frequent in the winter, whereas poliomyelitis is most common in the summer. The infectious diseases are not the only diseases influenced by climate, for climate also affects such noninfectious diseases as hypertension (5), eclampsia of pregnancy (6), peptic ulcer, coronary thrombosis (7), pulmonary embolism (8), arthritis (9), lupus erythematosus, scleroderma and carcinoma (10).

Thus, medical bioclimatology adds another aspect to the understanding and treatment of disease; for, whereas it is recognized that drugs, diet, rest and certain physical and psychological measures are often indispensable to the proper management of disease, it adds another important factor, the environment.

CLIMATOLOGY AND MAN

Man lives at the bottom of an atmospheric sea several hundred miles deep. The circulation of the atmosphere about the earth is responsible for climate. Weather represents acute variations in climate, i.e., day-to-day variations in the circulating atmosphere.

The Adaptation of Man to Climate. Throughout the eons of evolution, the survival of all species, including man, has depended upon how well they adapted to existing climatic and weather conditions. For example, the extinction of the great dinosaurs coincided with a decrease in the mean temperature of the earth's atmosphere. All species of animals, except man, are restricted by climate to particular geographic areas. Man's ability to transgress climatic barriers is due to a combination of circumstances, not the least of which are his intelligence and inventiveness. Man devotes a great deal of time and energy adjusting to climate and weather. Countless daily activities such as putting on and taking off clothing, turning the dial of a thermostat, walking on the shaded side of the street, opening and closing windows, taking cold or hot baths, and reading and listening to weather reports are performed almost subconsciously by man so that he may modify his *microclimate.* Climate, itself, alters many physiologic processes; for example, it influences susceptibility to disease, is partially responsible for racial characteristics, influences the vigor of nations, and modifies individual temperament, energy and capacity for sustained effort. Indeed, no interpretation of human history could be accurate if it disregarded the effect of weather and climate on human affairs.

A great deal of scientific data has been amassed to support the hypothesis of climatic pulsations. Examination of deep sea cores by the method of Urey (11) has shown that these pulsations occur in 40,000-year cycles. This method has provided man with a paleothermometer by which it has been demonstrated that the great dinosaurs became extinct during a period when the earth was cooling. By the same technique it has been shown that millions of years ago the waters of the arctic were considerably warmer than they are today. This agrees with the geologic knowledge that Greenland was at one time covered with pine and spruce forests (12).

When civilization arose in Mesopotamia and Egypt these regions enjoyed a more favorable climate than they do at present. As these areas became hotter and annual rainfall declined, migrations occurred which carried man out of the fertile crescent to the northern shores of the Mediterranean basin. The periodic invasions of Europe by barbaric tribes from the East, many of whom were nomadic, were probably in part the result of unfavorable climatic conditions in eastern and central Asia. As man became more civilized, he was able to inhabit even climatically unfavorable regions through the use of clothing and the construction of dwellings.

Within the spectrum of the fantastic cold of interstellar space and the tremendous heat of the blue stars, there is a small band of temperature ranging from about —90° F. to +125° F. in which it is possible for biologic processes, as we know them, to exist. The number of planets in the universe satisfying this temperature requirement has been conservatively estimated by Shapley to be about one hundred million (13). As already mentioned, certain species are adapted to live within a certain temperature range. However, man is able to live anywhere on earth that he chooses. Today, no portion of this planet can be considered uninhabitable by man. This is so because of his ingenuity and his complex physiologic thermal regulatory mechanisms which make it possible for him to maintain a body temperature of about 98.6° F. regardless of the environmental temperature and humidity.

One of man's greatest assets is the high development of his eccrine sweat glands. It seems that the evolutionary process has been directed toward the development of a completely eccrine glandular system for the skin at the expense of the apocrine sweat glands. Thus, man depends on either diffusion of water through the skin (insensible perspiration) or eccrine sweating (sensible perspiration) for about 90% of heat loss from the body when he is in a warm or hot environment. Many animals depend greatly upon heat loss from the respiratory tract rather than through the skin. This process requires panting, a comparatively inefficient method of heat loss. Furthermore, it demands the cessation of physical activity, which may make the animal more vulnerable to his enemies. This does not mean that man is the only animal that can live in a hot environment. Some animals are admirably suited to such habitats. The desert rodent can live on a dry grain diet because of his ability to produce a highly concentrated urine (14). These rodents can derive all the water they need to live through metabolic processes. However, the same species, in contrast to man, could not survive the arctic cold. The Eskimo has survived in the arctic for centuries because of his ingenuity. The igloo is constructed in such a way that, even at outside temperatures of —50° F., the ambient air within the igloo may be maintained at a comfortable temperature (15).

Although it is possible for man to survive wide ranges in temperature, there are definite differences between man living in a hot and humid environment and man living in a cold environment. C. A. Mills (16) noted that American children who lived in the Panama Canal Zone for two years or more were physically and mentally inferior to American children of comparable ages who had just arrived in the Canal Zone. Nutrition and parasitism were not factors because adequate sanitation and the importation of food from America eliminated these problems. He assumed that the only difference between the two groups of children was the climate in which they developed.

Children living in hot climates develop more effective and a greater number of sweat glands than their northern counterparts. Body weight is less for body length in the moist tropical regions so that the ratio of body surface to mass is high.

Physical Anthropology and Climate. The differences between man (as well as other animals) living in hot and cold climatic areas have been studied for a long time and have given rise to what may be called "physical anthropologic" rules. Although these are by no means proven, they are of sufficient interest to be described.

Gloger's Rule. "In mammals and birds, races which inhabit warm and humid regions have more melanin pigmentation than races of the same species in cooler and drier regions."

Bergmann's Rule. "The smaller-sized geographic races of a species are found in warmer parts of the range, the larger-sized races in the cooler districts."

Allen's Rule. "Protruding body parts such as tails, ears, bills, and extremities are relatively shorter in the cooler parts of the range of the species than in warmer parts."

There are psychological as well as physical differences between man living in a tropical climate and man living in a temperate climate. In the tropics where the climate varies little from day to day, the monotony of the weather produces a mental lassitude in which initiative and creative thought are impaired. By contrast, in a temperate climate with rapidly changing barometric pressures and stormy days followed by clear, sunny days, man is energetic, imaginative and creative. These differences raise the question of the ideal climate for man.

It is no accident that civilization began in a region of the world which 6,000 years ago enjoyed a mild, subtropical climate. Only when man was released from the necessity of constant toil in order to survive could he direct his attention to cultural things. The projection of culture is civilization. Only in a land of plenty where agriculture was easy and game abundant could the struggle be won and leisure gained. Such a place was Mesopotamia 6,000 years ago, and it was here that man first began to write history. In the short span of these 6,000 years the fertile crescent has become an arid desert. Civilization died or moved on to more fertile ground as the original climatic conditions for cultural development changed unfavorably. In the short history of human effort climate has taken its toll of many civilizations. Climatic change contributes not only to the dissolution of empire but also to the formation of empire.

The "Ideal" Climate. Although the *ideal climate* for man cannot be defined in absolute terms, it is possible to make certain generalizations. Comfort and efficiency depend upon temperature, humidity and air movement. Therefore, any consideration of ideal temperature must take into account humidity and air movement. Man is relatively comfortable when he is quiet and the temperature is 90° F. and the relative humidity 35%. However, in the same temperature with a relative humidity of 80%, man is extremely uncomfortable. Generally, most people are comfortable when the *wet bulb* temperature is between 50° and 60° F. and are uncomfortable when it is above 70° F. A wet bulb temperature of 78° F. has been considered the limit of tolerance by some observers. With adaptation to heat and cold man can overcome even less favorable climatic conditions. However, the closer the mean wet bulb temperature of a particular country approximates the ideal range of 50° to 60° F., the more virile the nation.

Clothing and Climate. It must be emphasized that the comfort of an environment depends upon man's activity. The more active a person and the greater the rate of heat production, the greater the need for heat loss and the lower the temperature and relative humidity of the atmosphere must be for comfort. Clothing also influences man's comfort. A lightly clad person resting quietly finds a temperature of 78° F. and a relative humidity of 60% or less to be comfortable in the summer and a temperature of 75° F. and relative humidity of 60% or less to be comfortable in the winter. Gagge, Burton and Bazett (17) have devised the *clo unit* to express thermal insulation, particularly that derived from clothing. A clo unit of thermal insulation is described as the amount of insulation required to maintain a resting-sitting man, whose metabolic rate is 50 kg-cal./m^2/hr., indefinitely comfortable in an environment of 21° C. (70° F.) and less than 50% relative humidity, and air movement of 20 ft./min. Many of the problems of thermal regulation have been discussed by Burton (18).

In a tropical climate the annual range of temperature seldom exceeds the diurnal range. Tropical weather may occur even in temperate zones. So-called "heat waves" may impose a great stress on the cardiovascular system of unacclimatized individuals. Hospital admission rates for myocardial infarction in temperate zones increase during the first few days of a heat wave (19).

Man does not have to inhabit a tropical zone to experience tropical weather.

The purpose of this monograph is to present some of the physiologic effects of a hot and humid environment on the cardiovascular system of man. It was necessary to include more than a study of the heart and circulation since thermal regulation involves the interaction of many organ systems. Nevertheless, the heart and circulation are greatly concerned with thermal regulation. Death from excessive exposure to heat is usually due to failure of the cardiovascular system. The nature of the processes which ultimately lead to cardiovascular failure must be understood before the influence of a hot and humid environment upon the cardiovascular system can be fully appreciated. An understanding of these phenomena is important for the proper management of patients with a wide variety of diseases, particularly those with cardiovascular disease.

REFERENCES

1. Hippocrates: *The Loeb Classical Library.* New York, Putnam, 1931.

2. Dexter, E. G.: *Weather Influences.* New York, Macmillan, 1904.

3. Horvath, L. G.: Weather changes and accidents in industry. *Idojaras,* Budapest, *60:*88, 1956.

4. Tholuck, H. J.: Suicide and weather. *Beitr. Gerichtlichen Med., 16:*121, 1942.

5. Sarre, H. and Betz, L.: Climatic influences on the blood-pressure of hypertensives. *Annalen der Meterologie, Medizin-meteorologische Hefte* No. 4: 26, 1950.

6. Berg, H.: Causation of diseases by meteorological and solar influences. *Naturwissenschaftliche Rundschau, 3:*161, 1950.

7. DePasquale, N. P. and Burch, G. E.: The seasonal incidence of myocardial infarction in New Orleans. *Am. J. M. Sc., 242:*468, 1961.

8. Geppert, M. P.: On statistical techniques in bioclimatic research. *Annalen der Meteorologie, Medizin-meteorologische Hefte,* No. 9:21, 1954.

9. Whiten, A. J.: Rheumatism and fronts. *Weather, 8:*10, 1953.

10. Bittner, J. E.: *Prevention of heart disease and cancer (bioclimatology and etiology).* Yakima, Wash. Bittner Research Foundation, 1955.

11. Urey, H. C.: Thermodynamic properties of isotopic substances. *J. Chem. Soc.,* p. 562, 1947.

12. Gamow, G.: *Biography of the Earth.* Its Past, Present and Future. New York, The Viking Press, 1959.

13. Shapley, H.: *Climatic Change: Evidence, Causes, and Effects.* (Chapter 1) Cambridge, Harvard University Press, 1959.

14. Schmidt-Nielsen, B. and Schmidt-Nielsen, K.: Pulmonary water loss in desert rodents. *Am. J. Physiol., 162:*31, 1950.

15. Newburg, L. H.: *Physiology of Heat Regulation and the Science of Clothing.* (Chapter 1) Philadelphia, Saunders, 1949.

16. Mills, C. A.: *Climate Makes the Man.* New York, Harper and Brothers, 1942.

17. Gagge, A. P., Burton, A. C. and Bazett, H. C.: A practical system of units for the description of the heat exchange of man with his environment. *Science, 94:*2445, 1941.

18. Burton, A. C. and Edholm, O. G.: *Man in a Cold Environment: Physiological and Pathological Effects of Exposure to Low Temperatures.* London, Edward Arnold (Publishers) Ltd., 1955.

19. Ferris, E. B., Jr., Blankenhorn, M. A., Robinson, H. W. and Cullen, G. E.: Heat stroke: clinical and chemical observations on 44 cases. *J. Clin. Invest., 17:*249, 1938.

II

THE ROLE OF THE SKIN IN THERMAL REGULATION

THE cutaneous envelope of man is an efficient inhibitor of water and electrolyte loss. Death would occur within a few hours from water and electrolyte imbalance were man completely denuded of skin. The skin and subcutaneous tissues thermally insulate man from his environment. Thermal gradients between the "core of the body," the subcutaneous tissues, the skin and the ambient air determine the rate, amount and direction of heat exchange across the cutaneous envelope. Thus, the integument behaves as a thermal barrier as well as a water barrier.

THE INTEGUMENT AS A THERMAL BARRIER

In man the skin is the organ primarily concerned with the dissipation or conservation of body heat. It is well adapted for the protection of man from thermal imbalance. The tough epidermis is perforated by numerous sweat glands which are capable of pouring water onto the body surface or of remaining almost totally inactive to ensure a dry dermal surface, depending upon environmental conditions. The epidermis possesses an inhibiting layer which controls the rate of diffusion of water through the skin, and the dermis contains highly developed sensory organs which are sensitive to the slightest changes in temperature. Moreover, the integument, which behaves as an almost perfect black body radiator, has excellent physical and architectural characteristics to provide for efficient heat transfer between the body and the environment.

Heat exchange through the skin ultimately depends on the rate of dermal blood flow. Beneath the malpighian layer there is a rich plexus of capillaries, arterioles and venules which allow rapid and marked changes in blood flow to the skin. These dermal vessels are arranged and function in such a way that when cool environmental conditions require conservation of body heat, heat transported from the core of the body can be shunted away from the skin through a process involving arteriovenous heat exchange and countercurrent flow (1) (Chapter 8). The numerous arteriovenous anastomoses aid in controlling cutaneous blood flow to vary heat exchange. These arteriovenous anastomoses appear to be under the control of the hypothalamus, the heat regulating center of the body (2). Furthermore, certain arteriovenous anastomoses, the "glomus bodies," are specialized in structure and function. These structures contain specialized epithelioid cells which arise either from primitive neuroderm or from smooth muscle (3). The exact role of the glomus bodies is not known. However, they seem to function as specialized arteriovenous shunts which assist in the control of the dermal circulation. It is obviously impossible to understand the factors influencing heat loss from the surface of the body without taking into account the characteristics of both the cutaneous envelope and the dermal circulation. However, for convenience of presentation, the dermal circulation will be discussed in a separate chapter (Chapter 7).

THE INTEGUMENT AS A WATER BARRIER

Water is lost from the body of normal man primarily through the skin, lungs, urine, feces and saliva. The approximate daily rates of water loss through these various routes for an average-sized adult under basal conditions are shown in Table 1. The water loss through the skin and lungs varies with the ambient temperature and humidity.

TABLE 1
APPROXIMATE AVERAGE DAILY WATER LOSS THROUGH VARIOUS ROUTES FOR NORMAL MAN UNDER BASAL CONDITIONS (MODIFIED FROM BEST AND TAYLOR [4])

Skin	500 ml.
Expired Air	350 ml.
Urine	1,500 ml.
Feces	150 ml.
Milk (lactating female)	500-900 ml.
Saliva	Negligible

At comfortable temperatures about 75% of total heat loss takes place through radiation and convection. However, as the environmental temperature rises, these avenues of heat loss become less and less effective. When the environmental temperature equals or exceeds skin temperature, heat loss occurs through evaporation of water from the surface of the body. The water is secreted onto the skin surface by the eccrine sweat glands as an extremely dilute fluid made from the plasma. With each milliliter of water vaporized at room temperature, there is a loss of 0.59 Calorie of heat from the body. At extremely high environmental temperature and relative humidity water loss through the skin and expired air may reach 5 to 20 liters per day. Thus, the vaporization of water from the skin surface is the chief protective mechanism against overheating of the body when the ambient temperature exceeds body temperature. When the vapor pressure of the ambient air is so high that vaporization of water is limited, serious thermal difficulty develops unless the environmental conditions are modified. Furthermore, if the rate of sweating and the relative humidity of the air are high, much of the sweat drips and pours off the body surface without being vaporized and therefore does not participate in heat loss.

Loss of water by diffusion through the skin independent of sweat gland activity is termed *insensible perspiration.* At comfortable room temperature and relative humidity the water diffused through the skin evaporates as quickly as it is formed so that the skin appears dry. *Sensible perspiration* usually refers to visible water which appears on the surface of the skin as a result of sweat gland activity. If the rate of sweating exceeds the rate of vaporization of water from the surface of the body, the sweat is visible and the skin appears moist. However, when the rate of vaporization of sweat equals the rate of sweating, the skin appears dry. This latter situation has been termed "occult sweating" to distinguish it from insensible perspiration in which the skin also appears dry but the sweat glands are inactive. This distinction is of importance. Subjects with ectodermal defects with an absence of sweat glands remain in thermal balance at comfortable room temperatures because at such temperatures heat loss takes place primarily through radiation, convection, conduction and insensible perspiration. However, at high temperatures difficulty with thermal regulation develops because of the decrease in efficiency of radiation, convection and conduction in the absence of sweating.

REFERENCES

1. Burch, G. E. and Hale, A. R.: Relation of morphology of volar cutaneous blood vessels in man to countercurrent thermal flow in thermal regulation. *Angiology;* in press.
2. Freeman, W. J. and Davis, D. D.: Effects on cats of conductive hypothalamic cooling. *Am. J. Physiol., 197:*145, 1959.
3. Hale, A. R. and Burch, G. E.: The arteriovenous anastomoses and blood vessels of the human finger. *Medicine, 39:*191, 1960.
4. Best, C. H. and Taylor, N. B.: *The Physiological Basis of Medical Practice.* Ed. 4, Baltimore, The William. and Wilkins Co., 1945.

III

METHODS OF MEASURING SENSIBLE AND INSENSIBLE WATER LOSS FROM THE SURFACE OF THE BODY

STUDIES by many investigators indicate marked variations in the rates of total sensible and insensible water loss. This variability is due in part to significant individual physiologic differencs between the rates of water loss from the skin and lungs as well as to such variables as diet and season. However, differences in quantitative accuracy among the methods used to measure rates of water loss account for some of the variability reported. For this reason, the methods developed in this laboratory for measuring the rates of total insensible water loss and insensible water loss from the skin and from the lungs are described in detail. A more sensitive technique for measuring the rate of water loss from the lungs is described in Chapter 8.

THE MEASUREMENT OF THE RATE OF TOTAL WATER LOSS FROM THE BODY

Total insensible water loss was measured by means of a specially constructed human balance* which weighs a man to an accuracy of less than ± 150 mg. (1). The balance consists of a heavy steel frame which supports the fulcra and suspension arms above. The subject was suspended on one arm of the balance and the weights were suspended on the other arm (Figs. 1, 2). The ratio of the lever lengths or the weight ratio for the balance is 4:1. Special air dampers (Fig. 2, insert A) were constructed according to the principle of the air dampers used in the Curie-type analytic balance. They consist of a group of metal interdigitating cylinders made of 26-gauge galvanized iron sheeting. The outer cylinder has a diameter of 14 inches and the inner ones are made successively smaller so that there is ⅜-inch clearance between their walls. The cylinders a and a′ (insert A) are closed to form pistons. The set of cylinders labeled b and b′ (insert A) are clamped to the upper and lower surfaces of the bottom shelf of the weight-bearing side of the balance. The outer cylinders, labeled c and c′ (insert A), are arranged so that they may be moved to avoid contact with the inner cylinders when the weight-bearing end of the balance oscillates. The rigid arm (d) and wooden platform (e) permit adjustments of the outer group of cylinders. The dampers bring the balance from maximal oscillation to standstill in 6 minutes.

The Photographic and Recording Portions of the Balance. The movements of the balance are magnified and recorded

* Buffalo Scale Co., Buffalo, New York.

Fig. 1. Photograph of the human balance. (From *Am. J. M. Sc.*, *209*:220, 1945.)

through a specially constructed system (Fig. 2). An aluminum plate (f) fixed to the beam of the balance near the main fulcrum is so arranged as to prevent friction between the parts when the balance oscillates. An aluminum rod (g) is attached to the plate (f) so that the center of the rod is at the center of the knife-edge of the main fulcrum of the balance. The distal end of the rod which extends three inches beyond the side frame of the balance holds a mirror (h, insert B) which is concave and has a 2-meter focal length. Aluminum joints permit adjustment of the mirror in any direction. A 21-candle power, 6-volt lamp and housing (i) are mounted at the base of the balance. The lamp hous-

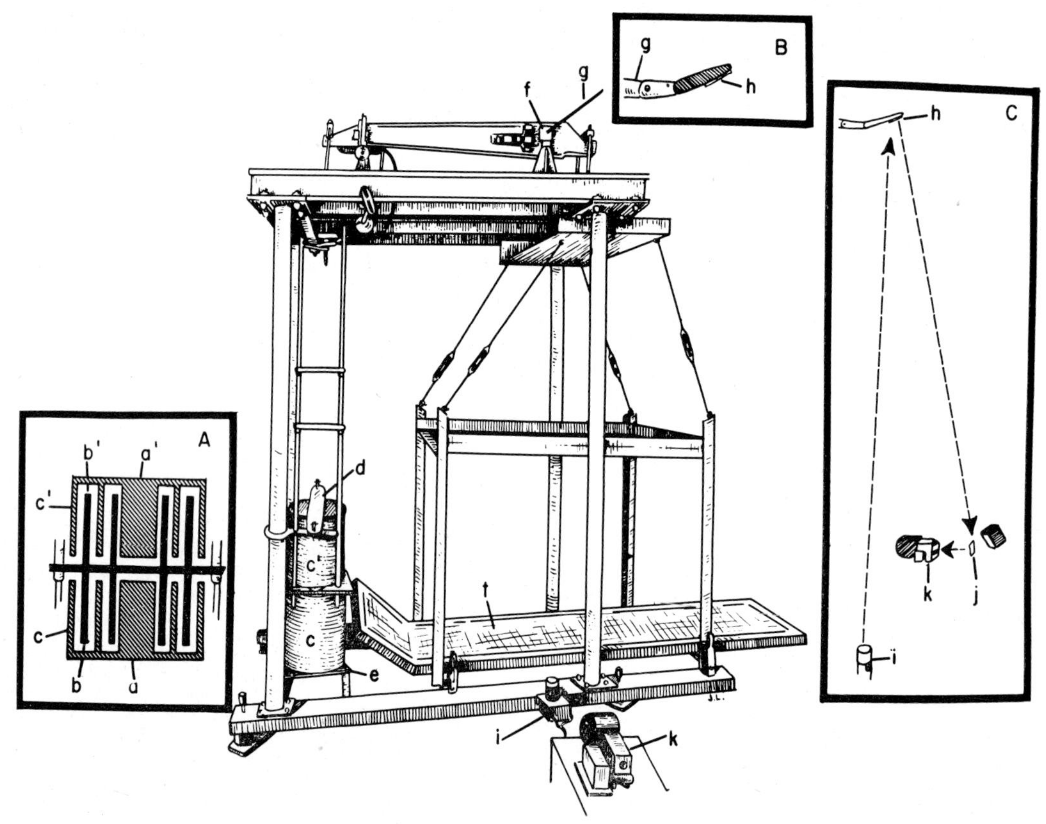

Fig. 2. Drawing of the human balance. Insert A shows details of the special air dampers. Insert B shows the mirror mounted on the end of the rod used in photographing the movement of the balance. Insert C shows travel of light beam to the camera slit for recording. Consult text for details.

ing has an adjustable slit so that a line of light can strike the mirror (h, insert C) and be reflected onto a plane mirror (j) which, in turn, reflects it onto an electrocardiographic type of photographic recording camera (k). Figure 3 shows an original tracing obtained by this method.

Method of Use of the Balance. The balance is used in the following manner. The atmospheric conditions of the room are maintained at a relatively constant level before and during the weighing of the subject. The subject rests in the supine position on the specially constructed all-metal wire-mesh cot (Fig. 2, t) for at least 15 minutes. The balance is then unlocked and the beam released. To facilitate the evaporation of moisture from the skin of the axillae, groin and genitalia, the subject's arms and legs are abducted. Weights are added to the opposite arm of the scale until it is balanced. The light is then turned on and the light beam reflected onto the camera. After the scale is balanced, the air-conditioning unit is turned off to eliminate air currents in the room. The illumination in the room is then reduced so as not to interfere with photography. The shift in the beam of light as water is lost from the body is recorded by the camera. Recordings can be made for any desired period of time.

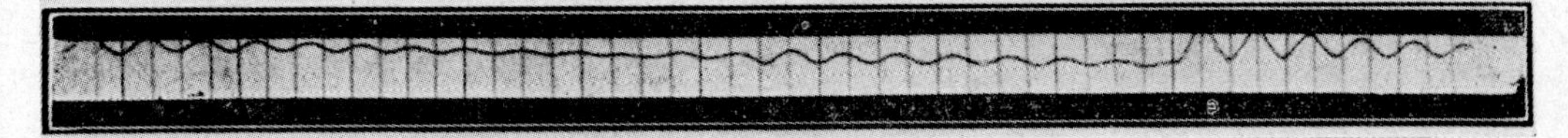

Fig. 3. Original tracing obtained by use of the human balance. The coarse, smooth waves on the horizontal line produced by the light beam from the concave mirror of the balance represent slow pendulous oscillations of the balance due to slight movement of the subject. The sudden rise in the tracing and large, smooth waves seen to the right of the tracing were produced by the addition of 5 gm. to the subject's side of the balance for calibration. The vertical lines are produced by flashes of the timer light at 15-second intervals. Every fourth vertical line is darker than the others, thus marking a minute. (From *Am. J. M. Sc.*, *209*:220, 1945.)

Calibration of the Balance. Just prior to completion of the recording, a known weight (usually 5 gms.) was added to the subject's side of the balance in order to calibrate the balance (Fig. 3). This procedure moved the light beam a measurable distance in the opposite direction, making it possible to convert millimeters of deflection of the light beam on the photographic record to change of weight in grams.

THE MEASUREMENT OF RATE OF WATER LOSS THROUGH THE SKIN AND/OR THE LUNGS

Weight loss measured with the subject lying quietly on the balance in a comfortable environment represents weight loss through the diffusion of water from the entire body. Utilizing the techniques described below, it was possible to measure the water loss from the skin and lungs separately.

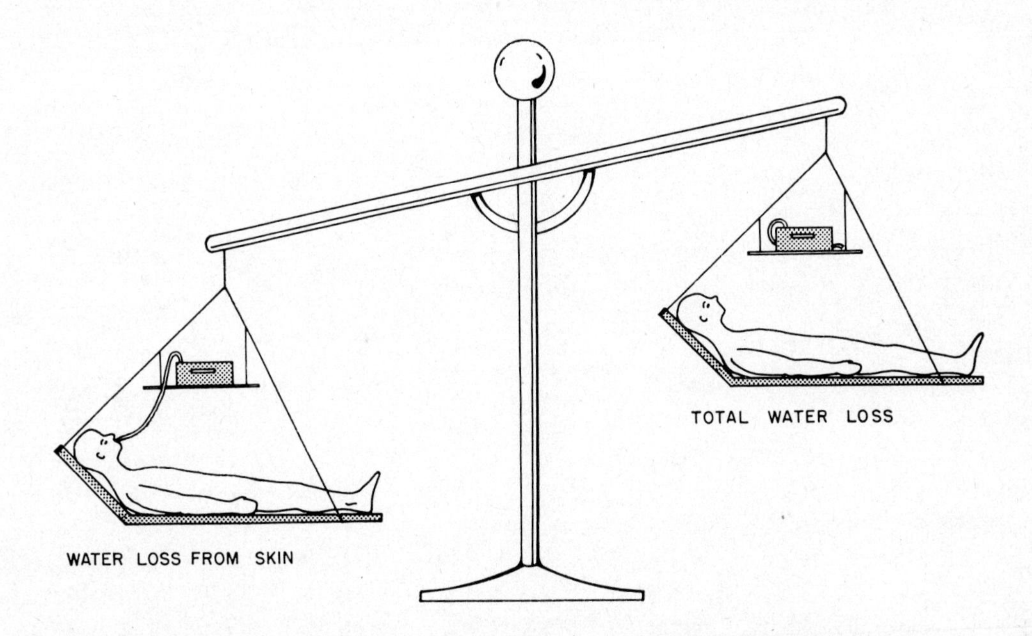

Fig. 4. Schematic representation of one of the methods used to measure water loss from skin and lungs separately.

Insensible Water Loss from the Skin. To determine insensible water loss from the *skin alone,* measurement is first made of total insensible weight loss with the subject breathing atmospheric air while resting on the cot of the balance in a comfortable, temperature-controlled room. This loss in weight represents total water loss from the skin and lungs. Then, while the subject breathes into a Benedict-Roth BMR machine suspended with him on the subject arm of the balance, the weight loss is again recorded. Since no water or gaseous exchange occurs between the lungs and the atmosphere, the change in weight represents change due to water loss through the skin only. Corrections are made for change in manifested weight due to a decrease in buoyancy as the volume of the bellows of the BMR apparatus decreases with absorption of oxygen. In effect, the decrease in buoyant force exerted by the atmosphere makes the BMR apparatus heavier. By subtracting the loss of weight while breathing through the BMR apparatus (water loss through the skin) from the loss of weight while breathing atmospheric air (total insensible water loss), the insensible water loss from the lungs is determined (Fig. 4).

Insensible Water Loss from the Lungs. The procedure can be modified so that water loss from the skin is controlled and water loss from the lungs measured. This is accomplished by placing a large

Fig. 5. Cylindrical metal tank in which the subjects were enclosed to control water loss through the skin while water loss through the lungs was measured. The metal cot is shown on the balance above the tank. The subject rested on this cot in order that the total insensible loss in weight could be measured. The subject was then sealed in the cylindrical tank and water loss from the lungs measured as described in the text. From both measurements the rate of water loss from the entire body as well as from the lungs and skin was obtained. (From *Am. J. M. Sc., 209:*226, 1945.)

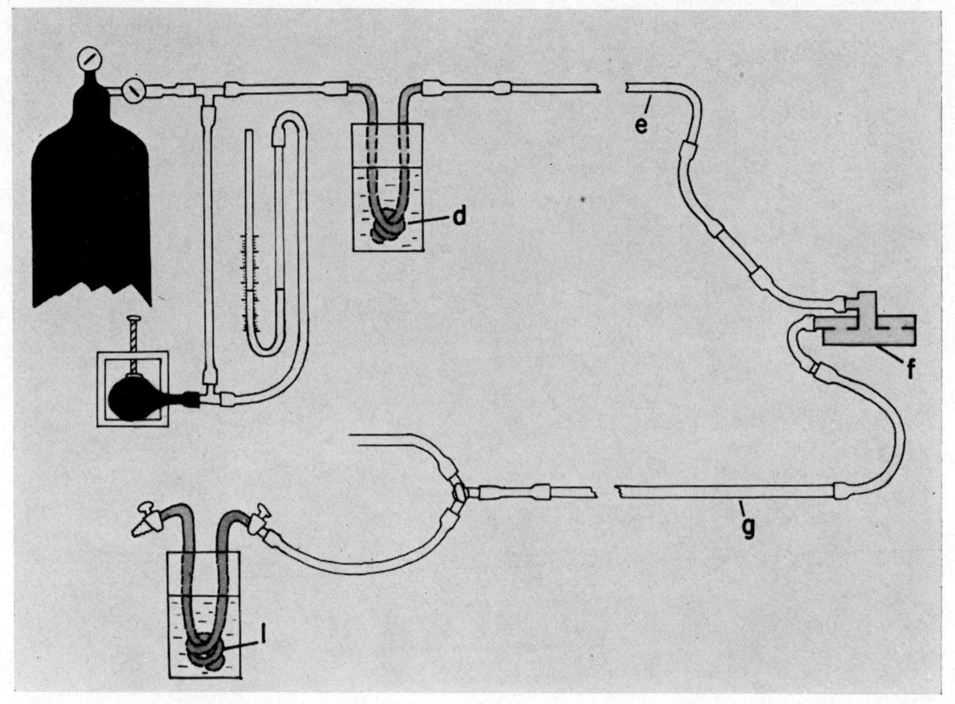

Fig. 6. Apparatus used for the quantitative measurement of water loss from small areas of skin. The brass chamber (f) was sealed onto the area of skin to be studied. Afferent (e) and efferent (g) tubes circulated dry oxygen to the skin. The aluminum coil (d) packed in solid carbon dioxide dried the oxygen prior to passage over the skin, whereas the aluminum coil (l) trapped the water of the water-laden oxygen returning from the skin. From the difference in weight of coil (l) prior to and after collection of the water, the rate of water loss for the area of skin was obtained. Consult text for details.

vapor and gas-tight cylinder on the subject arm of the balance (Fig. 5). The subject then lies in this cylinder which is sealed by means of a vapor-tight metal cover. He breathes into the atmosphere through an orifice in the wall of the tank specially adapted for this purpose. Since the chamber is vapor and gas-tight, any loss of weight which occurs must take place through the lungs.

THE MEASUREMENT OF THE RATE OF WATER LOSS FROM ISOLATED AREAS OF SKIN

The methods thus far described measure total insensible water loss from the entire body, the skin or the lungs. In order to measure *sensible* and *insensible* water loss from isolated areas of skin, other methods were employed which involved the use of brass chambers (2) or brass cylinders (3) as described below.

Intact Living Skin. The apparatus diagrammatically shown in Figure 6 was used to measure quantitatively the rate of water loss from small areas of intact living skin. It consists of a brass chamber (Fig 6, f and Fig. 7) fitted with an afferent (Fig. 6, e) and an efferent (Fig. 6, g) tube and sealed onto the skin surface to isolate a known area (5 to 10 cm.^{2}) for study. Dry oxygen from a cylinder is dried further by passing it

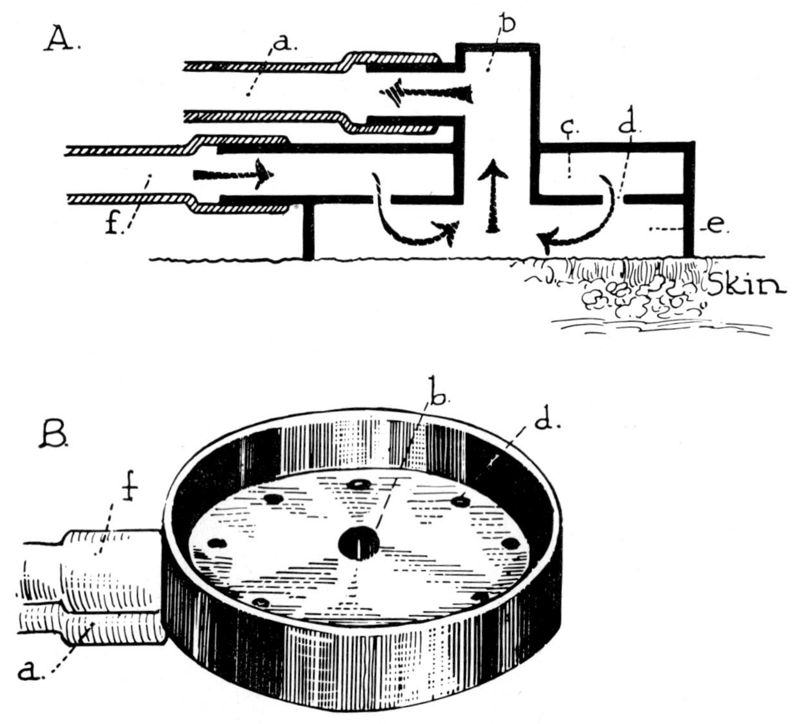

Fig. 7. The brass collecting chamber. A. Cross-section drawing of the chamber; the arrows indicate the direction of oxygen flow. B. Collecting surface of the chamber shown in detail. (a) Efferent tube, (f) afferent tube, (b) portal of exit of water-laden oxygen returning from area of isolated skin, (c) diffusing chamber in which dry oxygen is distributed so that it is delivered equally through portals (d) to splash upon the surface of the isolated skin where the water was vaporized. (From *Am. J. Physiol.*, *138:*603, 1943.)

through aluminum coils (Fig. 6, d) cooled to —70° C. with solid carbon dioxide. It is then circulated to the skin through the afferent tube of the specially designed collecting chamber where the oxygen collects the water as vapor from the surface of the isolated area of skin. This water-laden oxygen leaves the collecting chamber through the efferent tube and passes through another aluminum coil (Fig. 6, 1) cooled to —70° C. by solid carbon dioxide, where the water vapor is trapped by freezing allowing only dry oxygen to escape into the atmosphere. The coil is weighed before and after known periods of collection. The differences in weight represent the water loss for known intervals of time from a known area of skin. Such measurements of the rates of water loss were made with subjects resting in comfortable, cool, and hot and humid environments.

Intact Dead Skin. The water loss measured from isolated areas of intact living skin, as described above, represents water loss by both diffusion and glandular secretion. Many investigators fail to differentiate between water lost sensibly through the secretion of sweat and water lost insensibly by diffusion. Since water lost through dead skin must be lost by diffusion and not by secretion by the sweat glands, the rate of diffusion

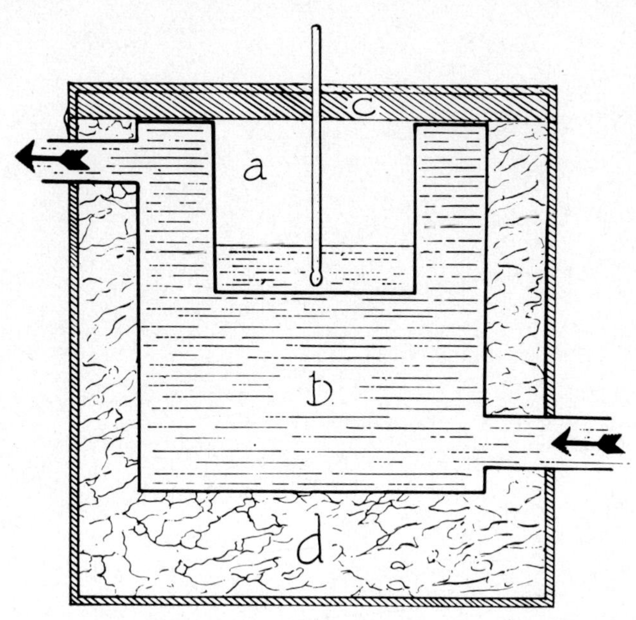

Fig. 8. Cross-sectional drawing of the water bath used in measuring diffusion of water through dead skin. (From *Arch. Int. Med.*, *74*:437, 1944.)

of water through skin may be studied by measuring the rate of loss through dead human skin. The rate of diffusion of water through dead skin was measured in two ways.

The *first method* utilizes brass chambers, similar to those employed in the study of living skin, sealed to the external surface of skin collected from subjects shortly after death. By means of a specially constructed water bath (Fig. 8) the dead skin can be maintained at any desired temperature. The rate of water loss is measured by collecting water from the skin with dried oxygen and condensing it in aluminum coils for weighing, as described for studies in living intact skin.

The special *water bath* (Fig. 8) consists of a one foot cubic container (Fig. 8, b) constructed of 26-gauge galvanized iron sheeting with a smaller eight inch cubic container (Fig. 8, a) fitted inside of it (4). Afferent and efferent water lines are connected to the larger chamber (Fig. 8, b) which is insulated with wood and cork (Fig. 8, d) and covered with an insulated, hinged cover (Fig. 8, c). Isotonic saline is placed in the smaller container (Fig. 8, a) with a thermometer inserted into the saline solution through a hole in the cover for thermal observations. The water circulated through the large container is pumped from a 12-gallon water bath, the temperature of which is controlled within 1° C. automatically by refrigerating and heating units. The centrifugal pump which circulates the water has a capacity of 400 gallons per hour.

The *second method* for the study of diffusion of water through dead skin involves mounting the skin over the orifice of a specially designed brass cylinder as shown in Figure 9. The cylinder (Fig. 9, e), which contains loose cotton, is filled with an isotonic saline solution (0.85% NaCl in H_2O) in such a way that the solution and wet cotton just touch the under surface of the skin. The cot-

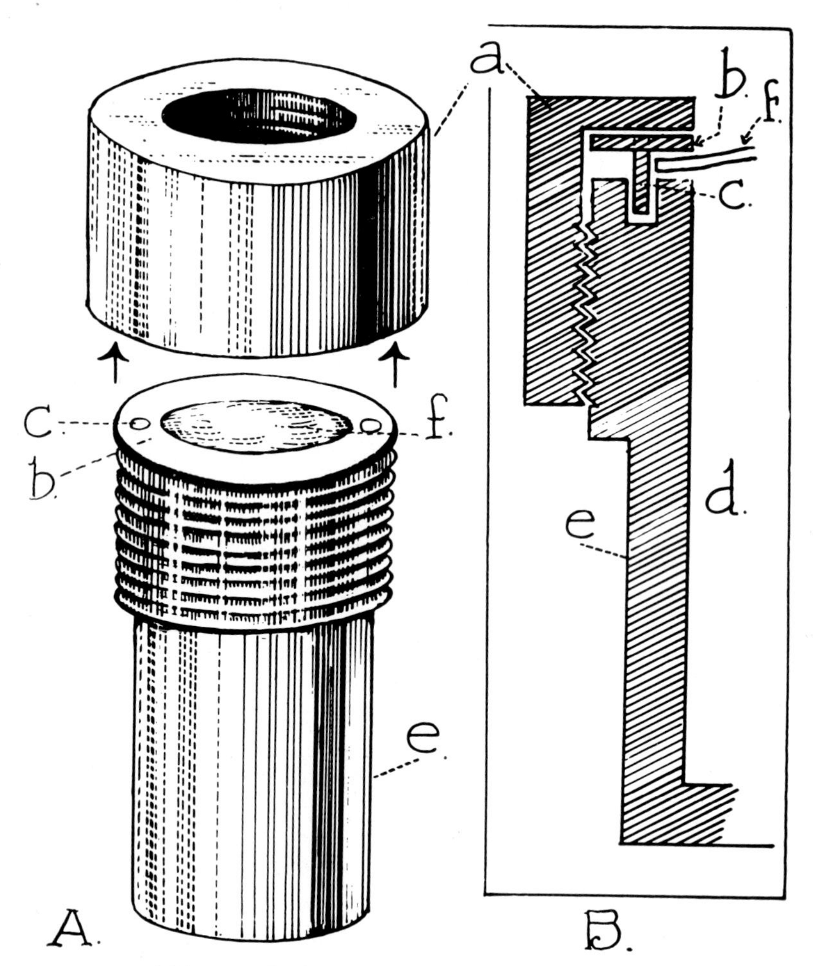

Fig. 9. A. Drawing of brass cylinder used for measuring the diffusion of water through dead skin. B. Cross-section of cylinder showing manner in which the skin (f) is secured to the top of the cylinder to make an air and vapor-tight seal. (From *Arch. Dermat. & Syph.*, *53*:39, 1946.)

ton provides a means for keeping the solution in contact with the skin at all times. A brass ring (Fig. 9, b) with stopcock grease on its under surface is placed over the skin. Two pins soldered to the ring 180° apart are slipped into holes in the top of the cylinder (Fig. 9, c) to prevent the skin from twisting when the cap is screwed into place. The threaded portions are greased with stopcock grease. Thus, a diaphragm of skin 2 cm.^{2} in area (Fig. 9, f) is sealed tightly over the brass cylinder.

The cylinder with the mounted skin is placed in a room of desired temperature and relative humidity and allowed to reach equilibrium. It is then weighed on an analytic balance to an accuracy of 0.1 mg. After periods varying from a few minutes to several hours the unit is weighed again. Weighings are repeated several times for at least two successive days. Any loss in weight represents diffusion of water through the skin. The temperature and relative humidity of the room are varied to produce different environmental conditions. For more frequent weighings a preparation is left on the pan of the analytic balance so that by merely releasing the beam of the balance at selected intervals a record of the change in weight due to water loss by diffusion can be obtained.

REFERENCES

1. Burch, G. E.: A method for measuring small amounts of weight loss in man. *Am. J. M. Sc., 209:*220, 1945.

2. Burch, G. E. and Sodeman, W. A.: Regional relationships of rate of water loss in normal adults in a subtropical climate. *Am. J. Physiol., 138:*603, 1943.

3. Burch, G. E. and Winsor, T.: Diffusion of water through dead plantar, palmar and torsal human skin and through toe nails. *Arch. Dermat. & Syph., 53:*39, 1946.

4. Burch, G. E. and Winsor, T.: Rate of insensible perspiration (diffusion of water) locally through living and through dead human skin. *Arch. Int. Med., 74:*437, 1944.

IV

SENSIBLE AND INSENSIBLE WATER LOSS

THE weight of the body is not constant but fluctuates from moment to moment. The gains and losses in body weight over a 24-hour period may amount to several pounds. These gains and losses are attributable in large part to the ingestion of food and drink and to the excretion of urine and feces. However, a portion of the weight loss is due to the insensible loss of water vapor from the skin and lungs. In the studies described below, change in weight of subjects was observed for predetermined periods of time during which there was no ingestion of food or water and no elimination of excretory products (1). Thus, decreases in weight represented loss of water from the skin and lungs.

THE RATE OF TOTAL INSENSIBLE WATER LOSS

Total insensible water loss from the body was measured with the subjects resting on the human balance in a comfortable air-conditioned room while breathing atmospheric air (1). The mean loss in weight (total insensible water loss) for 12 normal subjects was 3.418 gm./m²/10 min. (range, 2.396 to 5.503). The mean rate of total insensible water loss for ten subjects studied during summer and winter under similar laboratory environmental conditions was slightly greater during a cool winter month than during a hot summer month.

Rate of Insensible Water Loss from the Skin and Lungs with Loss from the Lungs Controlled. By having the subjects breathe through a Benedict-Roth type BMR machine while resting on the human balance, it was possible to determine the proportion of the total insensible water loss that occurred through the skin and lungs separately since the loss in weight with the subject breathing through the BMR machine represented water lost through the skin alone and the difference between this quantity and the total insensible weight loss represented water loss through the lungs (Chapter 3). Employing this technique the mean rates of water loss through the skin and lungs for the 12 subjects were 1.633 gm./m²/10 min. (range, 0.955 to 2.753) and 1.789 gm./m²/10 min. (range, 0.873 to 2.869), respectively. Thus, in these subjects 48% of the total insensible water loss occurred through the skin (Table 2).

Rate of Insensible Water Loss from the Skin and Lungs with Loss from the Skin Controlled. When the subjects were placed in metal tanks in order to control weight loss through the skin while permitting water loss through the lungs, the results were essentially simi-

TABLE 2

Insensible Loss in Weight (gm./m²/10 minutes) from the Skin and Lungs of 12 Normal Adult Males, Ages 23–28
(Water Loss through the Lungs Controlled)

Subject No.	*Room* *Temp.* (°C.)	*R.H.* (%)	*Total Loss*	*Skin Loss*	*Lung Loss*
1	23.6	22	3.073	1.708	1.365
2	23.6	43	2.651	1.778	0.873
3	23.6	44	5.503	2.753	2.750
4	22.5	30	4.615	1.746	2.869
5	23.6	46	2.396	0.955	1.441
6	23.6	39	3.045	1.396	1.649
7	23.6	48	2.720	1.690	1.030
8	23.6	55	3.066	1.050	2.016
9	24.6	30	3.226	1.674	1.552
10	23.6	46	2.868	1.310	1.558
11	23.6	55	4.564	1.880	2.684
12	23.6	55	3.335	1.660	1.675
Mean			3.418	1.633	1.789
Max.			5.503	2.753	2.869
Min.			2.396	0.955	0.873
Percent of total loss from lungs, 52.23					

lar to those obtained with the previous technique except that the percent of water lost through the lungs tended to be slightly greater than when the BMR machine was used. The mean rate of total insensible weight loss for 4 subjects studied in the metal tanks was 2.752 gm./m²/10 min. (range 1.783 to 3.463). The mean rates of weight loss from the skin and lungs were 1.087 gm./m²/10 min. (range, 0.600 to 1.741) and 1.665 gm./m²/10 min. (range, 1.115 to 2.124), respectively (Table 3).

These results differ from those of other investigators in that the proportion of water lost through the lungs is somewhat higher than that reported by others. In general, less than 30% of the water vapor eliminated insensibly has been estimated to come from the lungs. However, Benedict and Benedict (2) and Galeotti (3) found the loss from the lungs to be about 40% of the total insensible water loss. This value approaches that found on the subjects of these experiments (Table 2). The high rate of water loss from the lungs with the subjects enclosed in the metal tanks was probably a result of psychic influences since the subjects were noted to breathe more rapidly and more deeply while in the tank than when on the cot outside of the tank.

THE RATES OF INSENSIBLE WATER LOSS IN WHITES AND NEGROES

The mean rates of total insensible loss in weight for ten young white and ten young Negro male adults studied under comparable conditions were 3.483 and 3.582 gm./m²/10 min., respectively. The difference was not statistically significant. That the rates of total insensible water loss for Negro and white subjects were equal is in agreement with the observations of other investigators. Any racial differences in adaptation to humid heat must be explained by factors other than racial differences in the dissipation of heat by insensible perspiration.

THE RATE OF WATER LOSS THROUGH THE SKIN OF CADAVERS

The measurement of insensible water loss through the skin of living subjects is accurate only if no sweating (sensible perspiration) occurs. In order to eliminate errors due to water loss through sensible perspiration, the rate of water loss from the surface of cadavers was measured. These experiments also provided an estimation of the accuracy of the measurement of the rates of insensible water loss through the skin of living subjects. A comparison between living and dead bodies is justified because studies on isolated living and dead skin showed that the rates of insensible water loss through both were the same (vide infra).

TABLE 3

INSENSIBLE LOSS IN WEIGHT (GM./M²/10 MINUTES) FROM THE SKIN AND LUNGS OF 4 NORMAL WHITE ADULTS

(Water Loss through the Skin Controlled)

Subject No.	*Total Loss*	*Skin Loss*	*Lung Loss*
1	2.724	0.600	2.124
2	3.463	1.741	1.722
3	3.038	1.338	1.700
4	1.783	0.668	1.115
Mean	2.752	1.087	1.665
Max.	3.463	1.741	2.124
Min.	1.783	0.600	1.115
Percent of total loss from lungs, 60.50			

The loss in weight of ten bodies was studied shortly after death. The mean loss in weight was 0.92 gm./m²/10 min. (range, 0.39 to 1.51), which was lower than the mean rate for the total surface of living skin (Tables 2, 3, 4). This difference may be explained in part by additional losses in water through the skin of the living subjects due to occult sweating which was absent in the dead bodies. Furthermore, the warmth of the

TABLE 4

LOSS IN WEIGHT (gm./m²/10 minutes) THROUGH THE SKIN OF THE ENTIRE BODY SHORTLY AFTER DEATH

Subject No.	*Age*	*Sex*	*Color*	*Room Temp. (°C.)*	*Room R.H. (%)*	*Hours After Death*	*Weight Loss*
30	47	M	W	27.2	35	3.5	1.51
31	49	M	C	27.2	35	2.5	0.87
32	50	F	C	27.2	37	3.3	0.95
33	54	F	C	27.4	50	2.5	0.39
34	59	M	W	25.5	64	2.0	0.71
35	33	M	C	25.5	36	3.8	1.00
36	51	F	W	25.5	52	3.6	0.75
37	26	M	C	25.5	78	6.0	0.93
38	62	M	C	25.5	78	1.3	1.25
39	18	M	W	24.0	50	4.0	0.85
Mean							0.92
Max.							1.51
Min.							0.39
Standard error of mean							0.095
Standard deviation							0.302
Standard error of standard deviation							0.068
Coefficient of variation							32.83%
Standard error of coefficient of variation							7.34%

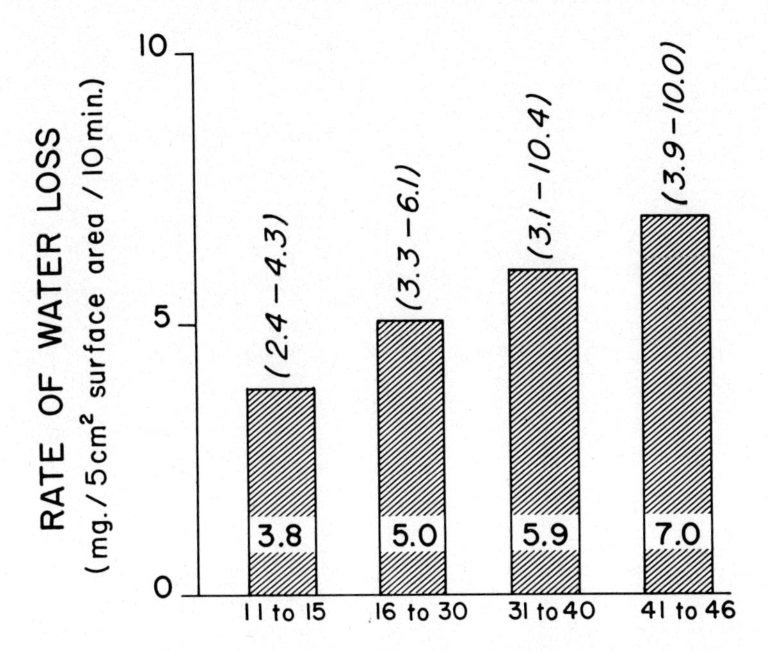

Fig. 10. The influence of skin temperature on the rate of diffusion of water through dead skin. (From *Arch. Int. Med.*, 74:437, 1944.)

skin of the living subjects contributed to the more rapid rate of insensible perspiration. Studies on isolated areas of skin, discussed below, showed that the rates of water loss through dead and living skin maintained at the same temperature were equal. When the temperature of the skin was lowered, however, the rate of water loss decreased more or less in direct proportion to the change in temperature. Since the skin of living subjects was at a higher temperature than that of the dead bodies, most of the differences in water loss through the skin of the living and dead bodies could be explained on the basis of the differences in the effects of skin temperature on the rate of diffusion (Fig. 10).

THE RATES OF WATER LOSS FROM VARIOUS AREAS OF SKIN

The rate of water loss from isolated areas of skin was studied by means of brass chambers (4) sealed to the surface of the skin, as described in Chapter 3. The most rapid rates of insensible perspiration for a comfortable environment occurred, in descending order, for the soles of the feet, palms of the hands, arms, forehead, legs and trunk (Fig. 11).

The rates of water loss from the same areas of skin studied under identical environmental conditions were essentially the same during summer months as during winter months (Fig. 12).

When sweating was stimulated by a hot and humid environment, the most rapid rates of water loss were from the axillae, forehead, arms and right index finger tip (Fig. 11).

In a hot and humid environment water loss through the skin involved both diffusion of water through the skin and water loss through sweat gland activity. Since at increased environmental temperatures all samples collected from the

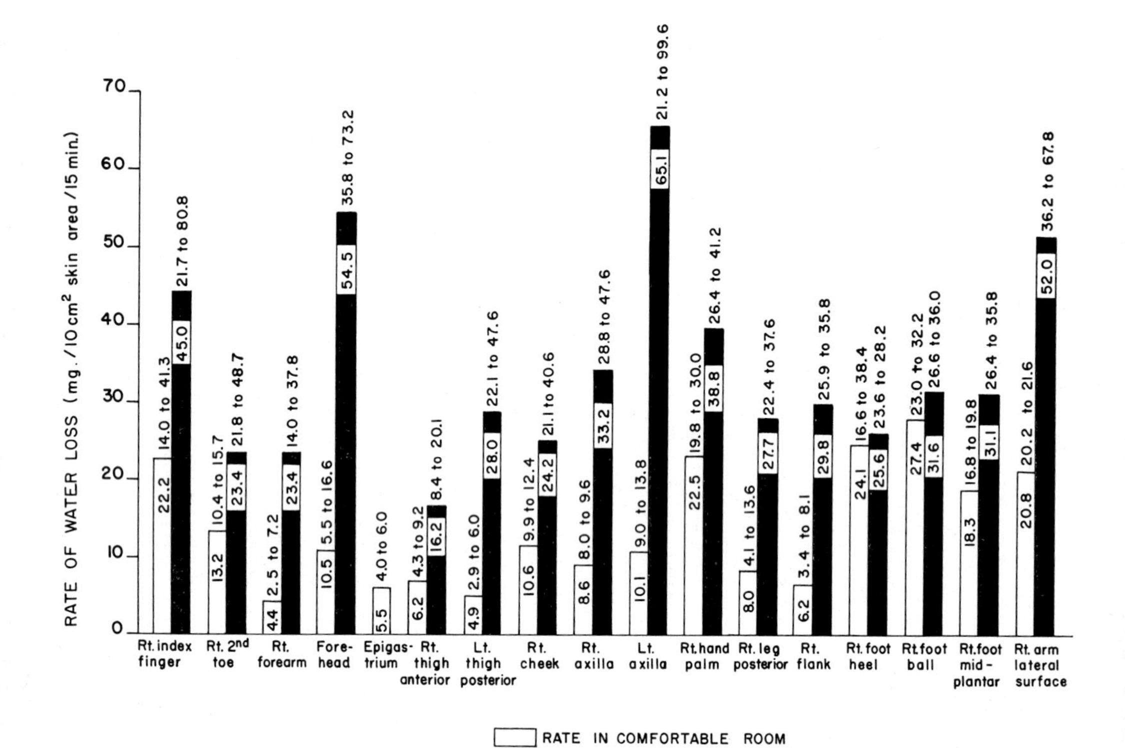

Fig. 11. The rate of water loss through the skin of various body sites with the subjects in a comfortable (75° F., 50% R.H.) and a hot and humid environment (95° to 100° F., 75% R.H.) (From *Am. J. Physiol.*, *138*:603, 1943.)

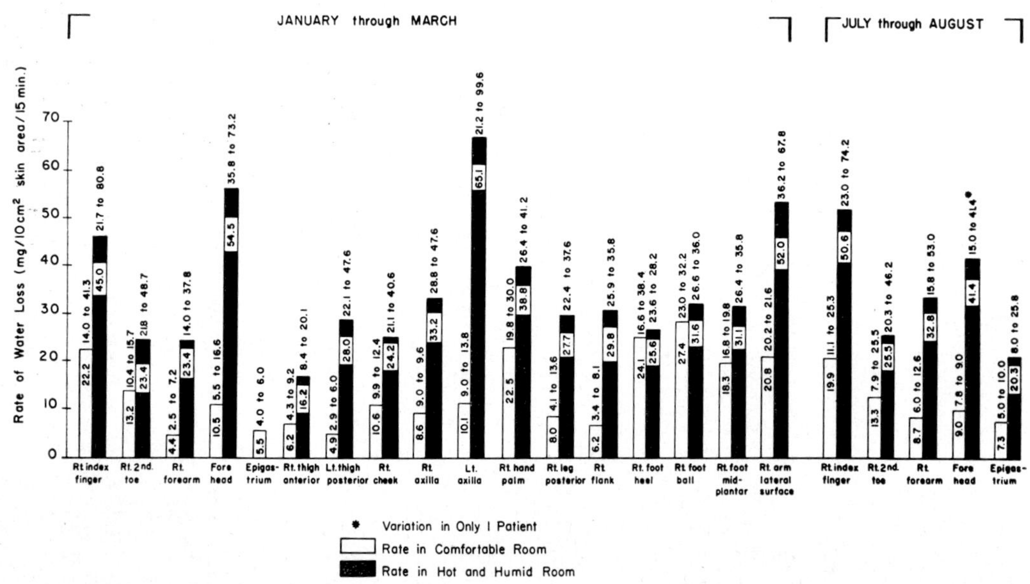

Fig. 12. Influence of season on the rate of water loss through the skin of various body sites with the subjects in a comfortable (75° F., 50% R.H.) and a hot and humid environment (95° to 100° F., 75% R.H.). (Modified from *J. Clin. Invest.*, *23*:37, 1944.)

skin contained sweat, the effect of a hot and humid environment on insensible water loss could not be determined.

THE RATE OF WATER LOSS THROUGH ISOLATED DEAD SKIN

In order to differentiate between water lost insensibly by diffusion of water through the skin and water lost through sweat gland activity (occult sweating), the brass chambers were sealed to dead human skin, as described in Chapter 3, and the rate of water loss studied at controlled atmospheres (5). Additional measurements of water loss by diffusion were made for dead human skin mounted on brass cylinders (6) (Chapter 3).

The rate of water loss through dead skin was essentially the same as that through living skin in a comfortable environment and at the same temperature (Fig. 13). The greatest rates of water loss by diffusion were through the skin of the palms and soles and through toenails. The higher the environmental temperature, the greater was the rate of water loss through dead skin. There was no significant difference between the rates of water loss through skin of Negro and white subjects (Fig. 14). The rate of water loss through dead human skin was essentially the same whether the skin was obtained from bodies dead two hours or one week (Fig. 15). The variation in the rate of diffusion of water through a sample of skin over a continuous 61-day period is shown in Figure 16. The mean rate of water loss through the skin of 2 subjects with atrophic sweat glands was found to be essentially the same as that through dead skin of normal subjects (Fig. 17).

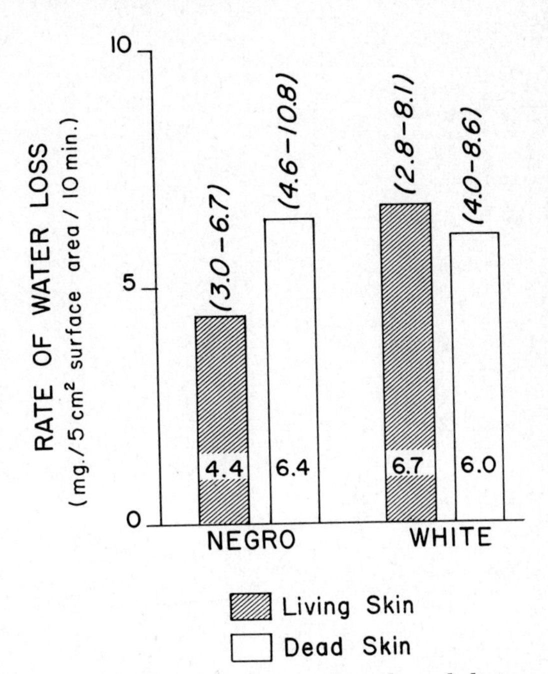

Fig. 14. The rate of water loss through living and dead skin of Negro and white subjects. (From *Arch. Int. Med.*, *74*:437, 1944.)

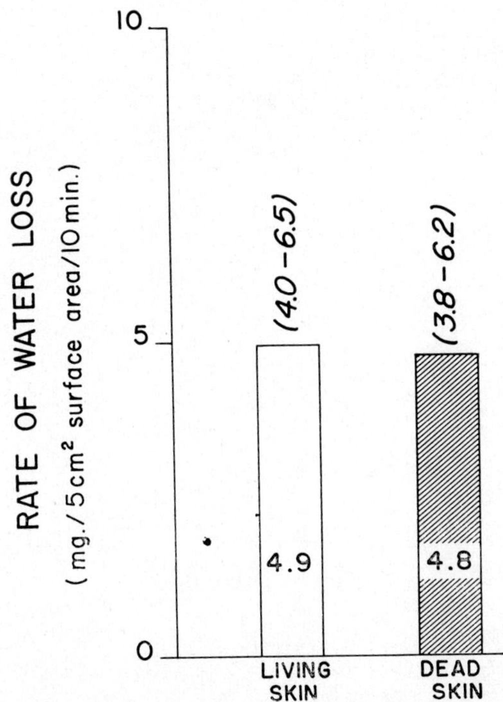

Fig. 13. Rate of water loss through living and dead skin observed under the same environmental conditions. (From *Arch. Int. Med.*, *74*:437, 1944.)

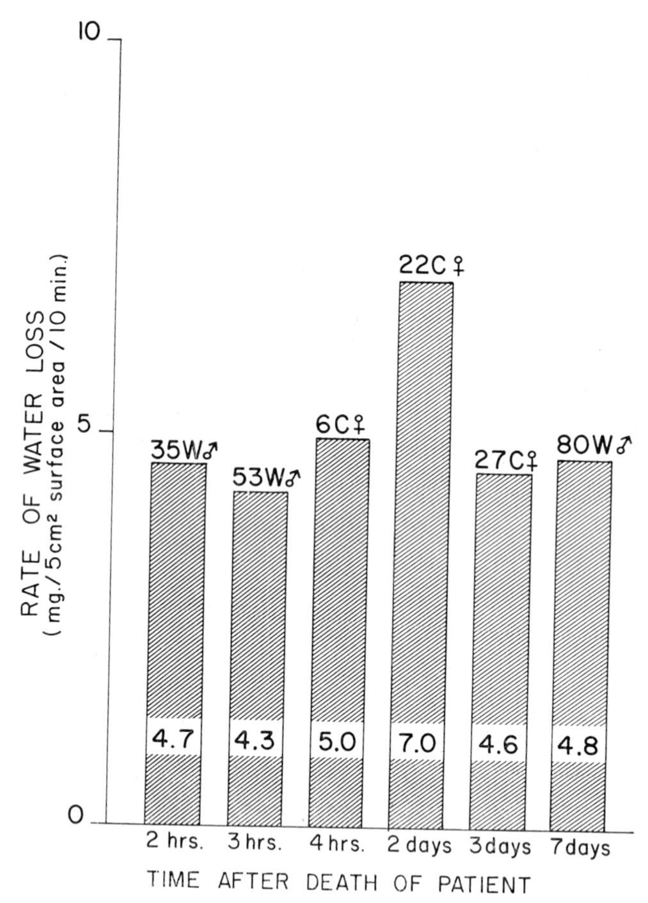

Fig. 15. The rate of water loss through 6 specimens of dead skin taken at various intervals of time after death. Age, color and sex are indicated at the top of each column. (From *Arch. Int. Med.*, *74*:437, 1944.)

THE RATE OF WATER LOSS THROUGH ISOLATED LIVING SKIN

When insensible water loss was measured through isolated areas of living skin by passing dry oxygen over the skin, it was not possible to know whether the water collected represented water of diffusion alone or water of diffusion plus water secreted by the sweat glands. Therefore, to provide an opportunity for sweat to accumulate on the surface of the skin of living subjects resting quietly in a comfortable environment, the flow of oxygen through the brass chamber sealed to the skin was interrupted for various periods of time. It was found that there was no accumulation of sweat gland secretion since the difference between the amount of water collected prior to and after stopping the oxygen flow was approximately 1.5 mg. whether the period allowed for accumulation of sweat was ten minutes or 60 minutes (Fig. 18). If sweat had been accumulating, the quantity that accumulated should have increased as the time allowed for accumulation increased. Therefore, water collected from the skin of a subject resting in a comfortable, quiet environment was water of diffusion and not water secreted through sweat gland activity. This is supported

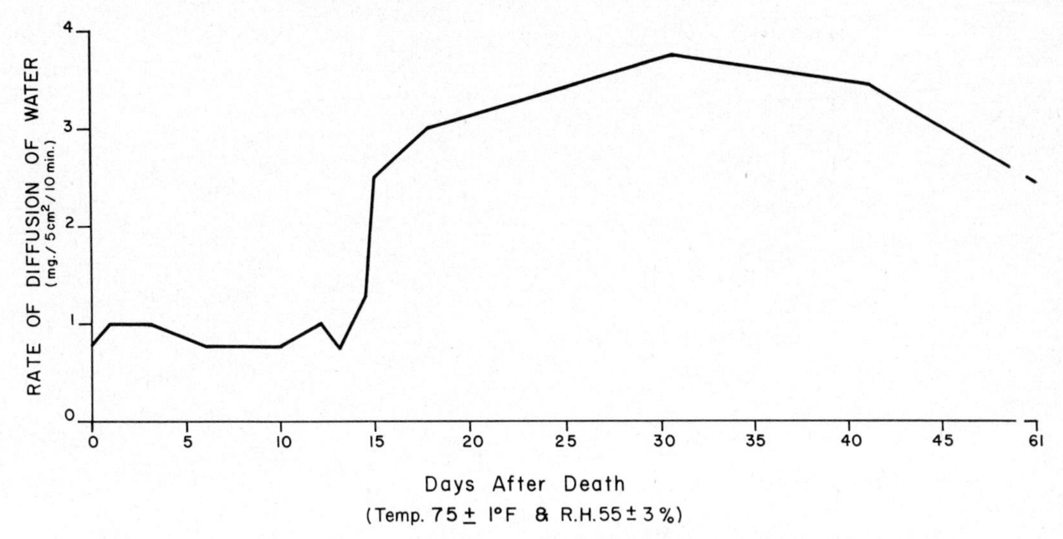

Fig. 16. The rate of water loss from epigastric skin obtained from a patient at autopsy and measured at various intervals of time following the death of the patient. (From *Arch. Dermat. & Syph.*, 53:39, 1946.)

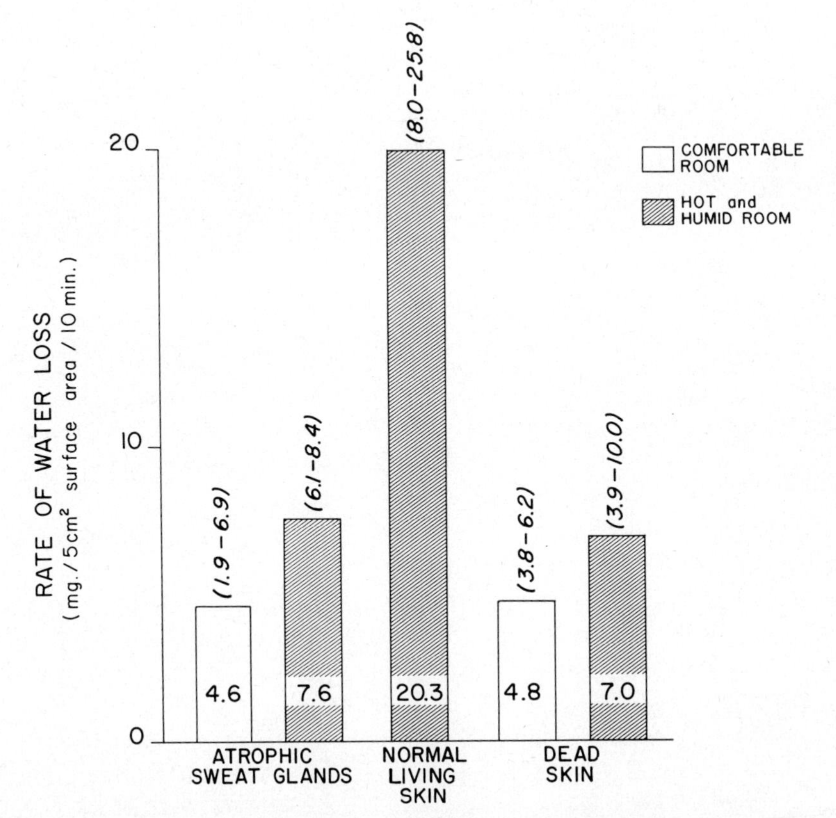

Fig. 17. The rate of water loss through the skin of the epigastrium of 2 patients with atrophic sweat glands, through the skin of normal subjects and through dead skin for a comfortable (75° F. ((38° C.)), 50% R.H.) and for a hot and humid environment (115° F. ((60° C.)), 80% R.H.). (From *Arch. Int. Med.*, 74:437, 1944.)

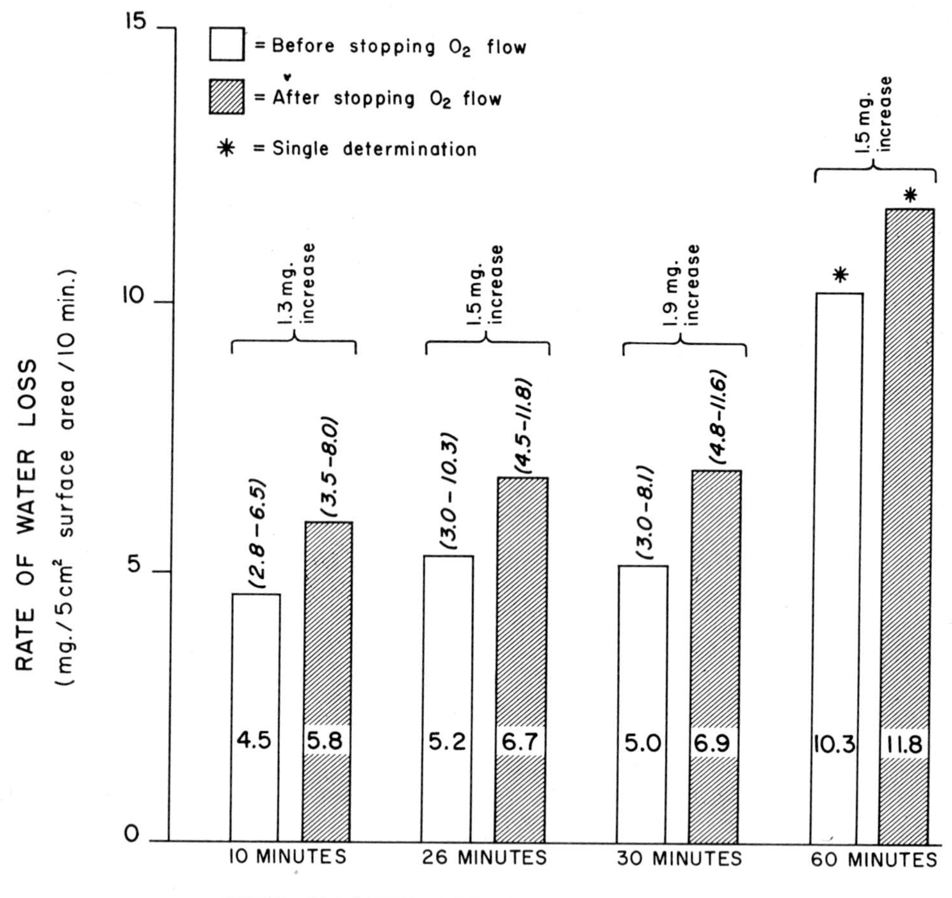

Fig. 18. The rate of water loss through living skin before and after allowing for accumulation of water in the brass chambers. The increase in the amount of water collected for a 10 minute interval after stopping the flow of the oxygen was the same even though the time allowed for sweat to collect varied from 10 to 60 minutes. The larger amount of water collected after stopping flow of the dry O_2 was due to previous "drying" of the skin. (From *Arch. Int. Med.*, *74*:437, 1944.)

by the following facts: 1) the rate of water loss from the surface of the skin of subjects resting quietly in a comfortable environment is the same as the rate of water loss through dead skin maintained at the temperature of living human skin; 2) the rate of water loss is essentially the same from the epigastrium of normal subjects and from that of subjects with atrophic sweat glands; and, 3) there is no significant difference between the amounts of water collected for a given period of time from the epigastrium of living subjects prior to and after allowing time for sweat to accumulate on the surface of the skin.

DEFINITION OF SENSIBLE PERSPIRATION, INSENSIBLE PERSPIRATION AND OCCULT SWEATING

Because of possible confusion in the literature and because it is possible to separate water loss by diffusion from water loss through sweat gland activity, it is advisable to define sensible, insensible and occult perspiration. Perspiration has been distinguished as either *insensible* or *sensible.* The former has been defined as "those gaseous emanations from the body which do not appear in the form of sensible sweat or moisture, such as gaseous productions arising from the lungs in exhalation and from the skin by vaporization." Sensible perspiration or sweating is defined as "perspiration which appears as moisture on the skin." However, if the rate of sweating and the vapor pressure of the ambient air are low so that sweat evaporates as rapidly as it is secreted, then sweat will not accumulate on the surface of the body. By definition, such water loss would be called "insensible" perspiration even though it was produced by the sweat glands. However, it seems best to consider water which is lost from the body independent of sweat gland activity as *insensible perspiration* and that due to sweat gland activity, whether it is visible on the surface of the body or not, as *sensible perspiration.* That portion of the sensible perspiration which is not visible as moisture on the surface of the body because of prompt evaporation would be referred to as *occult sweat.*

PATHOPHYSIOLOGIC INTERPRETATIONS

The rate of insensible water loss is related to metabolic activity and is greatly influenced by food intake and muscular activity. It has been pointed out (7) that insensible perspiration (I. L.) is equal to the weight of water loss (I. W.) plus the weight of the carbon dioxide exhaled minus the weight of oxygen absorbed, i.e.,

$$\text{I. L.} = \text{I. W.} + CO_2 - O_2. \quad (1)$$

If the diet is known, it is possible to calculate the amount of carbon dioxide inhaled and the oxygen absorbed. Therefore, if the subject is in metabolic equilibrium, it is possible to compute the insensible water loss.

There is an essentially linear relationship between insensible perspiration and heat production. Therefore, those foods which increase heat production will also increase the rate of water loss from the body. Protein with its high specific dynamic action (SDA) will greatly increase water loss by diffusion. The importance of these factors to survival under conditions of water shortage and deprivation is obvious.

In patients suffering from febrile illness the rate of total insensible water loss may be great. This must be considered when estimating daily fluid requirements. Furthermore, diseases with high rates of metabolic activity will be associated with high rates of water loss, whereas the converse is true for diseases with low metabolic rates. Obviously, the environmental temperature and relative humidity greatly influence the rate of total insensible water loss.

Sensible perspiration in a resting adult is not marked until the environmental temperature and humidity limit the loss of heat by radiation, conduction and convection (Chapter 13). For example, at a room temperature of 95° F. and a relative humidity of 75%, a subject resting quietly in bed was relatively comfortable. Although the rate of sweating was greater than normal, it was not marked since heat loss by radiation just maintained thermal balance. At this critical level sweating was cyclic. As

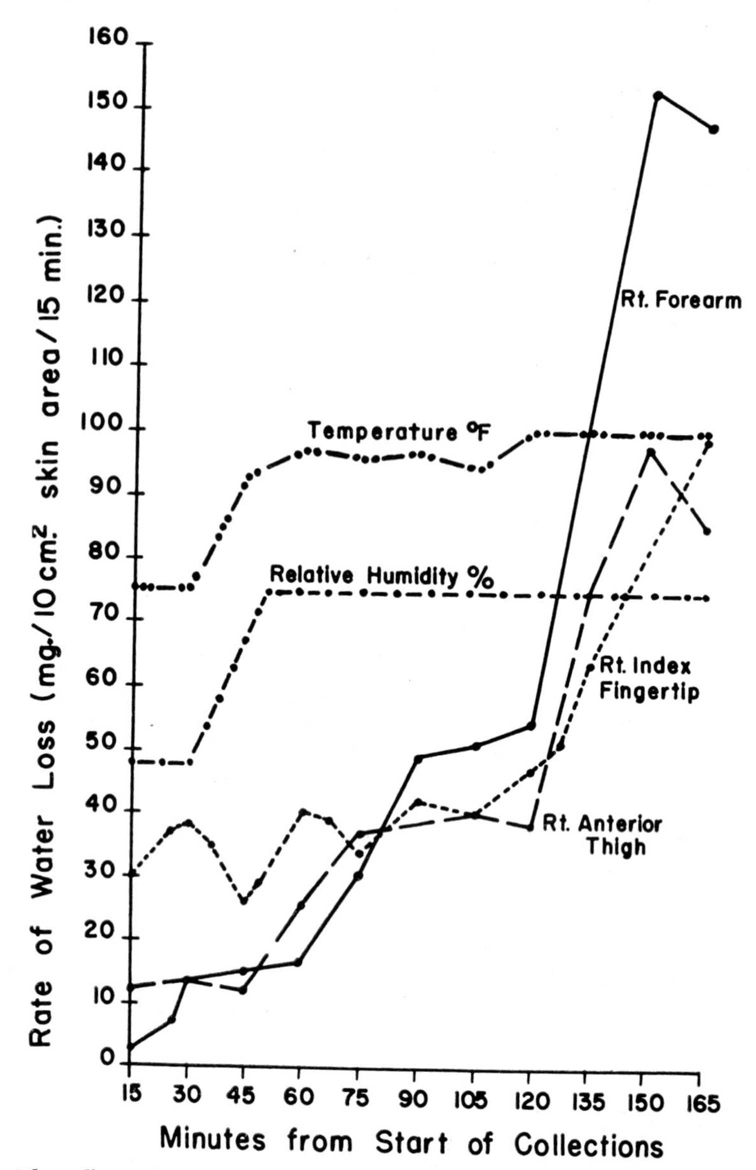

Fig. 19. The effect of variations in room temperature and humidity on the rate of water loss from three skin areas of one subject. (From *Am. J. Physiol.*, *138*:603, 1943.)

the body accumulated heat, sweating developed, the body cooled and sweating ceased. Soon the body reaccumulated heat and sweating again developed to cool the body. These oscillations in sweating continued as long as the environmental temperature remained at the critical level (Chapter 13).

When the room temperature was increased to 100° F. and the relative humidity maintained at 75%, there was an immediate and marked increase in the rate of water loss even though this represented a rise in temperature of only 5° F. (Fig. 19). Under such circumstances heat was transferred from the atmosphere to the body and convection currents (less than 20 ft./min.) could not

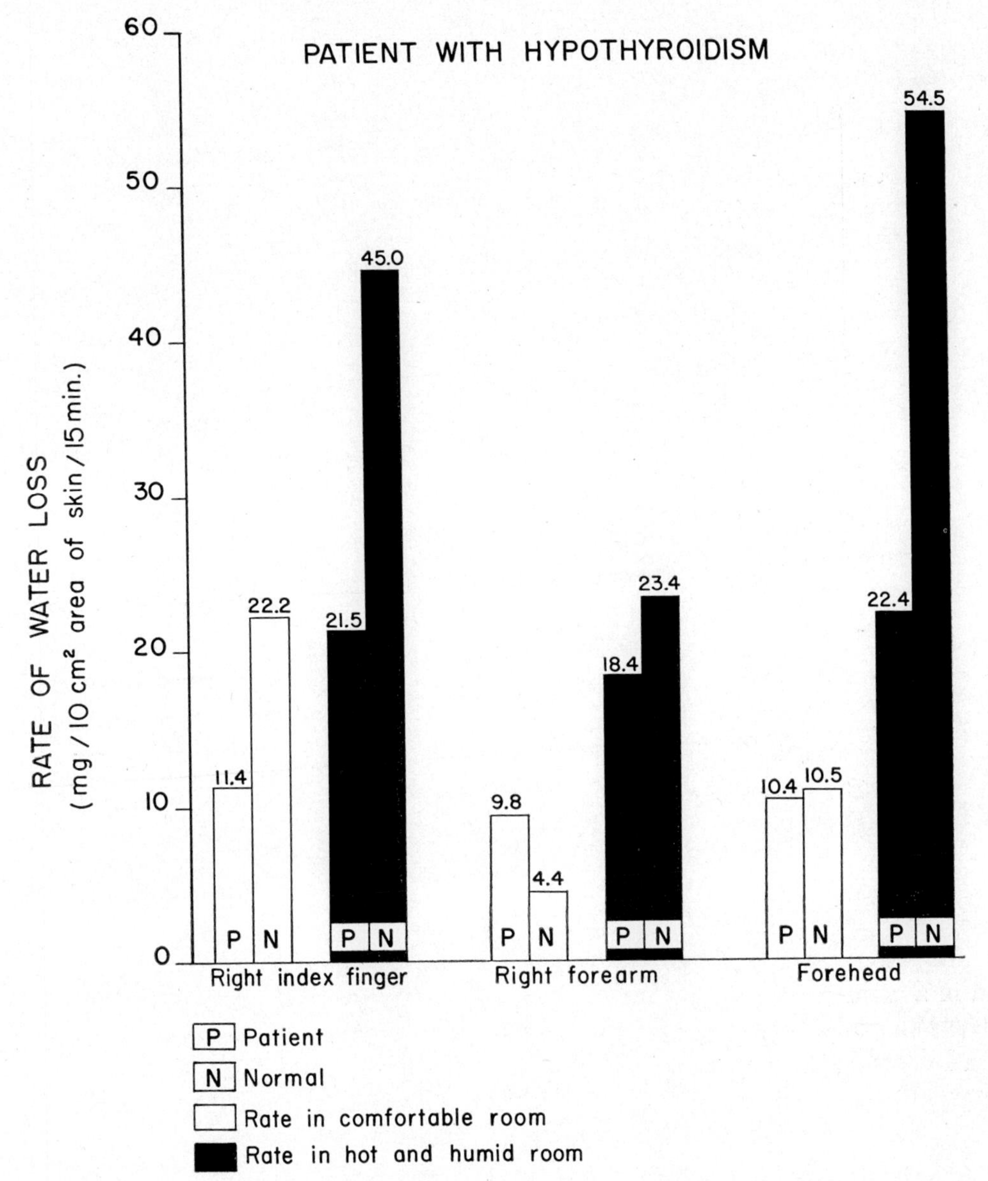

Fig. 20. The rate of water loss through the skin of several body areas of a patient with hypothyroidism. (From *J. Clin. Invest.*, 23:37, 1944.)

cool the body, but instead helped to heat it. The only possible source of heat loss was through evaporation. However, heat loss through evaporation was impeded by the high relative humidity. Sensible perspiration, even though relatively ineffective, was stimulated and copious amounts of sweat were produced. Marked sweating over prolonged periods of time in an unacclimatized person may produce serious illness.

THE RATE OF WATER LOSS FOR VARIOUS PATHOLOGIC STATES

The rate of water loss through the skin of patients with various diseased

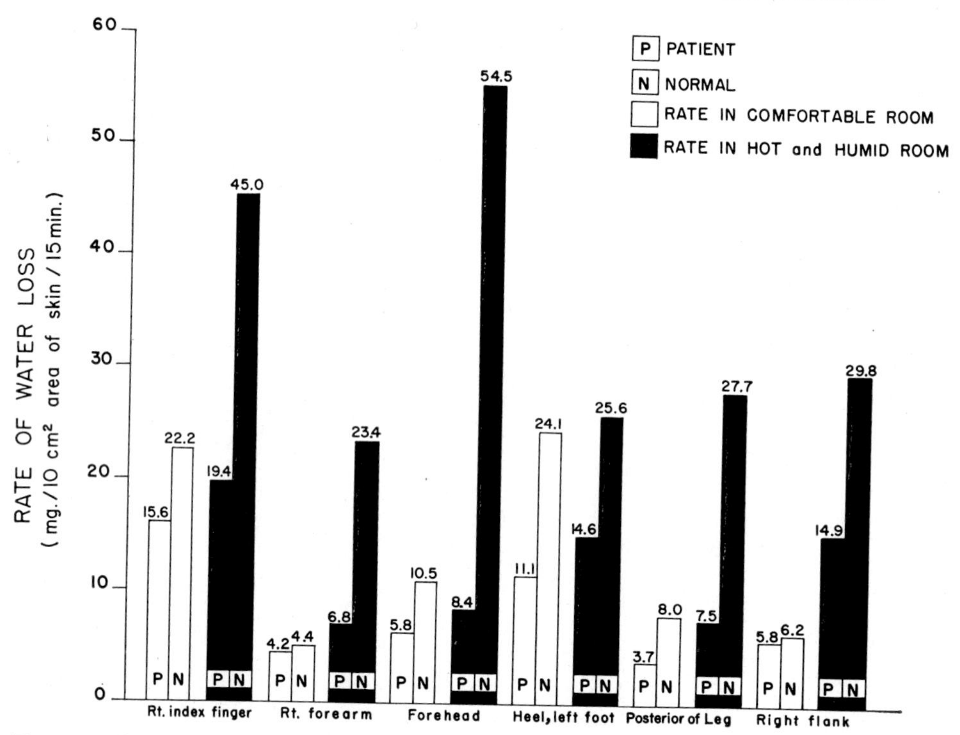

Fig. 21. The rate of water loss through the skin of several body areas of a patient with heat intolerance. (From *J. Clin. Invest.*, 23:37, 1944.)

states was measured. The patients were studied while resting in a hospital-type bed in a comfortable environment.

Hypothyroidism. In general, patients with hypothyroidism had lower rates of water loss from the skin than normal subjects. The rate of water loss from the right index finger tip was less than normal, from the right forearm above normal, and from the forehead within the normal range (Fig. 20). Rates of water loss for the index finger tip and forehead in a hot and humid environment failed to reach those of the normal.

Heat Intolerance. A female patient who complained of the summer weather was unable to work in hot weather without quickly becoming fatigued. Nothing was found in the clinical evaluation of the patient to account for this complaint. The rates of water loss through the skin were consistently below the average normal rates. These differences from the normal were markedly accentuated in a hot, humid room (Fig. 21).

Nervous Sweating. The regional rates of water loss for a patient with "nervous" sweating are shown in Figure 22. The rates of water loss were normal in all areas except the right index finger tip where it greatly exceeded the normal. This conforms to the clinical observation that, besides the axillae, the hands are primarily involved in psychogenic sweating. The eccrine sweat glands of the hands differ from the eccrine glands of other areas of the body in that they readily respond to emotional stimuli.

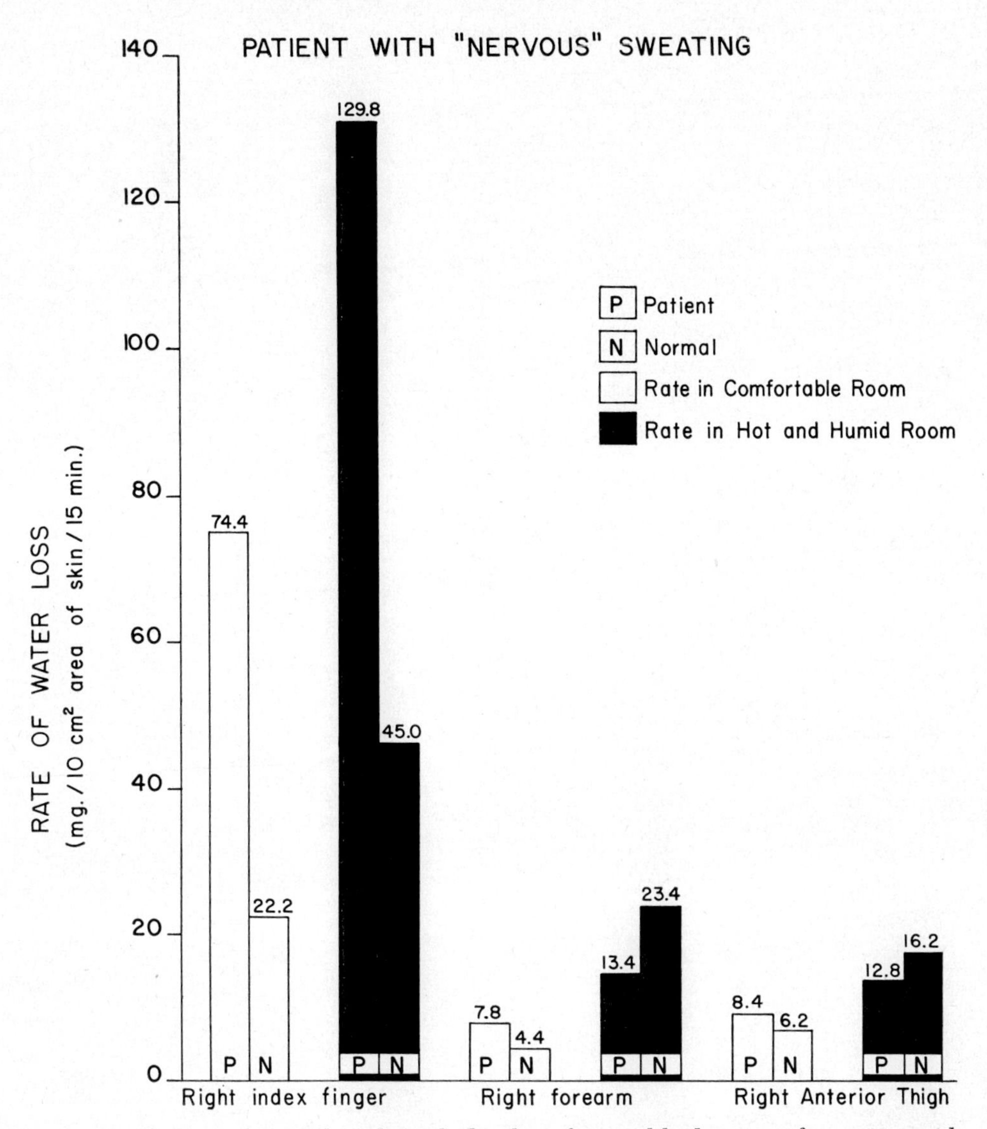

Fig. 22. The rate of water loss through the skin of several body areas of a patient with neurocirculatory asthenia and "nervous sweating." (From *J. Clin. Invest.*, *23*:37, 1944.)

Scleroderma. The involved areas of skin of patients with scleroderma exhibited low rates of water loss (Fig. 23).

Acromegaly. Acromegaly is often associated with profuse sweating. A patient with acromegaly studied in the laboratory was found to have rates of water loss from the right index finger tip, the axillae and the forearm which were higher than normal for the comfortable environment, but which, with the exception of the finger, were essentially normal for a hot and humid environment. This phenomenon may be related to the hypermetabolic state often found in patients with acromegaly.

Occlusive Vascular Disease. Patients with occlusive vascular disease associ-

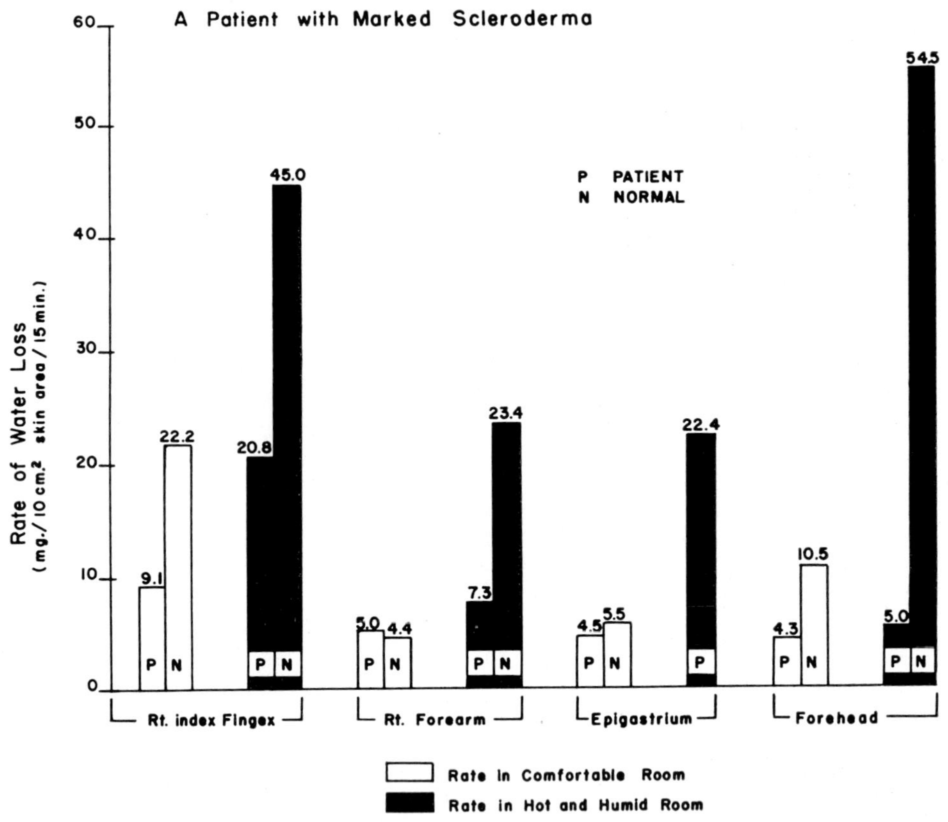

Fig. 23. The rate of water loss through the skin of several body areas of a patient with scleroderma. (From *J. Clin. Invest.*, 23:37, 1944.)

ated with impairment of blood flow exhibited decreased rates of water loss from ischemic areas.

Congestive Heart Failure. In patients with congestive heart failure the rates of water loss studied simultaneously for the finger tip, forearm and leg were found to be slightly lower than normal. In general, the more severe the failure, the less was the water loss (Fig. 24). In a hot and humid environment the rate of water loss from the skin of patients with progressing congestive heart failure was considerably less than normal. The reduction in the rate of water loss in a hot and humid environment may result in impairment of thermal regulation. Because of the physical effort and anxiety associated with congestive heart failure, there is an increased rate of heat production. Furthermore, because of the impaired circulation and venous stasis, there is also a decrease in the rate of heat elimination through the skin by conduction, radiation and convection. The heat produced in the muscles and viscera internally is not satisfactorily transported by the blood to the surface of the body for elimination. With the reduction in sensible perspiration (sweating) there is a restriction of all avenues of heat loss in patients with congestive heart failure, i.e., radiation, convection, conduction and evaporation. The fever often encountered in congestive heart failure has been attributed to impaired ability to eliminate body heat (8). Indeed, at high environmental tempera-

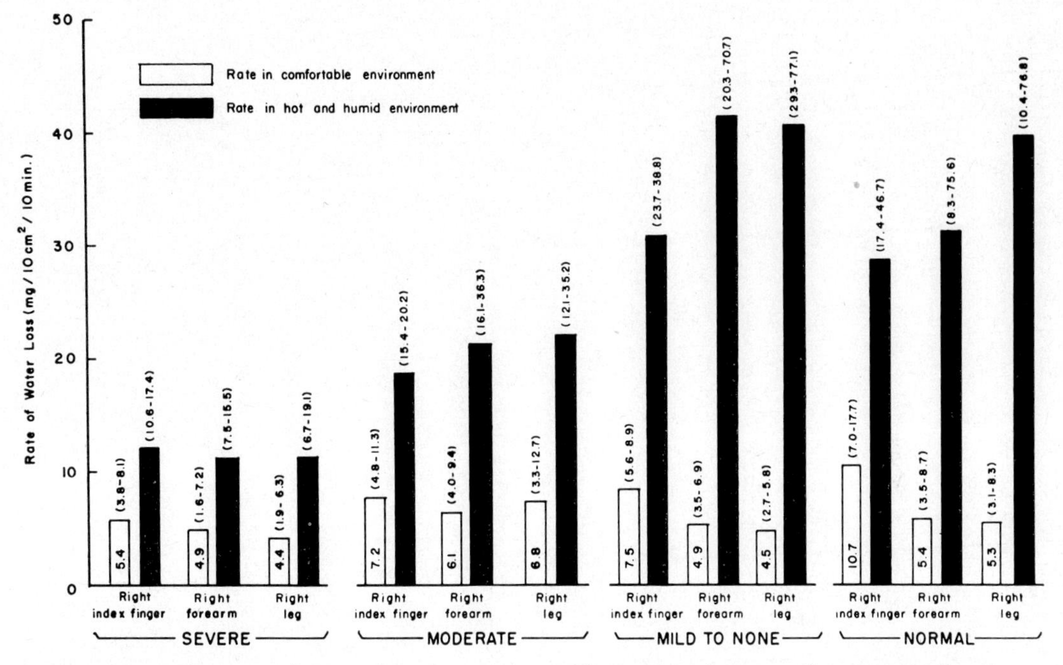

Fig. 24. The rate of water loss in patients with varying degrees of congestive heart failure and in normal subjects studied in a comfortable and in a hot and humid environment. The more progressive the congestive heart failure, the lower the rate of water loss both in the comfortable and in the hot environment for each of the three skin sites studied. The rate of water loss in the hot and humid environment was relatively more depressed than the rate of water loss in the comfortable environment for the same degree of congestive heart failure. (Modified from *Am. J. M. Sci., 211*:181, 1946.)

tures patients with congestive heart failure may actually *accumulate* heat. Thus, a hot and humid environment is more likely to exert a deleterious effect upon the cardiovascular system of patients with congestive heart failure. An environmental situation which promotes the accumulation of heat and therefore the need for increased cardiac work to maintain thermal balance should be avoided in patients with congestive heart failure. This is discussed in more detail in other portions of this monograph (Chapter 11).

CLINICAL APPLICATIONS

The maintenance of electrolyte and fluid balance is one of the major problems in clinical medicine. Patients who lose significant quantities of body fluids present therapeutic difficulties. In such patients therapy is concerned in large part with electrolyte and water replacement. It is often difficult to estimate water losses quantitatively at the bedside when sweat cannot be measured. Thus, since it is not possible to measure accurately the amount of sweat lost by patients, it is a good practice to eliminate this loss when possible by providing a comfortable cool environment with air-conditioning. The daily losses of water through the various channels can be estimated for clinical purposes. The rates shown in Table 1 are for an average-sized adult male. These rates must be adjusted for body build, the clinical state of the patient and the environmental conditions.

A man resting comfortably in bed in a neutral environment has an average total insensible water loss of 3.418 cc./m^2/10 min. Assuming a body area of 1.7 square meters, the total insensible water loss in 24 hours would be about 850 cc. However, insensible water loss through the skin is greatly accelerated by pyrexia or a high environmental temperature, so that additional allowances must be made for these conditions. If the ventilatory rate is increased for any reason, water loss from the respiratory tract increases. When the environmental temperature is high, sensible water loss must be added to insensible water loss. In a hot and humid environment, four to five liters of fluid may be lost through the skin and respiratory tract in a 24-hour period. Obviously, such losses must be replaced to prevent dehydration. In patients who are able to take adequate amounts of fluid orally, simply having water available at the bedside is all that is required to insure adequate hydration. However, very ill patients may be too weak to drink and may require parenteral replacement. Also, it should be remembered that older patients often have impairment of the thirst mechanisms and therefore will not maintain water and electrolyte balance without assistance from others.

Precise fluid replacement is even more critical in anuric patients. Therefore, water loss through all channels must be estimated carefully, taking into consideration the factors mentioned.

In patients with congestive heart failure the rate of water loss through the skin is low, and at the same time there is impairment of heat loss from the body. A high environmental temperature and relative humidity will also result in further impairment of heat loss. Under such circumstances physical exertion and heat production should be kept as low as possible.

The problems associated with estimating nonurinary water loss in a warm and humid environment are in part eliminated by a comfortable air-conditioned atmosphere. Since the body surface is kept cool, the rate of water diffusion through the skin is normal. In addition, water loss through sweating is eliminated.

REFERENCES

1. Burch, G. E. and Winsor, T.: The relation of total insensible loss of weight to water loss from the skin and lungs of human subjects in a subtropical climate. *Am. J. M. Sc., 209:*226, 1945.
2. Benedict, F. G. and Benedict, C. G.: Perspiration Insensibilis: Ihr Wesen und ihre Ursachen. *Biochem. Ztschr., 186:*278, 1927.
3. Galeotti, G.: Uber die Ausscheidung des Wassers bei der Atmung. *Biochem. Ztschr., 46:*173, 1912.
4. Burch, G. E. and Sodeman, W. A.: Regional relationships of rate of water loss in normal adults in a subtropical climate. *Am. J. Physiol., 138:*603, 1943.
5. Burch, G. E. and Winsor, T.: Rate of insensible perspiration (diffusion of water) locally through living and through dead human skin. *Arch. Int. Med., 74:*437, 1944.
6. Burch, G. E. and Winsor, T.: Diffusion of water through dead plantar, palmar and torsal human skin and through toe nails. *Arch. Dermat. & Syph., 53:*39, 1946.
7. Isenschmid: Die Bestimmung der Wasserbilanz am Krankenbett. *Med. Klin., 14:*1128, 1918.
8. Cohn, A. E. and Steele, J.: Unexplained fever in heart failure. *J. Clin. Invest., 13:*853, 1934.

V

THE CUTANEOUS WATER AND ELECTROLYTE BARRIER

THE integument, the most massive organ of the body, protectively envelops man. Chemicals, microorganisms and debris do not easily penetrate the intact skin. However, the skin is penetrable. Certain substances can enter the body through intact skin via either the ducts of the sweat and sebaceous glands or directly through the epidermis (1). Although the skin can withstand considerable amounts of physical trauma, if its protective mantle is disrupted through physical injury, foreign material and microorganisms readily enter the body. For example, a small scratch by a needle contaminated with the virus of infectious hepatitis may result in disease, whereas blood of a patient with infectious hepatitis in contact with intact skin is innocuous.

As previously indicated, one of the most important functions of the skin is to inhibit the free passage of fluid and electrolytes from the body, for without skin man would become desiccated and die within a few minutes of exposure to a gentle, warm, dry breeze. Experiments were therefore designed to study the mechanisms by which the skin regulates water and electrolyte loss. The methods employed to measure rates of water loss in these experiments were described in Chapter 3.

THE ROLE OF THE VARIOUS LAYERS OF THE HUMAN SKIN IN LIMITING WATER LOSS FROM THE BODY

One of the first problems was to learn whether or not living processes were necessary for the skin to inhibit water loss (2, 3). The answer to this problem was available from previous experiments which showed that the rate of diffusion of water was no different for dead skin than for living intact skin (Chapter 4, Fig. 13). If living processes were essential for a functioning cutaneous water barrier, dead skin would have allowed a greater rate of water loss than living intact skin.

Also, from previous experiments it was found that measurements of the rate of diffusion of water through white skin and dark Negro skin failed to exhibit significant racial differences (Chapter 4, Fig. 14). Thus, the factors which inhibit the free diffusion of water through skin are independent of melanin or other racial attributes.

Experiments were then designed to determine which layer of the skin was chiefly responsible for the inhibition of loss of body water (2). Accordingly, the epidermis was removed from living and dead skin by various methods and the rate of water loss through the de-

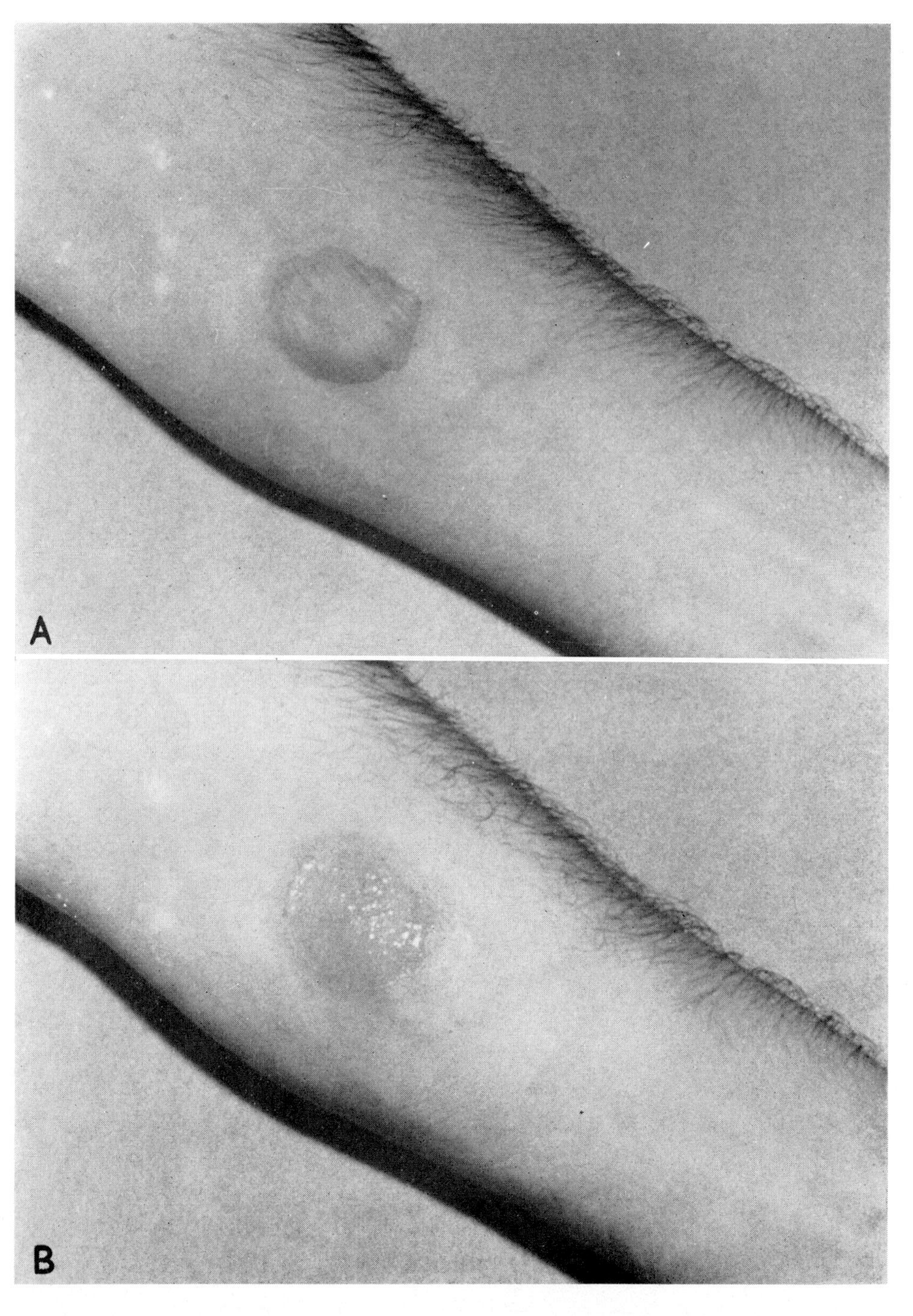

Fig. 25. A. A blister raised on the forearm by means of cantharides plaster. Note that there is little inflammatory reaction at the base of the blister. B. The denuded area of skin exposed by removal of the blister top.

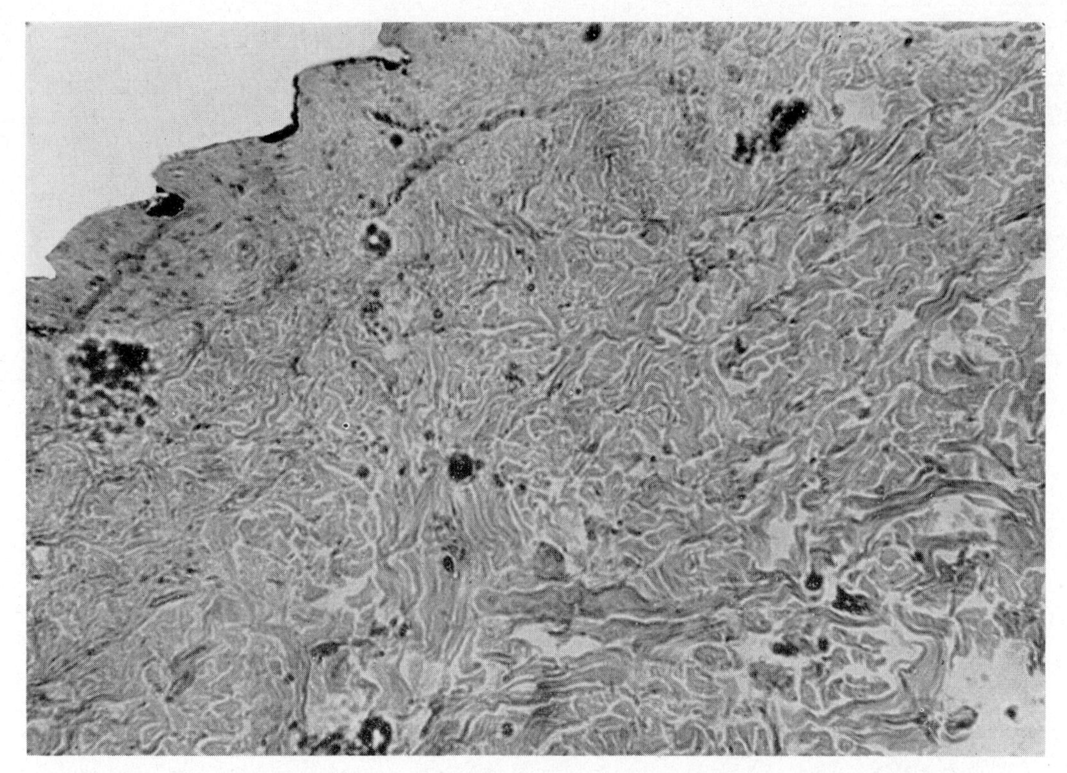

Fig. 26. Histologic section of skin after removal of the epidermis. The epidermis has been almost completely removed except for a few isolated cells of the stratum germinativum located between the dermal papillae. (From *Arch. Int. Med., 74:*428, 1944.)

nuded skin and through the epidermis after its removal from the body was measured.

Formation of the Cantharides Blister. To remove the epidermis from living skin a blister was raised on the skin with cantharides plaster, an agent frequently used in this laboratory as a vesicant to study dermal physiology. The technique for producing the blister consisted of applying to the skin a sufficient amount of cantharides cerate on a disc of Whatman No. 2 filter paper to cover an area of approximately 5 or 10 sq. cm. The paper disc with the plaster was taped to the skin surface for about 10 hours, after which the plaster was removed. A well-formed blister was usually present at the end of this time (Fig. 25a). Most of the mild inflammatory reaction that occurred usually subsided in another 12 hours. Careful removal of the top of the blister exposed the denuded surface of the skin for study (Fig. 25b). The extent to which the epidermis had been removed could be determined by histologic examination (Figs. 26, 27). It is characteristic for a blister formed in this manner to separate the epidermis through the stratum spinosum. Histologic studies have shown that the denuded surface after the removal of the top of the blister consists of stratum germinativum, the malpighian layer and a few cells of the stratum spinosum (2).

Water Loss through Skin Denuded by Vesication. The rate of diffusion of water through the denuded living and denuded dead skin was more rapid than

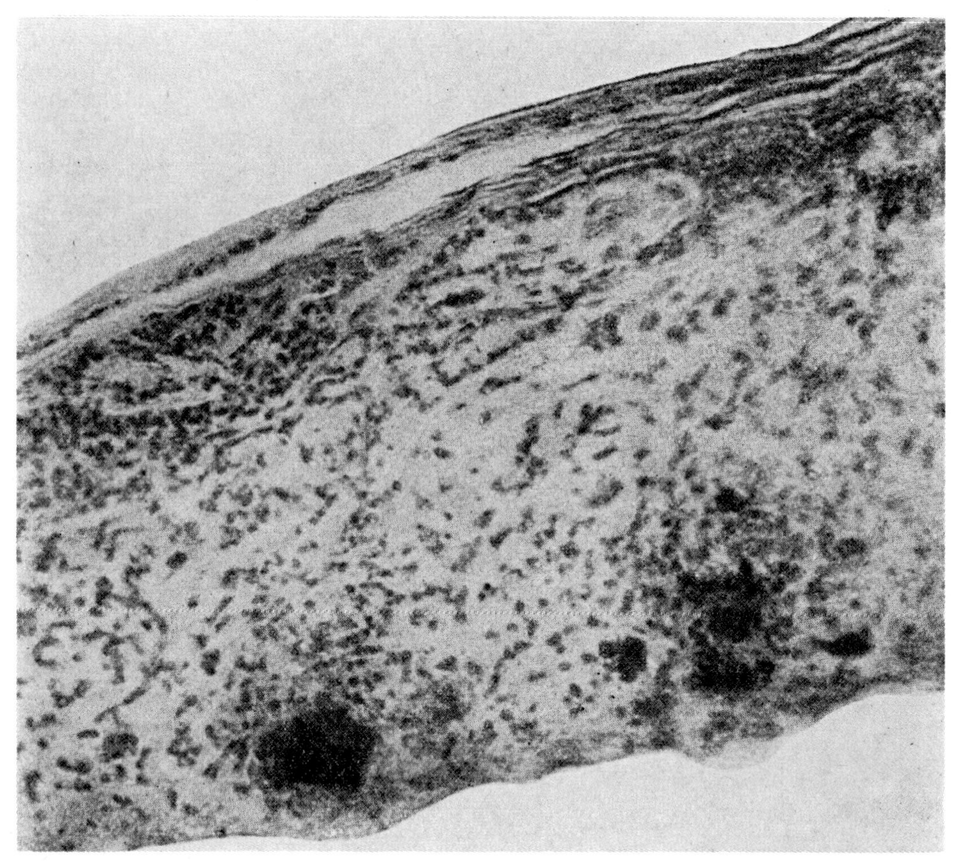

Fig. 27. The top of the blister consisting of the stratum corneum and a few inflammatory cells underlying this layer. (From *Arch. Int. Med., 74*:428, 1944.)

that through normal skin with the epidermis intact (Figs. 13, 28). Since diffusion of water through the denuded skin prepared by the cantharides plaster was uninhibited, part of the epidermis superficial to the stratum spinosum must have contained the layer responsible for the inhibition of water loss.

Water Loss through the Blister Top. The rate of the diffusion of water through the blister top was studied with the blister in situ and found to be similar to that of normal intact skin (Fig. 29). The blister top was then removed by carefully cutting it away from the base of the blister with sharp scissors. The rate of water loss through the blister top thus removed from the body was studied by means of the brass chamber and water bath (Chapter 3) to make certain that osmotic pressure within the blister due to the high protein content of the blister fluid was not a factor in preventing diffusion of water through the blister top. Again the rate of the diffusion of water through the blister top was similar to that of normal intact skin (Fig. 29). In the cantharides-induced blister the sweat ducts are separated from the functional glomeruli of the sweat glands. Thus, the fact that diffusion of water through the blister top was similar to that through normal skin again demonstrated that man rest-

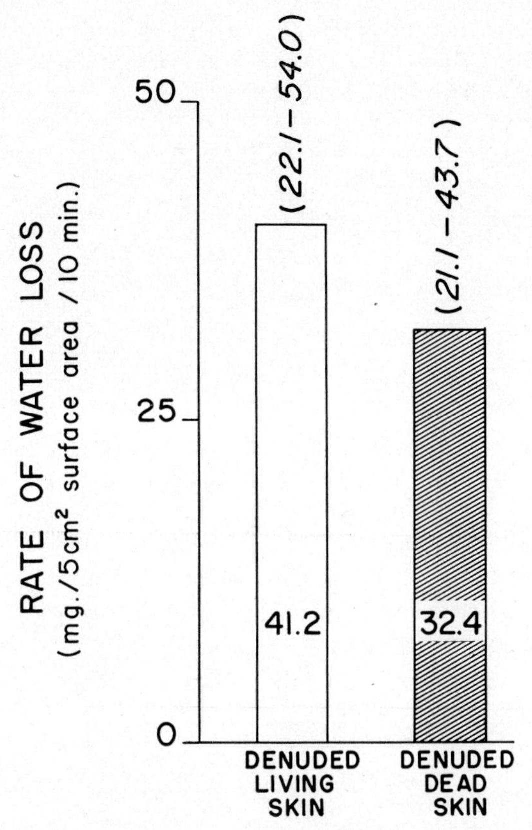

Fig. 28. The rate of the diffusion of water through the dermis of denuded living and dead skin. See text for details. (From *Arch. Int. Med.*, 74:428, 1944.)

ing quietly in a comfortable environment loses water primarily through insensible perspiration or diffusion. Furthermore, if any of the insensible water loss was due to sweating, the intact skin next to the blister should have exhibited a higher rate of diffusion than the intact blister cap, but this was not the case (Fig. 29).

The results of the studies of water diffusion through the blister top were anticipated for the following reasons. Since removal of the blister top allowed free diffusion of water through the remaining denuded skin, the diffusion-inhibiting layer must have been removed with the blister top. As already indicated, direct measurements of the rate of diffusion of water through the blister top confirmed indirect evidence that the diffusion-inhibiting layer of the skin was superficial to the stratum germinativum. Since the blister top consisted chiefly of the stratum corneum, this most likely was the water-retaining layer. The possibility that the stratum lucidum was the diffusion-inhibiting layer was unlikely since the experiments

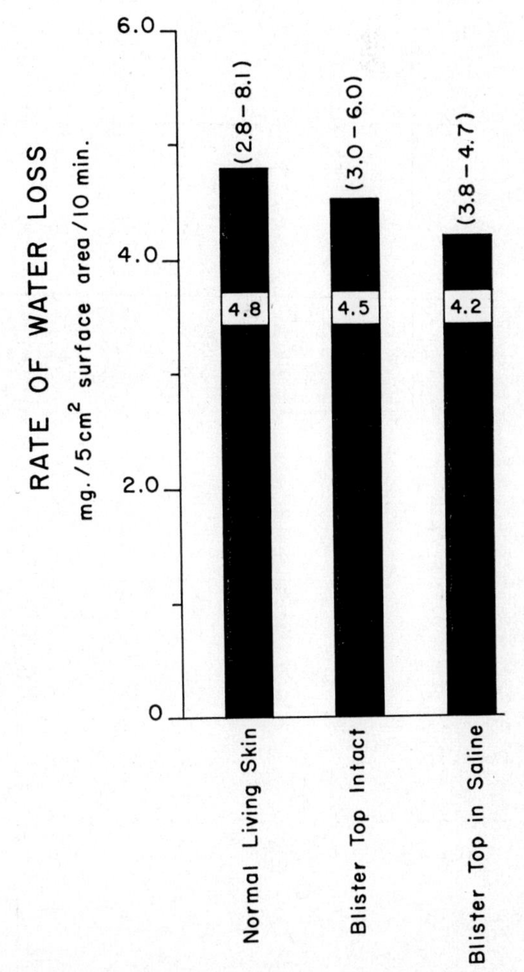

Fig. 29. The rate of water loss through normal living skin and through a blister top prior to removal from the body and in the normal saline bath after removal from the body. (Modified from *Arch. Int. Med.*, 74:428, 1944.)

included samples of skin removed from the epigastrium, in which region the stratum lucidum is absent.

Water Loss through Skin Denuded by Abrasion. Because the cantharides plaster may have altered the permeability of the blister top, experiments were performed in which the corneum of intact skin was removed by abrasion. The intact skin was abraded lightly with number 00 sandpaper so that little of the corneal layer was removed. The rate of diffusion of water through this lightly abraded area of skin was essentially normal (Fig. 30). Intact skin was then abraded moderately to remove more of the corneum. The rate of diffusion of water through the moderately abraded skin, although partially inhibited, was greater than normal (Fig. 30). Finally, the skin was abraded heavily to remove the entire corneum. The rate of the diffusion of water was now essentially uninhibited (Fig. 30). Therefore, it was concluded that the dense corneum was the layer chiefly responsible for inhibiting the diffusion of water through the skin.

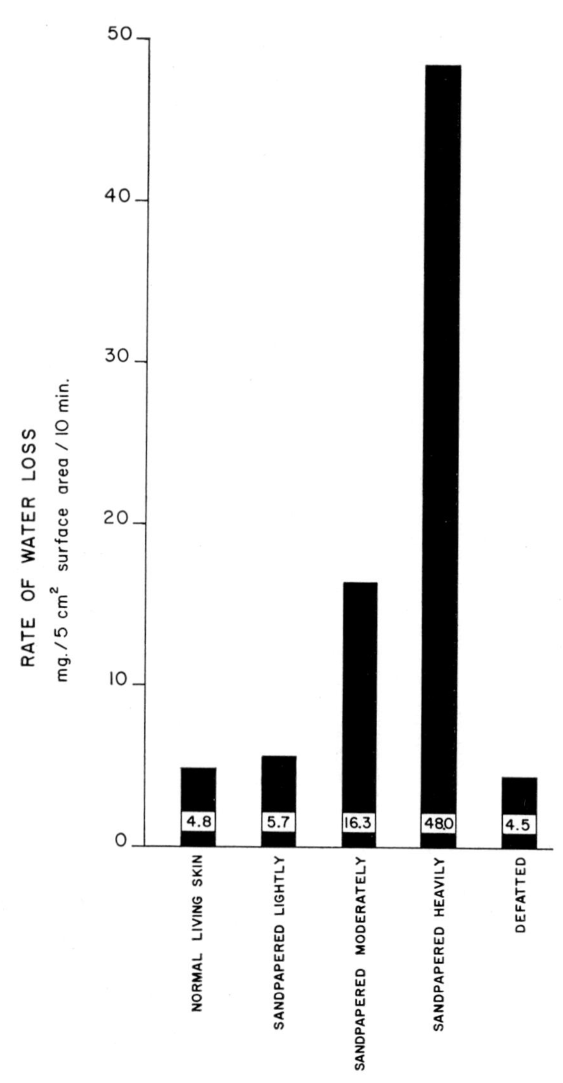

Fig. 30. The rate of water loss through normal skin, through skin sandpapered lightly, moderately and heavily, and through skin which has been cleansed of fats and oils by rubbing lightly with gauze saturated with acetone. (Modified from *Arch. Int. Med.*, *74*:428, 1944.)

NATURE OF THE WATER BARRIER

An attempt was made to identify the factor or factors in the corneum which inhibit diffusion of water through skin. First, abdominal skin was rubbed lightly with gauze saturated with acetone and then with ether to remove the fats and oils of the skin surface. The rate of the diffusion of water through the area of skin cleansed of fats and oils was essentially the same as that through uncleansed skin (Fig. 30). Therefore, either the fatty substances on the surface of the skin are not responsible for the inhibition of diffusion of water through the skin, or the method did not remove a significant amount of the lipid material.

Removal of Lipids from the Epidermis. In order to determine whether or not the extraction of more lipid material would alter the rate of diffusion of water through the skin, specimens of

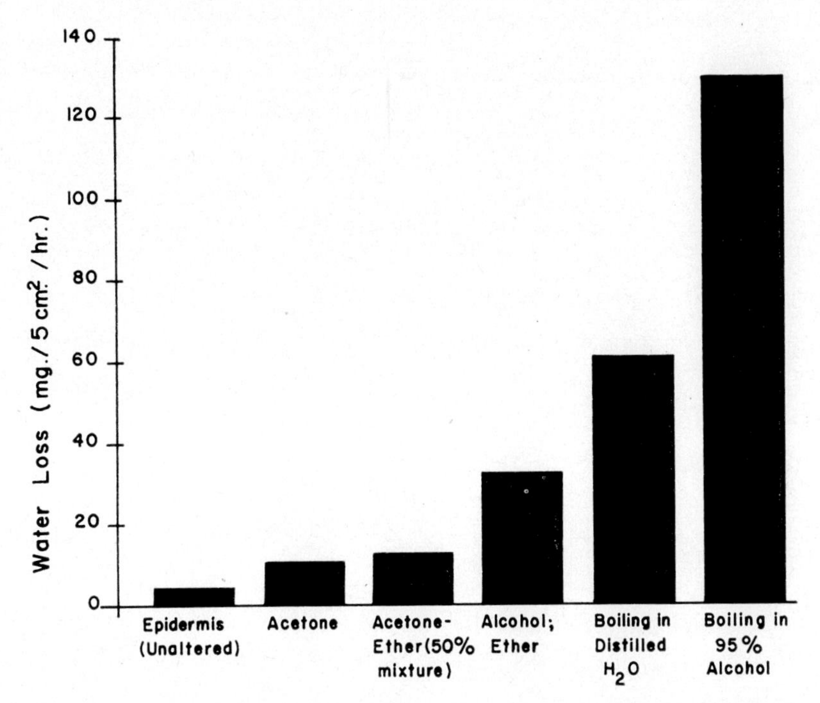

Fig. 31. Comparison of the mean rates of water loss through chemically untreated sheets of epidermis and sheets of epidermis altered by various types of chemical treatment primarily designed to extract lipid materials. (From *Am. J. Trop. Med.*, *31*:842, 1951.)

skin isolated from the abdominal wall of patients within a few hours after death were agitated in acetone, in a mixture of equal volumes of acetone and ethyl ether, and in 95% ethyl alcohol. Skin was also boiled in 95% ethyl alcohol for an hour while control specimens were boiled in distilled water (4). This group of experiments demonstrated that the more complete the extraction of lipid material from the skin, the more rapid was the rate of diffusion of water through the epidermis (Fig. 31). However, the chemical and thermal treatment employed was vigorous and must have produced changes in the epidermis other than removal of lipids. The lipid and related substances of the skin are present as (1) glycerides and free fatty acids, (2) nonsaponifiable fats and high molecular weight alcohols, esters of fatty acids, and (3) phospholipids.

Removal of Keratin from the Epidermis. Since one of the basic substances in the cornified layers of the epidermis is keratin, which is resistant to organic solvents, attempts were made to alter the quantity and physical state of that substance in the epidermis and to study the resultant influence of such alteration on the rate of diffusion of water through the epidermis. Samples of epidermis were placed in 0.001 normal solution of NaOH for 10 hours. Some specimens were exposed for 24 hours to 0.1 molar solution of sodium sulfide adjusted to pH 4.2. The property of skin to inhibit water diffusion was not significantly affected by substances used to alter keratin structure (4). It is likely that keratin acts merely as a framework

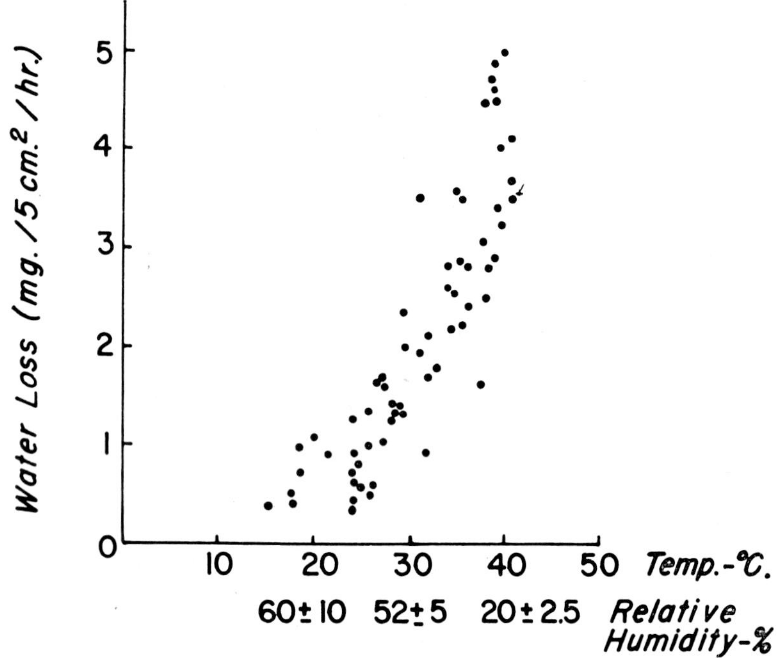

Fig. 32. The influence of increasing temperature and decreasing relative humidity of the atmosphere on the rates of water loss through segments of dead human skin from various sites of the body (abdomen, chest, breast and thigh). The conditions of the atmosphere are within the range of those frequently encountered by living man. (From *Am. J. Trop. Med.*, *31*:842, 1951.)

to hold lipids which are probably the chief barrier to loss of water through human skin.

It seems evident from these studies that the skin acts as an effective barrier to loss of water from the body and that the stratum corneum is the principal layer of the epidermis responsible for inhibiting water loss. Furthermore, the lipid substances contained in the interstices of the keratin matrix of the corneal layer produce a vapor seal which inhibits the diffusion of water through human skin.

THE INFLUENCE OF VARIOUS PHYSICAL FACTORS ON DIFFUSION OF WATER THROUGH ISOLATED HUMAN SKIN

To study the influence of certain physical factors of the environment upon the rate of diffusion of water through human skin, segments of skin were obtained from the abdomen of patients shortly after death and mounted on the orifice of brass cylinders, as described in Chapter 3. The rate of water loss through the skin was determined by weighing the cylinders periodically before and after exposing the skin to the various environmental factors (4). These experiments demonstrated certain interesting facts. For example, the diffusion of water through skin was influenced by atmospheric temperature and humidity (Fig. 32). The effect of *temperature* on the rate of water diffusion through the skin was almost linear for both white and Negro skins (Fig. 33).

The rate of diffusion of water through the skin was also dependent

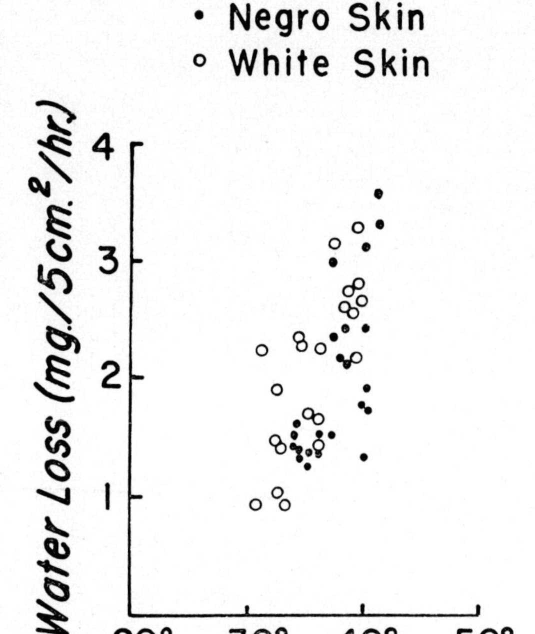

Fig. 33. The rate of water loss through dead, full-thickness human skin exposed directly to infrared radiation. The skin was obtained from white and Negro subjects. The rates of water loss were comparable to those shown in Figure 32 for the corresponding thermal levels. (From *Am. J. Trop. Med.*, *31*:842, 1951.)

upon the water *vapor pressure* adjacent to the surface of the skin. The higher the skin-to-atmospheric water vapor pressure gradient, the greater was the rate of water loss (Fig. 34). Thus, the higher the relative humidity of the ambient air, the lower was the rate of diffusion of water through the skin. Figure 35 demonstrates the effect of varying the relative humidity of the ambient air while maintaining a constant (dry bulb) temperature. Note the rapid decrease in the rate of diffusion when the relative humidity of the ambient air reached levels beyond 80%.

When skin was exposed to *infrared radiation* resulting in an increase in skin temperature, the rate of the diffusion of water through the skin increased as it did when the temperature of the atmosphere alone was increased. Thus, heat applied locally to the skin has the same influence upon the rate of water loss as an increase in temperature of the ambient air.

Skin *shielded* from infrared radiation by means of aluminum membranes 1/32 inch thick held a few centimeters from the surface of the skin had a lower rate of diffusion of water than either unprotected skin or skin shielded by the same aluminum membranes painted black (Fig. 36). The shiny aluminum membrane reflected more of the infrared radiation than did the black surface so that there was less heating of the skin protected by the shiny aluminum surface. The protective effect of shielding the skin with an aluminum membrane is therefore directly related to the skin temperature. Skin exposed to a *tanning* spectrum of ultraviolet

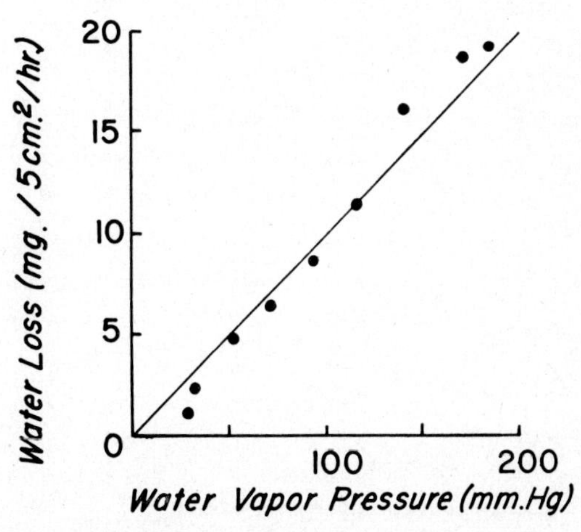

Fig. 34. Influence of water vapor pressure on the rate of water loss through full-thickness human skin. The temperatures ultimately reached were higher than those usually encountered by man. (From *Am. J. Trop. Med.*, *31*:842, 1951.)

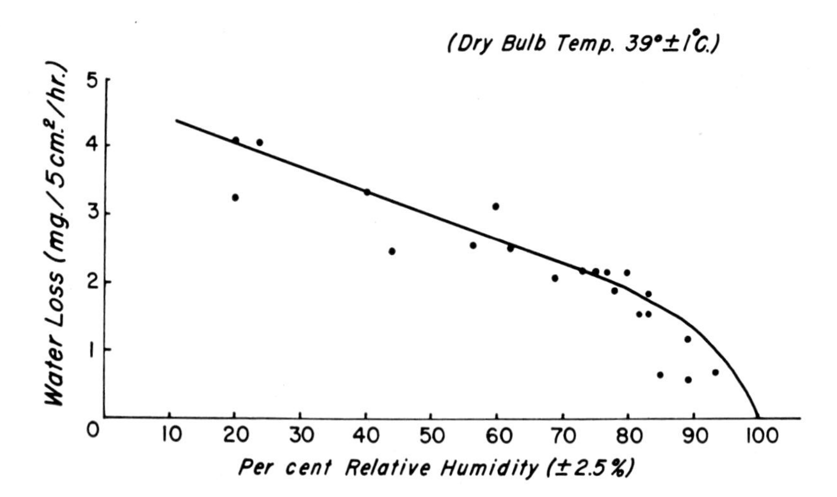

Fig. 35. The influence of relative humidity on water loss through dead, full-thickness human skin. The relative humidity varied by ± 2.5% at each level studied. The temperature (dry bulb) was maintained at a constant level of 39° ± 1° C., while atmospheric water vapor pressure was altered. The rate of water loss through the skin decreased rapidly at relative humidities beyond 80%. (From *Am. J. Trop. Med., 31*:842, 1951.)

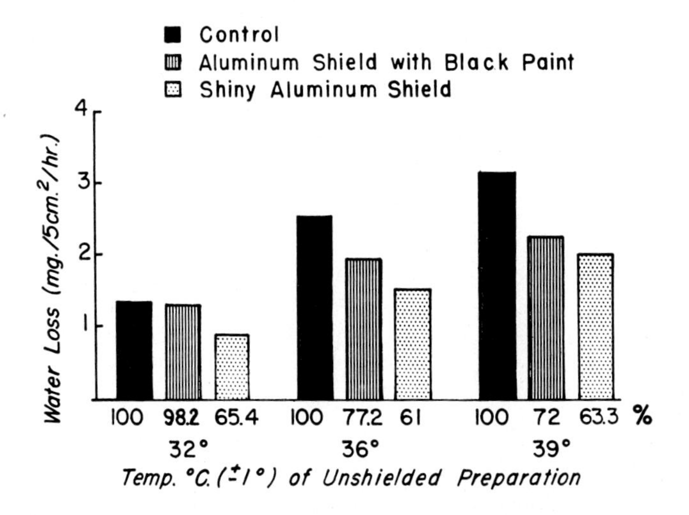

Fig. 36. The influence of infrared radiation on rates of water loss from preparations of skin unshielded and shielded by shiny aluminum or black-painted aluminum membranes. The temperature levels shown along the abscissa are those of the unshielded preparation. The mean rates of water loss of the shielded specimens expressed as percentage of the mean rates of water loss for the unprotected skin are shown along the abscissa. (From *Am. J. Trop Med., 31*:842, 1951.

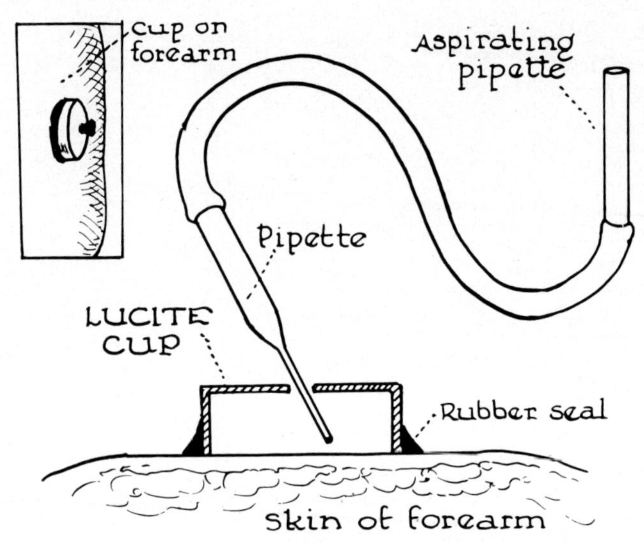

Fig. 37. Schematic drawing of the method of sampling from the extracorporeal compartment. The lucite cup was cemented to the skin over the denuded blister surface by means of inert rubber cement.

radiation for two and four hours had rates of diffusion of water similar to that of normal unexposed skin.

THE TRANSFER OF ELECTROLYTES ACROSS THE DENUDED SURFACE OF THE HUMAN SKIN

As shown above, water diffuses rapidly through the deep layers of the skin, the main barriers being external to the stratum spinosum. To study the kinetics of transfer of electrolytes across these deep layers, denuded blister surfaces were produced by means of cantharides plasters in the manner previously indicated. Although the cantharides blister surface is not a normal cellular surface, it is accessible, uniform and reproducible and it lends itself nicely to the study of rubidiokinetic, kaliokinetic, chlorokinetic and natriokinetic phenomena (5).

Method of Study. The technique employed in these studies consisted of first raising a vesicle on the volar surface of the forearm (Fig. 25a). The top of the vesicle was then removed and the exposed blister surface gently irrigated with warm isotonic saline (Fig. 25b). A circular lucite cup was then sealed over the blister surface with an inert cement (Fig. 37). Various test solutions were introduced into the cup through a hole which was stoppered at all times except when sampling the test fluid. With this technique aliquots of test fluid (0.5 ml.) were removed at predetermined intervals, usually thirty minutes or less. In experiments in which two isotopes were studied simultaneously it was necessary to separate the tracers either by suitable aluminum filters or by taking advantage of the physical decay of the tracer with the shorter half-life. In essence, the preparation consisted of two compartments separated by the denuded blister surface membrane. One compartment, the corporeal compartment, was composed of the entire body, whereas the other

CONCENTRATION TIME COURSE OF Rb^{86} IN EXTRACORPOREAL (BLISTER) COMPARTMENT CONTAINING SERUM

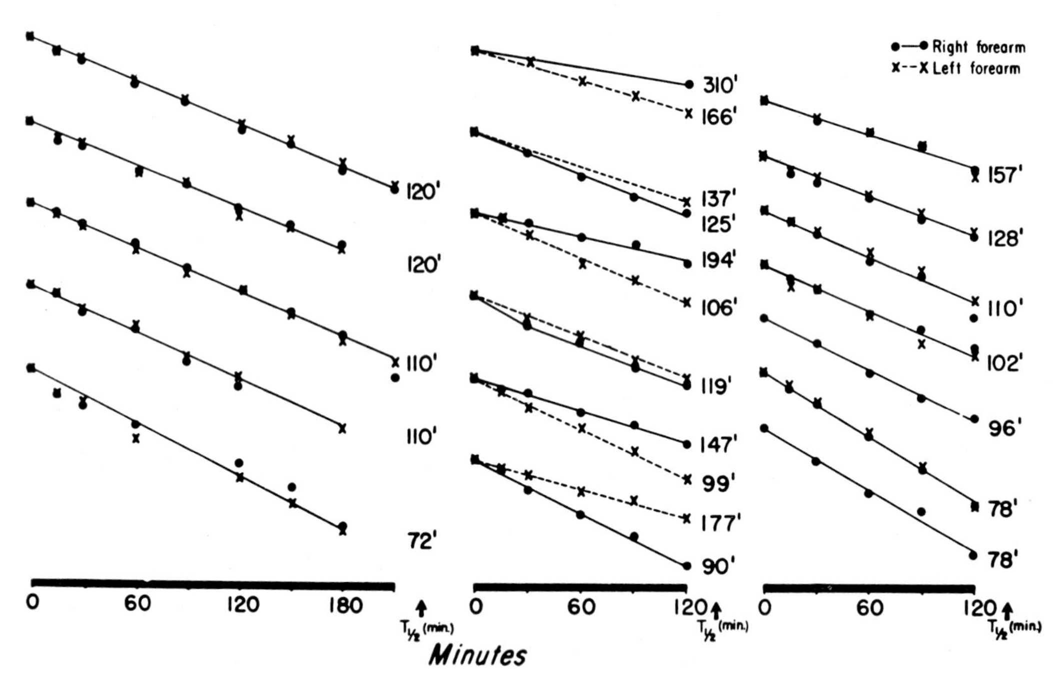

Fig. 38. Concentration-time courses of Rb^{86} in the extracorporeal compartment containing serum, with the $T_{1/2}$ values at the end of the respective curves. The group of curves to the left show no change in the rate of disappearance of Rb^{86} during observations lasting 120 to 210 min. The slower rates of change in concentration for 4 subjects shown in the middle group of curves were associated with a smaller area of blister surface. However, the rates of change in concentration of Rb^{86} were all equal when reduced to unit area and compartment size. Since the curves are exponential and the $T_{1/2}$ values of concentration are shown to the right of the respective curves, absolute ordinate values are unnecessary. (From *J. Appl. Rad. Isotopes, 4:*129, 1959.)

compartment, the extracorporeal compartment, consisted of the lucite cup containing the test fluid.

Transfer of Rb^{86}, Na^{22}, Cl^{36} and K^{42}. The transfer of Rb^{86}, Na^{22}, Cl^{36} and K^{42} across the denuded skin surface was studied in two groups of patients. One group included patients convalescing from diseases not associated with cardiovascular or renal disturbances. The other group included patients with varying degrees of congestive heart failure.

The subjects rested supine in bed in a neutral environment with the blister surface at about heart level. Both forearms were studied simultaneously so that one served as a control. A mixture of the subject's serum, 5% glucose in water, and distilled water with added tracers and electrolytes served as test fluids in most of the experiments.

The mean rate of disappearance of Rb^{86} from the extracorporeal compartment was expressed as $T_{1/2}$ (time required to reach half the initial concentration). After correction for area of blister surface and compartment size,

TIME COURSE OF CONCENTRATION OF Rb^{86} AND ΔK^{39} IN EXTRACORPOREAL (BLISTER) COMPARTMENT CONTAINING 5% GLUCOSE

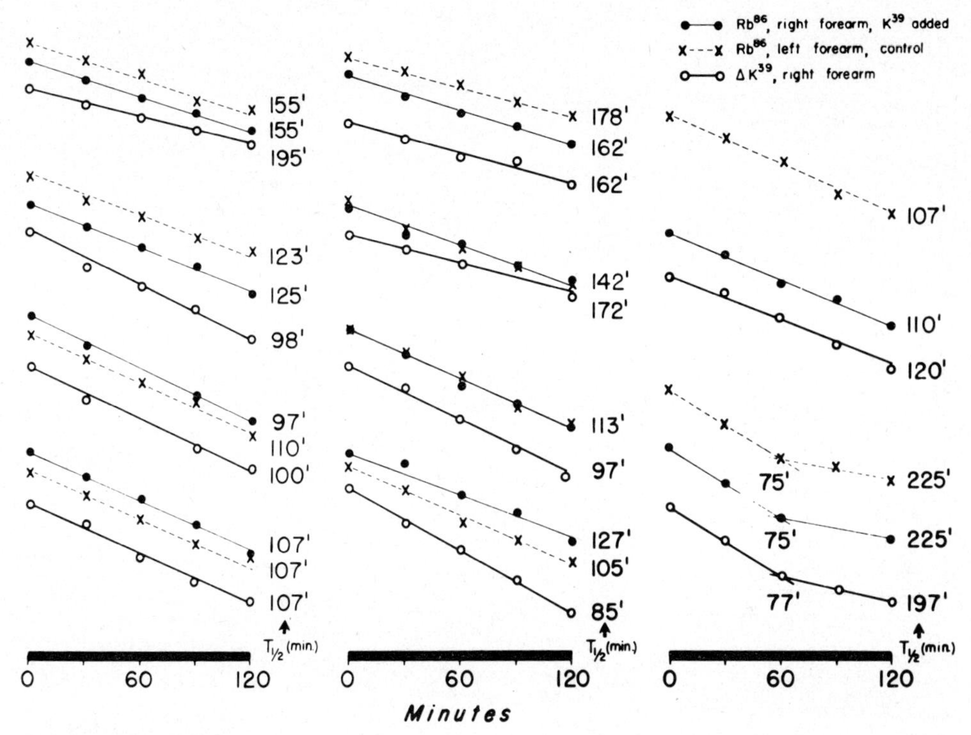

Fig. 39. Simultaneous concentration-time courses of Rb^{86} in the extracorporeal lucite compartments of both forearms. The compartment on the left forearm contained 5% glucose in distilled water with Rb^{86} as the test fluid and the compartment on the right forearm contained 5% glucose in distilled water and Rb^{86} with varying amounts of KCl (4-50 mEq./L) added. The time course of ΔK^{39} represents the change with time in the difference between the concentration of K^{39} in the extracorporeal compartment and that in serum. $T_{1/2}$ values in minutes are shown to the right of the respective curves. (From *J. Appl. Rad. Isotopes, 4*:129, 1959.)

the mean $T_{1/2}$ was 91.3 ± 21.7 minutes/10 cm.^{2} of the blister surface (Fig. 38). There was no significant difference between the mean values for the patients with and without congestive heart failure. Except for sampling, there was no significant net gain or loss of water, Na^{23}, K^{39} or Cl^{35} in the extracorporeal compartment during the course of the experiments (5).

The materials studied traversed a membrane composed of several layers of cells and intercellular substances. Monitoring of the forearm near the blister area as well as along the main lymphatic trunks draining the forearm failed to indicate significant local accumulations of Rb^{86}. It would appear, therefore, that Rb^{86} was removed mainly by the blood.

Rb^{86} traces K^{39} sufficiently well to justify calculation of certain kaliokinetic phenomena from the data obtained with Rb^{86}. It was possible to estimate the quantity of potassium which exchanged per day across the capillaries of

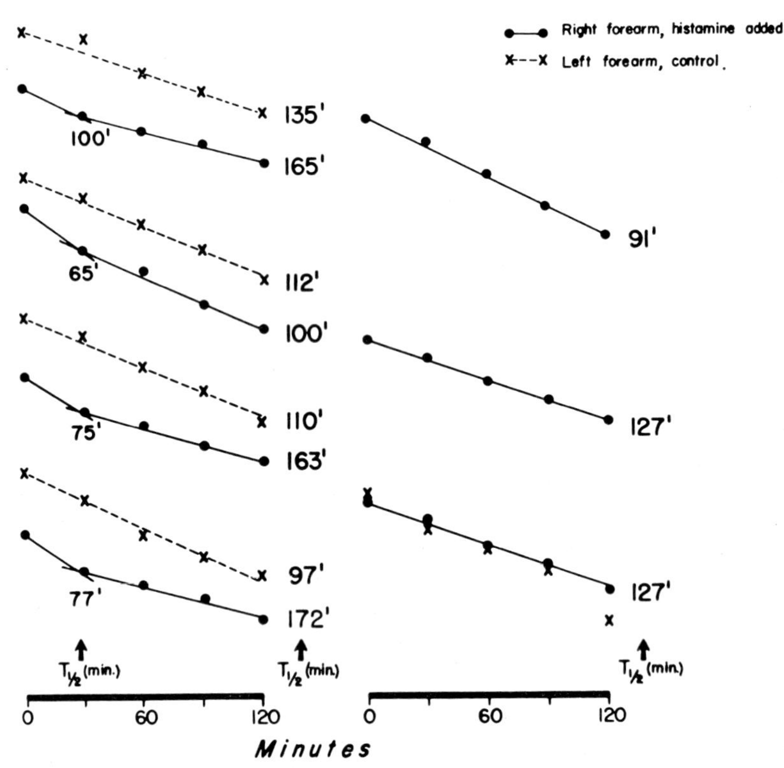

Fig. 40. The effect of histamine (added to compartment on the right forearm) on the rate of disappearance of Rb^{86} in 5% glucose from the extracorporeal compartment in 7 subjects. The compartment on the left forearm was used as the control. $T_{1/2}$ values in minutes are shown to the right of the respective curves. (From *J. Appl. Rad. Isotopes, 4*:129, 1959.)

an average-sized man. For example, the average unidirectional transfer of K^{39} was 0.00031 mEq./10 cm.^{2} blister base/min. When it was estimated that each square centimeter of blister base was in functional contact with about 0.1 cm.^{2} of capillary and venular surface area, the mean rate of transfer of K^{39} was 0.00031 mEq./cm.^{2} capillary/min. Therefore, if all the capillaries and venules of the body were exchanging at a rate observed for the blister base, approximately *1 ton of potassium* would transfer back and forth across the walls of these vessels each day. The quantity that would cross back and forth through the vessels of the skin per day would be about 0.13 lb.

The rate of disappearance of Rb^{86} from the extracorporeal compartment with varying amounts of K^{39} added to the test fluid was also measured. The mean rate of disappearance of Rb^{86} from the extracorporeal compartment, expressed as $T_{1/2}$, was 106.5 ± 22.1 min./10 cm.^{2} of blister surface (Fig. 39). Therefore, the addition of potassium to the test fluid had no detectable

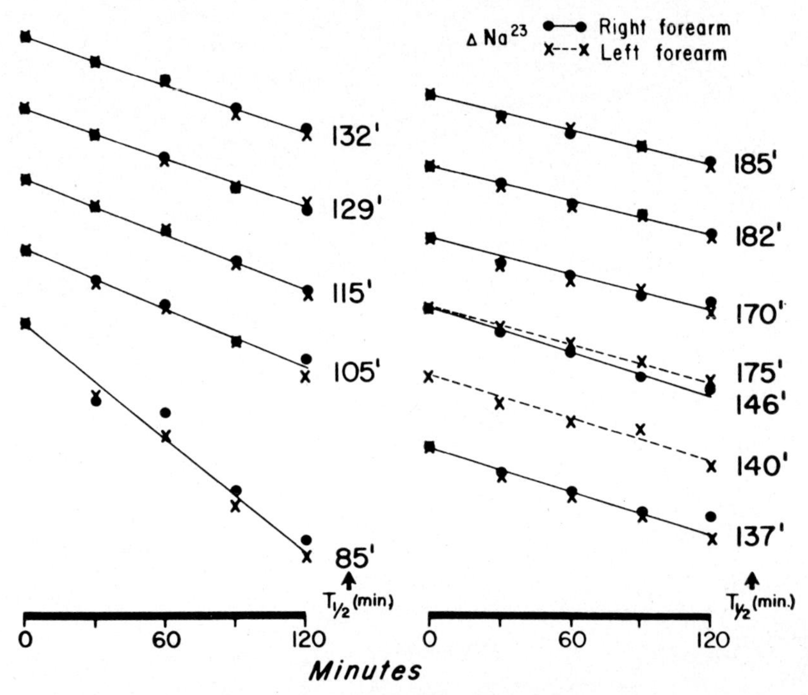

Fig. 41. Time course of the change in the difference between concentration of Na^{23} in the serum and in the extracorporeal compartment containing 5% glucose in distilled water ($\triangle Na^{23}$). These curves reflect the rate of transfer of Na^{23} into the extracorporeal compartment. The $T_{1/2}$ values in minutes are shown to the right of the respective curves. (From *J. Appl. Rad. Isotopes,* 4:129, 1959.)

influence on the rate of disappearance of Rb^{86}.

Influence of Histamine on Transfer of Rb^{86}. The addition of histamine to the test solution resulted in a more rapid rate of disappearance of Rb^{86} for the first 30 min. in four of seven experiments. After this 30-minute interval, the rate of disappearance of Rb^{86} tended to be slower than for the control side (Fig. 40).

Rate of Entry of Na^{23} into Extracorporeal Compartment. Since the test fluid of 5% glucose in water was sodium-free initially, it was possible to determine the rate of entry of sodium into the extracorporeal compartment. The mean rate was found to be 0.0052 ± 0.0007 mEq./10 cm.^{2} blister surface/min. In paired experiments, the addition of potassium to the lucite compartment on the right forearm did not change the rate of sodium transfer. The time course of the difference ($\triangle Na^{23}$) between the concentration of sodium in the serum (Na_s^{23}) and the concentration of sodium in the extracorporeal compartment (Na_e^{23}), expressed as

$$\triangle Na^{23} = Na_s^{23} - Na_e^{23}, \qquad (2)$$

was employed to determine the rate of

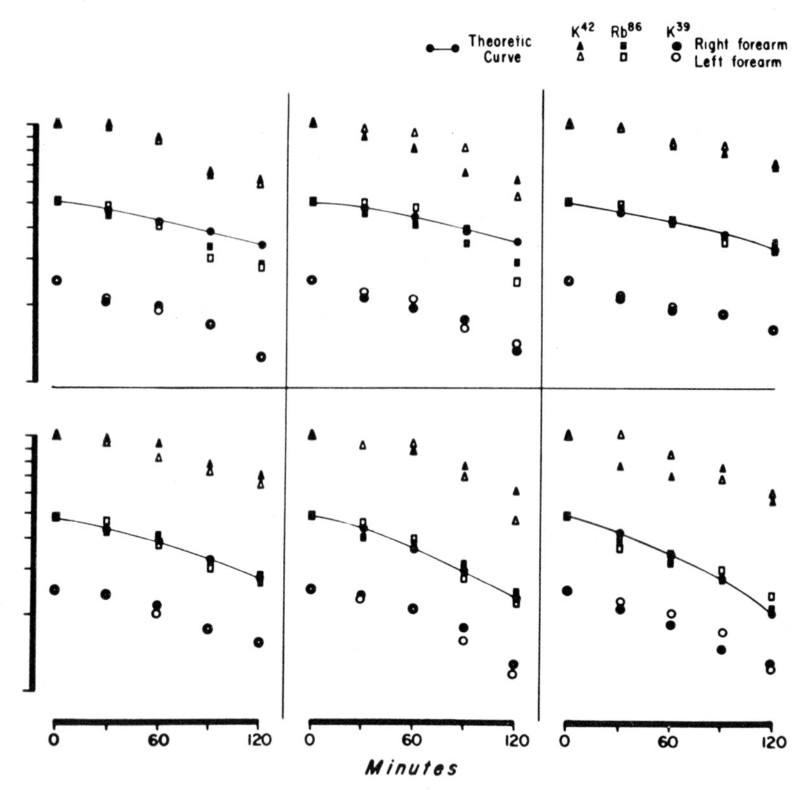

Fig. 42. Simultaneous concentration time-course curves of Rb^{86}, K^{42} and ΔK^{39} in the extracorporeal blister compartments of both forearms. Both the right and left compartments contained Rb^{86} and K^{42} in distilled water with 50 mEq./L of KCl. ΔK^{39} represents the difference between the concentration of K^{39} in the extracorporeal blister compartment and that in the serum. The theoretic concentration time-course curves were calculated on the basis of the rate of loss of Rb^{86} during the first 30-min. interval and measured decrements in volume of the test fluid during the entire experiment. The calculated and observed curves were strikingly similar. (From *J. Appl. Rad. Isotopes, 4*:129, 1959.)

exchange of Na^{23} (Fig. 41). This was expressed as $T_{1/2}$, or time in minutes required for the concentration in the extracorporeal compartment to reach one-half of the concentration in the serum. The mean $T_{1/2}$ value was 120 ± 25.1 min./10 cm.^{2} blister base (0.0078 ± 0.0018 mEq. Na/10 cm.^{2}/min.).

Rate of Entry of Cl^{35} into Extracorporeal Compartment. Similarly, since there was no chloride in the extracorporeal compartment initially, the rate of entry of chloride into the extracorporeal compartment could be measured using the same method of analysis employed for Na^{23}. The mean net rate of transfer of chloride was 0.0046 ± 0.0006 mEq. Cl/10 cm.^{2}/min. The mean $T_{1/2}$ value for Cl^{35} was 97.6 ± 17.6 min., with a rate of entry of chloride into the extracorporeal compartment of 0.0075 ± 0.0014 mEq. Cl/10 cm.^{2} blister base/min.

When Rb^{86}, K^{42} and K^{39} were added

to the extracorporeal compartment, the simultaneous time-course curves of concentration indicated an increasing rate of disappearance of these electrolytes with time (Fig. 42). This phenomenon was found only when the initial test fluid was hypotonic to serum. The loss of a constant amount of Rb^{86}, K^{39} and K^{42}, rather than a constant percentage of that remaining in the extracorporeal compartment, could result in these types of concentration time-course curves.

The average undirectional rate of transfer of Na^{22} from the extracorporeal compartment was 0.0079 mEq./10 cm.^{2} blister/min., which was exactly the same as the average rate of Na^{23} entering the compartment containing 5% glucose and water ($\triangle Na^{23}$).

The rate of disappearance of Cl^{36} from the extracorporeal compartment was of the same general magnitude as the rate of entry of Cl^{35} as determined previously by measuring the changes in concentration of Cl^{35} in the extracorporeal compartment.

Despite the complexity of the blister membrane, it is a convenient preparation for investigating aspects of the transfer of electrolytes and water. It appears that Rb^{86} is a satisfactory tracer of K^{39}. The rate of disappearance of Rb^{86} from the extracorporeal compartment was the same for normal subjects and patients with congestive heart failure. The fact that the rate of disappearance of Rb^{86} from the extracorporeal compartment was not altered when K^{39} was added to the test fluid indicated that there was no overloading of the transport mechanisms for K^{39}, Rb^{86}, Cl^{35} and Na^{23}, nor was there any selective competition between K^{39} and Rb^{86}. The greater the concentration gradient across the membrane, the greater was the mass of electrolyte transferred.

Influence of Norepinephrine on the Rate of Transfer of Na^{22} and Rb^{86} across the Blister Surface. The effect of norepinephrine on the rate of transfer of Na^{22} and Rb^{86} was variable. There was a tendency for norepinephrine to increase the rate of transfer of Na^{22} and Rb^{86} from the extracorporeal compart-

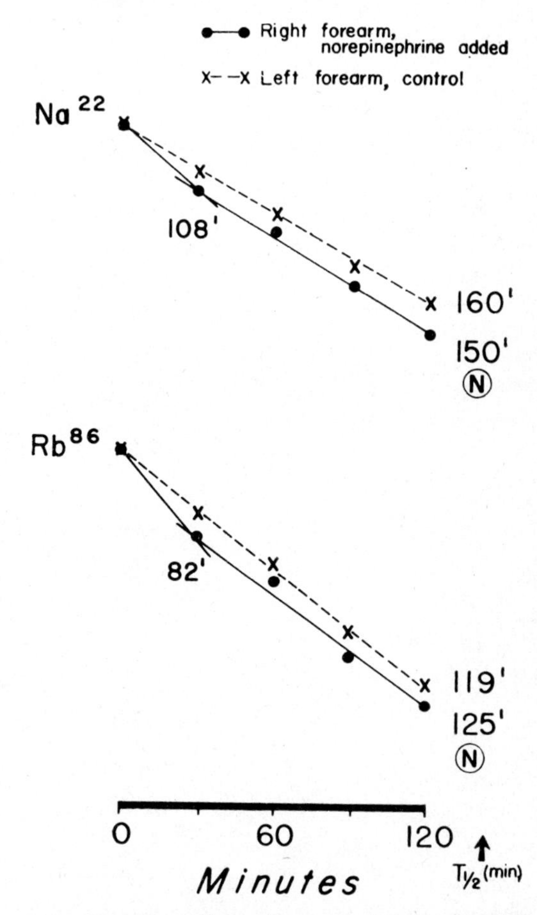

Fig. 43. The effect of norepinephrine on the rates of transfer of Na^{22} and Rb^{86} from the extracorporeal blister compartment containing serum. The norepinephrine (N) was added to the compartment on the right forearm in each instance. The $T_{1/2}$ values in minutes are shown to the right of the respective curves. (From *J. Appl. Rad. Isotopes,* 4:129, 1959.)

ment during the first part of the experiment (Fig. 43). There was no evidence of blanching of the blister base in response to norepinephrine. It is possible that the transient increase in the rate of transfer of Na^{22} and Rb^{86} observed in response to norepinephrine may have been in part the result of the influence of this agent on a chemical transport mechanism.

PATHOPHYSIOLOGIC INTERPRETATIONS

Injuries to the skin which disrupt the water-retaining corneum are associated with rapid rates of diffusion of water. If the area of skin involved is extensive, the water loss may be great enough to produce disease. The anuria which is frequently associated with extensive burns is not only dependent upon the toxic effects on the renal tubules of the products of tissue destruction but also upon the large losses of fluid through the denuded skin. The rapidity with which these losses occur makes proper replacement of fluid difficult. Skin diseases associated with the formation of large bullae which eventually rupture and leave denuded areas of skin present a similar problem. Pemphigus vulgaris and exfoliative dermatitis often end fatally due to serious fluid and electrolyte losses.

The rapidity with which electrolytes are transferred across the skin deprived of its protective barrier was studied by means of appropriate radioactive tracers. With certain rough estimations the calculated mass of NaCl transferred daily across the capillary surfaces of the body of man is between 60,000 and 70,000 pounds, whereas about 31,000 pounds of KCl are transferred across the capillaries daily. Although these estimations are for the entire body, they provide some appreciation of the magnitude of the electrolyte losses in patients with large areas of denuded skin from burns or exfoliative skin lesions. In such situations the rapid electrolyte loss may make it difficult to maintain homeostasis.

Lesions associated with thickening of the skin result in overinsulation of the body and a decrease in the rate of diffusion of water through the skin. Under such circumstances sweating is necessary to dissipate body heat.

If the skin is injured, not only may the barrier to free diffusion of water be impaired, but the ability of the skin to inhibit the entrance of injurious substances into the body is impaired. It is well known that the reaction of sensitive skin to poison ivy is usually more intense in an injured area of skin, as in a scratch, than in an intact area. Also, the skin lesion of sarcoid has a predilection for a biopsy site. Similarly, viruses and bacteria may gain access to the body through denuded areas of skin such as in lacerations, burns and scratches.

CLINICAL APPLICATIONS

Lesions which destroy the cutaneous water barrier cause a rapid loss of water, protein and electrolytes from the body. When extensive, this may be fatal. Survival often depends upon the promptness with which therapy is instituted.

REFERENCES

1. Rothman, S. (Editor): *The Human Integument.* Washington, D. C., American Association for the Advancement of Science, 1959.
2. Winsor, T. and Burch, G. E.: Differential roles of layers of human epigastric skin on diffusion rate of water. *Arch. Int. Med., 74:*428, 1944.
3. Burch, G. E. and Winsor, T.: Rate of insensible perspiration (diffusion of water) locally through living and through dead human skin. *Arch. Int. Med. 74:*437, 1944.
4. Berenson, G. S. and Burch, G. E.: Studies of diffusion of water through dead human skin; the effect of different environmental states and of chemical alterations of the epidermis. *Am. J. Trop. Med., 31:*842, 1951.
5. Ray, C. T. and Burch, G. E.: Rates of transfer of Rb^{86}, K^{42}, K^{39}, Cl^{36}, Cl^{35}, Na^{22} and Na^{23} across a blister surface on the forearm of normal man and patients with chronic congestive heart failure. *International J. Appl. Radiat., 4:*129, 1959.

VI

THE ELECTROLYTE CONTENT OF SWEAT AND THE KINETICS OF ELECTROLYTE EXCRETION BY THE SWEAT GLANDS

THE HUMAN APOCRINE AND ECCRINE SWEAT GLANDS

THERE are two morphologic types of sweat glands in man, the *apocrine* and *eccrine* glands. The apocrine glands are found in the hirsute regions of the body in close association with the hair follicles. The eccrine glands are distributed over the entire body except for the lips, glans penis, clitoris and prepuce (1). The fingers and toes possess a higher concentration of eccrine glands than other body areas. They occur with decreasing frequency on the dorsum of the hand, the forehead, the dorsum of the foot, the forearm, the arm, the abdomen, the lumbar region, the scapulae and the lower extremities (2). However, there is considerable variation in the number of eccrine glands from one individual to another. The sweat coil of the eccrine gland is smaller, less complex and located more superficially in the dermis than that of the apocrine gland (2). Also, the excretory tubule of the eccrine gland empties onto the surface of the skin (Fig. 44), whereas that of the apocrine gland usually empties into the pilary canal.

Although the secretory cycles of both the apocrine and eccrine glands are classified as merocrine, the character of the secretion of these two glands is different. In the apocrine glands a portion of the secretory cell grows inward toward the lumen of the sweat coil resulting in a protuberance which eventually breaks away from the cell and is discharged. In the eccrine glands a clear fluid is formed within the cells and discharged with no appreciable loss of cellular content. The apocrine secretion is a thick, viscid, milky-appearing substance hardly adaptable to thermal regulation. In lower animals the apocrine glands probably serve a sexual function which has become vestigial in man. These glands are activated primarily by emotional stimuli, such as anger or fear, but little by heat (2). The eccrine secretion, on the other hand, is a thin, watery secretion admirably suited for thermal regulation. Eccrine sweat is the most dilute excretion of the human body, consisting of about 99% water, a characteristic which makes it ideal for evaporative cooling owing to the high latent heat of vaporization of water.

The evolutionary trend seems to endow higher forms of life with more eccrine and fewer apocrine sweat glands. Thus, in man thermal regulation is primarily a function of the skin, whereas

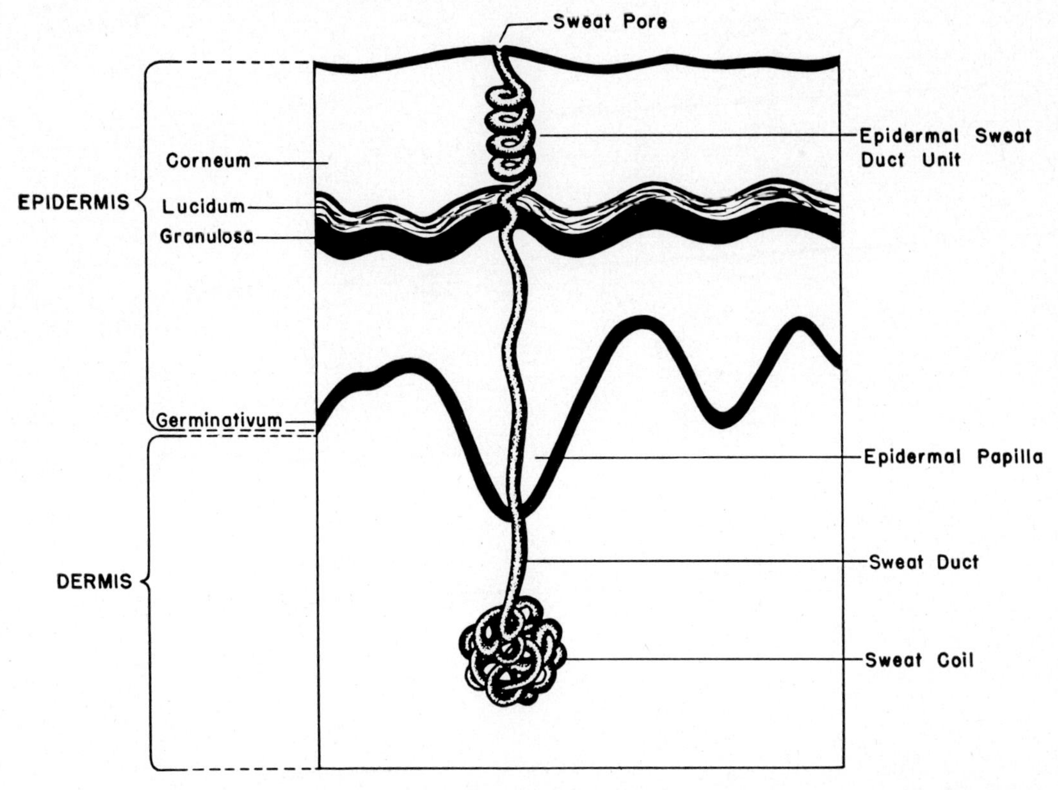

Fig. 44. Schematic drawing of the epidermis and dermis showing an eccrine sweat gland.

in lower animal it is primarily a function of the oral and respiratory passages.

In this discussion the terms "sweat gland" and "sweat" will refer to the eccrine sweat gland and its secretion. The apocrine glands, having no role in thermal regulation, are not considered.

Sweat is derived mostly from the serum. Since the concentrations of sodium, potassium and chloride in sweat differ from those of serum, work must be done by the sweat glands in excreting these electrolytes. The energy for this work probably originates in part from metabolic processes arising within the sweat glands themselves. Because concentration gradients between sweat and serum exist for other substances as well as for Na, K and Cl, some investigators (3) have considered the sweat duct to function in many ways like the renal tubule. The sweat tubule probably alters the sweat as it flows through its lumen.

METHOD OF COLLECTION OF SWEAT

There are many methods of collecting sweat for analysis. In this laboratory sweat was collected by means of clean, dry, transparent, lucite cups, 2 cm. high and with an opening of 10 or 15 $cm.^2$, sealed to the skin with an adhesive cement (Chapter 5, Fig. 37). The enclosed skin surface was accessible through a small orifice in the top of the cup which was stoppered except during periodic sampling (4). Samples were

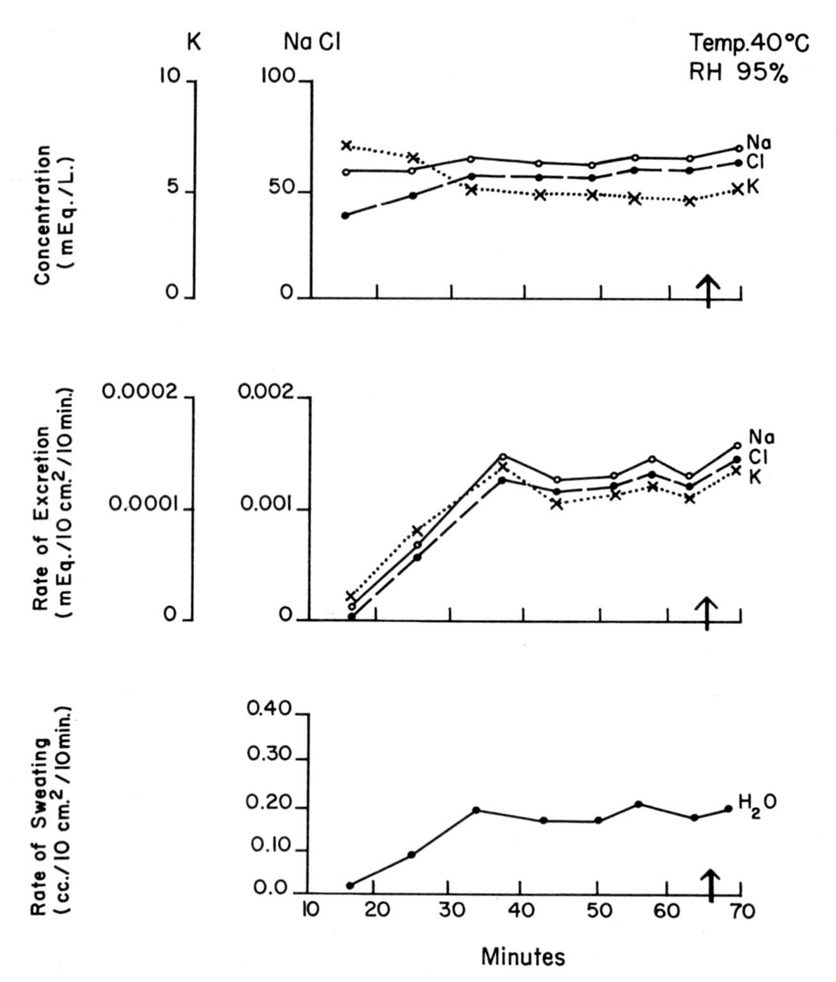

Fig. 45. Time courses of concentration and rate of excretion of Na, Cl and K in thermal sweat and the rate of sweating from the forearm of a representative normal subject. The arrow indicates the time that the temperature and humidity of the room air were made comfortable. (From *J. Lab. & Clin. Med., 42*:58, 1953.)

obtained with a pipette by thorough aspiration of all collectible sweat within the cup.

CONCENTRATION-TIME COURSES OF Na^{23}, K^{39} and Cl^{35} IN SWEAT

The Effect of Intense Thermal Stimulation on the Concentration-Time Courses of Na^{23}, K^{39} and Cl^{35} in Sweat. In subjects exposed to intense thermal stimulation for one hour (40° C., 95% R.H.), the concentrations of Na^{23} and Cl^{35} in sweat began at relatively low levels and increased concordantly as sweating progressed, always remaining hypotonic to serum (Fig. 45). The concentration of Cl^{35} was generally slightly less than that of Na^{23}. The concentration of K^{39} decreased as sweating continued, ultimately reaching an almost constant value, usually above the serum level. The rates of excretion of Na^{23}, K^{39} and Cl^{35} usually increased rapidly during the early period of exposure of the subject to a hot and humid environment but remained fairly constant thereafter. The

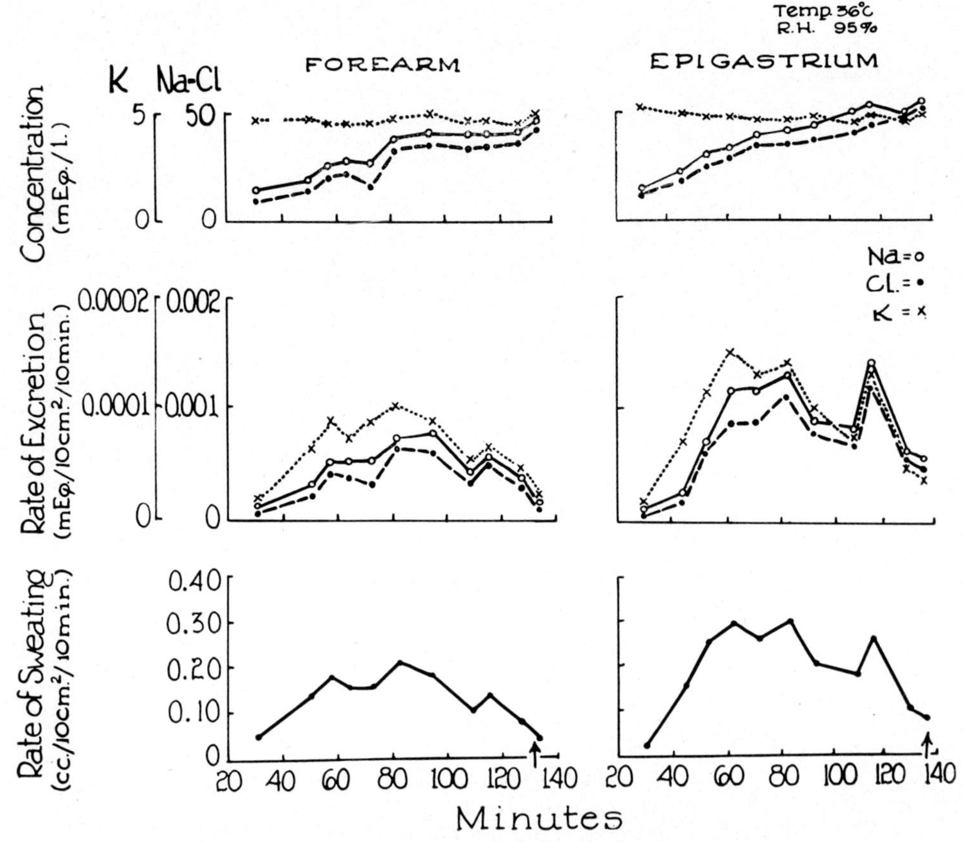

Fig. 46. Time courses of concentration and excretion of Na, Cl and K. in thermal sweat and the rate of sweating from the forearm and epigastrium of a representative subject exposed to the same humidity but lower temperature for a longer period of time than the subject shown in Figure 45. With prolonged sweating a decrease in the rate of sweating developed in association with a decrease in total excretion of the electrolytes. (From *J. Lab. & Clin. Med., 42*:58, 1953.)

rate of sweating also increased during the early period of thermal exposure to reach and maintain a maximal value if the duration of exposure to the hot and humid environment did not exceed sixty minutes. No significant changes were observed in the concentrations of Na^{23}, K^{39} and Cl^{35} in the serum nor in the hematocrit from blood obtained before and after exposure of the subject for about one hour to the hot and humid atmosphere. The rate of urine formation decreased considerably after an hour of exposure to the hot and humid atmosphere. This was associated with a slight decrease in the concentration of Na^{23} and Cl^{35} and a slight increase in the concentration of K^{39} in the urine. Under similar environmental conditions female subjects excreted considerably less sweat than did the male subjects.

The Effect of Prolonged Thermal Stimulation on the Concentration-Time Courses of Na^{23}, K^{39} and Cl^{35} in Sweat. Exposure to less intense thermal stimulation (36° C., 95% R.H.) for two hours resulted in time courses of concentration of Na^{23}, Cl^{35} and K^{39} in sweat

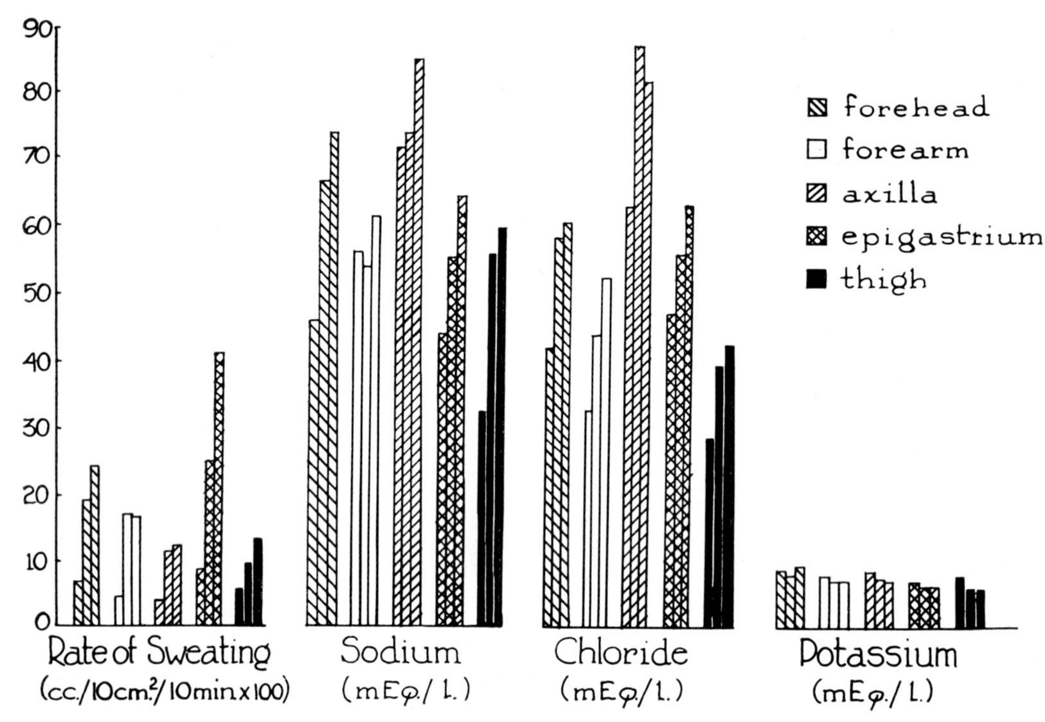

Fig. 47. Mean rates of sweating and concentrations of Na, Cl and K in sweat from 5 different body sites of 5 subjects. These mean values represent three periods of collection for each site during an hour of exposure to a hot and humid atmosphere. The greatest *total* excretion of all electrolytes occurred for the abdomen. (From *J. Lab. & Clin. Med.*, *42*:58, 1953.)

similar to those observed during exposure to a higher temperature for one hour, except that the rate of sweating decreased after reaching a maximum, resulting in a reduction in the total amount of electrolytes excreted (Fig. 46).

RELATION OF SITE OF THE SWEAT GLANDS TO THE RATE OF SWEATING

As already indicated, the number of sweat glands per unit area as well as the function of the sweat glands varies for different areas of the body (2). The glands of the palms of the hands and soles of the feet have relatively low rates of thermal sweating. This is an expression of the functional differences among the sweat glands located in different areas of the skin of man. It has been suggested that the eccrine glands of the fingers are transitional between the apocrine and eccrine glands (2). This assumption is supported by the fact that, whereas the eccrine glands in other regions of the body are activated primarily by heat, those of the finger tips are activated more by emotional stimuli than by heat. Furthermore, these glands function in the absence of thermal stimulation to keep the fingers moist to facilitate delicate tactile functions and grasping. The hypothesis that the eccrine glands of the finger tips are transitional between apocrine glands and eccrine glands of other areas of the body, however, must be based almost entirely on

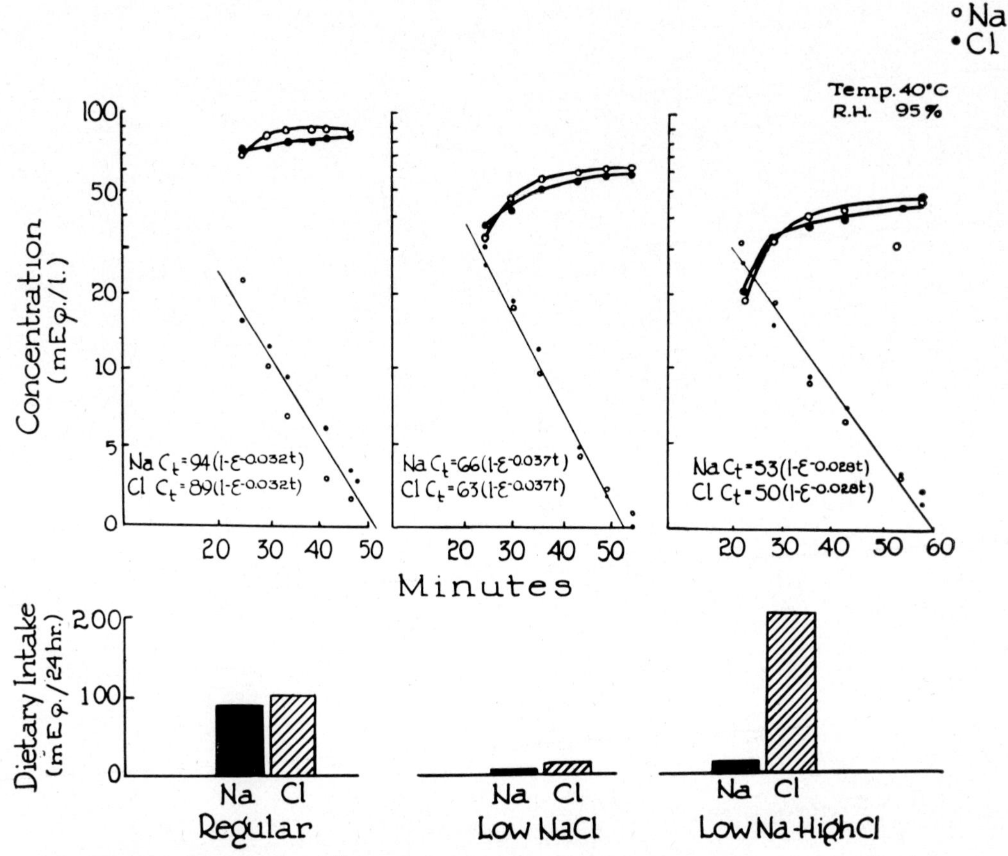

Fig. 48. Mathematical analysis of concentration time-course curves of Na and Cl for 3 experiments performed on a subject whose dietary intake of Na and Cl varied. The dietary intake influenced the absolute concentrations of Na in the sweat but the slopes of the concentration time-course curves were not changed. (From *J. Lab. & Clin. Med.*, *42*:58, 1953.)

functional characteristics since neither chemically nor histologically is the sweat or structure of the eccrine glands of the finger tip even remotely similar to those of the apocrine glands.

THE ELECTROLYTE CONCENTRATION OF NORMAL SWEAT

Because of the wide variations in the concentrations of Na^{23}, Cl^{35} and K^{39} from individual to individual as well as from different regions of the body of the same individual, it is hazardous to define the normal concentration of these electrolytes in sweat. In addition, factors such as diet, technique of collecting the sweat, method of inducing sweating, previous activity of the sweat glands, duration and rate of sweating, the state of the circulation, season and acclimatization influence the electrolyte concentration of the sweat of normal and abnormal individuals. Figure 47 indicates the magnitude of the differences in concentrations of Na^{23}, Cl^{35} and K^{39}, as well as the differences in the rates of sweating among different individuals and from various skin areas. Studies in this laboratory demonstrated variations in the concentrations of Na^{23} and Cl^{35} of

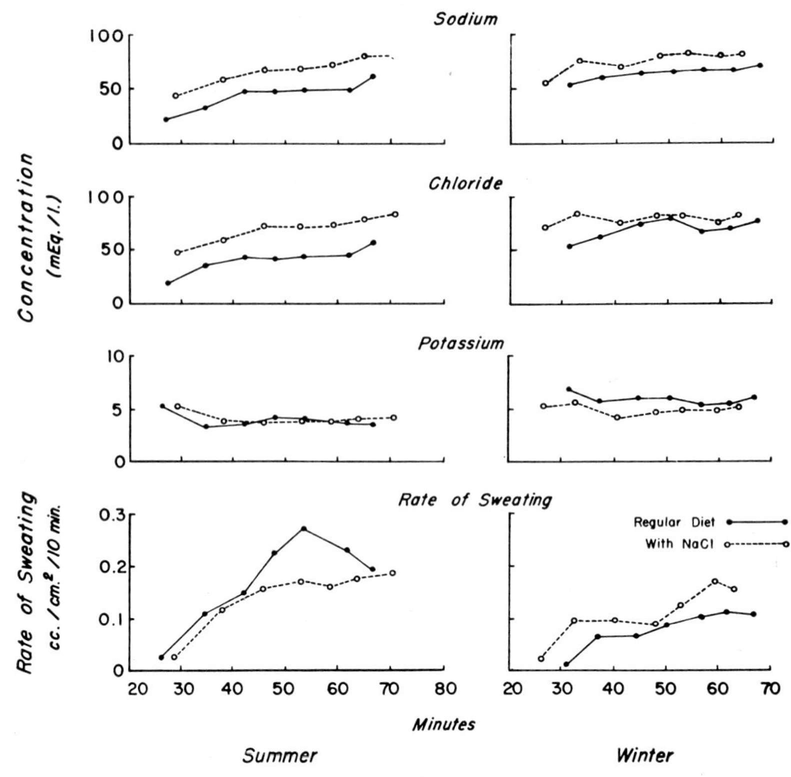

Fig. 49. Concentration time-course curves of Na, Cl and K in sweat and the rate of sweating for the same individual in summer and winter while on regular and high NaCl intake. (From *J. Lab. & Clin. Med.*, *42*:58, 1953.)

approximately 10 to 100 mEq. per liter from subject to subject, as well as from moment to moment in the same individual. Such wide variations make it difficult to reach definite conclusions concerning physiologic processes merely from the concentrations of Na^{23} and Cl^{35} in a single sample of sweat. Analysis of the concentration time-course curves of Na^{23}, Cl^{35} and K^{39} is more likely to lead to valid physiologic conclusions than are single determinations of concentration.

Certain generalizations are possible, however. The concentrations of Na^{23} and Cl^{35} in sweat are usually hypotonic to those in plasma, with the concentration of chloride slightly less than that of sodium and with the average Na/Cl ratio being slightly greater than unity. There were no differences between the concentrations of Na^{23} and Cl^{35} in the sweat of the Negro and the white subject. Males produced a more concentrated sweat than did females of both races. These differences may be related to the lower sweat rates found in women subjected to thermal stimulation. The concentration of K^{39} in the sweat was lower than that of either Na^{23} or Cl^{35} but was higher than the concentration of K^{39} in plasma. The Na/K ratio of concentration was usually about 15.

THE INFLUENCE OF DIET ON THE COMPOSITION OF SWEAT

There is disagreement on the effect of diet on the electrolyte concentration of sweat. However, it was found that the

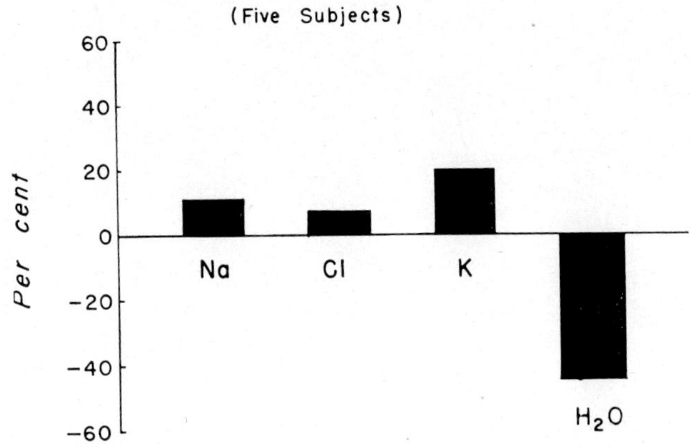

Fig. 50. Influence of ischemia on thermal sweat. The changes in concentration of Na, Cl and K are shown as percentage change from that for the contralateral control forearm. Similarly, the rate of sweating for the ischemic forearm is expressed as a percentage of the rate of sweating of the control contralateral forearm. There was relatively little change in concentration of Na and Cl while the K concentration increased and the rate of sweating decreased. (From *J. Lab. & Clin. Med.*, *42*:58, 1953.)

composition of thermal sweat could be influenced by the dietary intake of electrolytes. The sweat content of Na^{23} and Cl^{35} was influenced more by salt restriction than salt administration (Fig. 48). The changes in the concentrations of these substances occurred much more slowly and to a much lesser degree in the sweat than in the urine. The pattern of excretion of sweat for a given individual tended to remain constant, at least over a period of a few days. It was difficult to produce significant variations in the composition of the sweat.

THE INFLUENCE OF CLIMATE ON THE COMPOSITION OF SWEAT

The magnitude of the effect of climate on the concentration of electrolytes in the sweat and on the rate of sweating was variable. In a group of subjects studied during a warm and humid summer in New Orleans (mean temperature, 81.7° F.; mean relative humidity, 90%) and during a mild winter (mean temperature, 62.8° F.; mean relative humidity, 87%) the concentrations of Na^{23} and Cl^{35} in the sweat tended to be higher in the winter than in the summer in most subjects and the concentration of K^{39} was higher during the winter in all subjects (Fig. 49). The rates of sweating were higher in the summer in all subjects. Acclimatization to a hot environment is usually associated with a decrease in the concentration of Cl^{35} and an increase in the volume of sweat.

THE INFLUENCE OF ISCHEMIA ON THE COMPOSITION OF SWEAT

Arrest of the circulation to the forearm had a marked effect on the electrolyte concentration of sweat collected from this region. In experiments in which the concentrations of Na^{23}, Cl^{35} and K^{39} were measured simultaneously

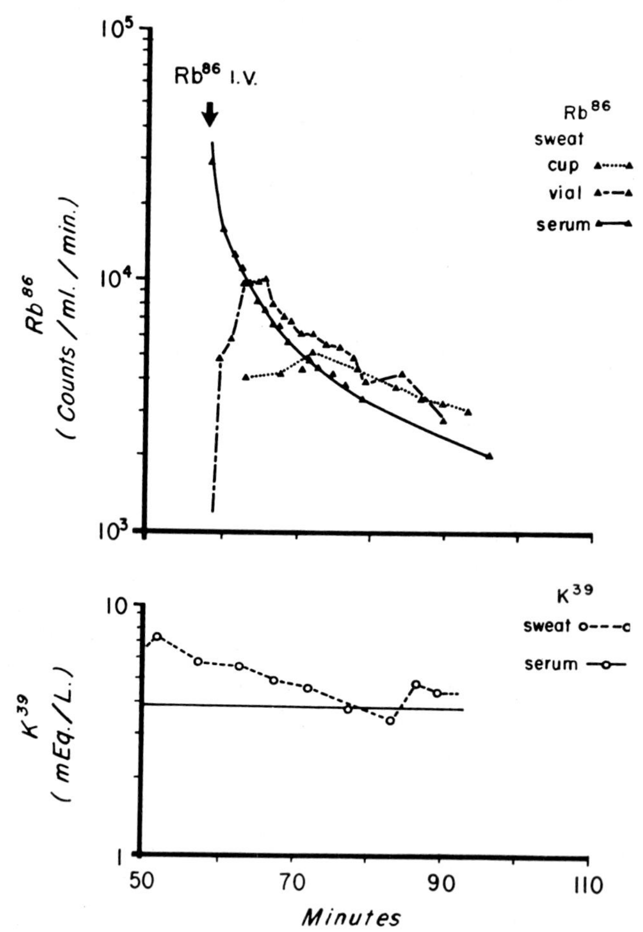

Fig. 51. Concentration-time courses of Rb^{86} and K^{39} in serum and in thermal sweat after a single intravenous administration of the tracer in a subject who was sweating profusely because of exposure to a hot and humid atmosphere for 56 minutes. "Cup" sweat refers to sweat collected in a lucite cup sealed to the skin. "Vial" sweat refers to the sweat collected by scraping the skin with the open orifice of a small vial. The straight horizontal serum level shown for K^{39} was based on one determination. (From *J. Lab. & Clin. Med., 49:*401, 1957.)

TABLE 5

Time Required for Detection of Radioactivity in Sweat after Intravenous Injection of Rb^{86} and K^{42}*

Subject No.	*Duration of I. V. Injection (Sec.)*	*Appearance Time (Min.: Sec.)*
1	3–7	0:30
2	3–7	1:00
3	3–7	0:15
4	3–7	0:15
5	5–10	0:15
6	40	0:30

* Measurements were obtained from sweat collected every 15 seconds on paper disks.

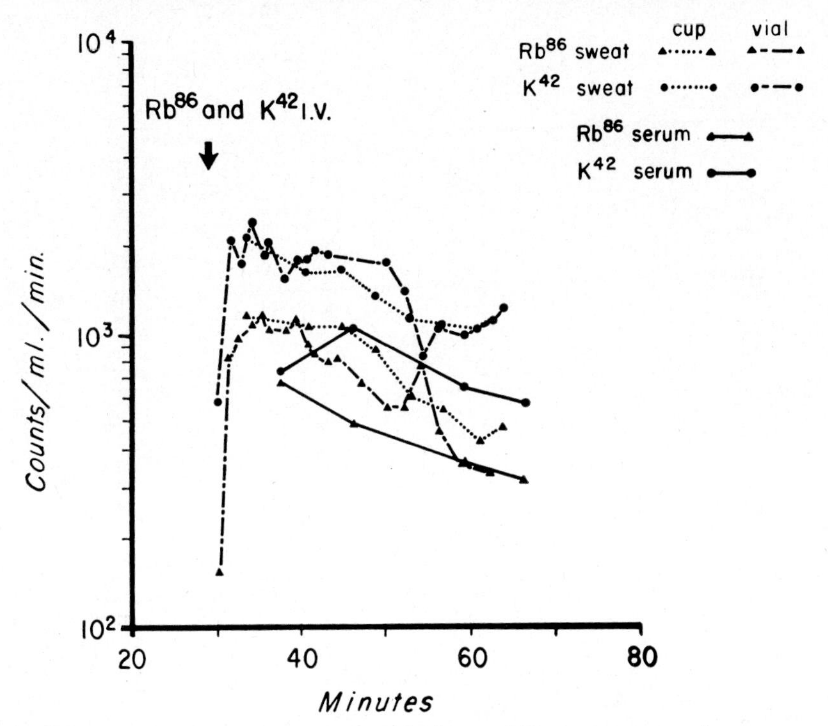

Fig. 52. The concentration-time courses of Rb^{86} and K^{42} in serum and sweat measured simultaneously following a single, sudden, simultaneous injection of the two tracers. The subject had been exposed to the hot and humid atmosphere for 29 minutes prior to administration of the tracers. See Figure 51 for definition of "cup" and "vial." (From *J. Lab. & Clin. Med.*, *49*:401, 1957.)

in the sweat from both forearms before and after acute circulatory arrest in one forearm by a blood pressure cuff, an increase was found in the concentration of K^{39} in the sweat collected from the forearm with the circulation interrupted. There were only questionable increases in the concentrations of Na^{23} and Cl^{35} in the sweat from the ischemic forearm. However, the most striking effect of ischemia was a progressive decrease in the rate of sweating (Fig. 50).

THE KINETICS OF ELECTROLYTE EXCRETION BY SWEAT GLANDS

Kinetic phenomena associated with the excretion of electrolytes in sweat were studied by measuring the excretion of certain radioactive substances by the sweat glands (5, 6).

Rate of Excretion of Rb^{86} and K^{42}. The rate at which Rb^{86} and K^{42} were transferred across the cells of the sweat glands was studied. These isotopes appeared in thermally induced sweat within 15 to 60 seconds after sudden intravenous injection of the tracer in the opposite arm (Table 5). Rb^{86} appeared within 15 seconds in sweat collected by means of filter paper disks placed on the skin of the forearm. The concentration of Rb^{86} in the sweat reached a maximal level in approximately six minutes. The concentration of Rb^{86} in whole blood and serum declined more rapidly and to levels lower than the concentration in sweat.

The concentration of potassium in serum changed little, whereas the concentration of potassium in sweat de-

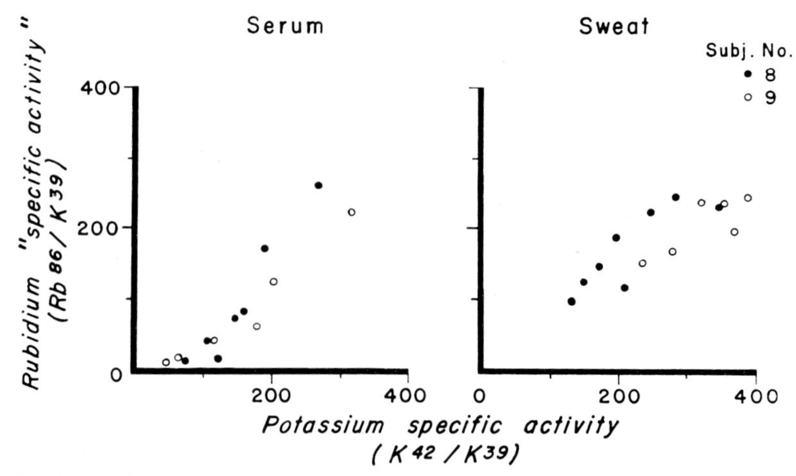

Fig. 53. Relationship of "specific activity" of rubidium (Rb^{86}/K^{39}) to specific activity of potassium (K^{42}/K^{39}) in serum and sweat. (From *J. Lab. & Clin. Med., 49:*401, 1957.)

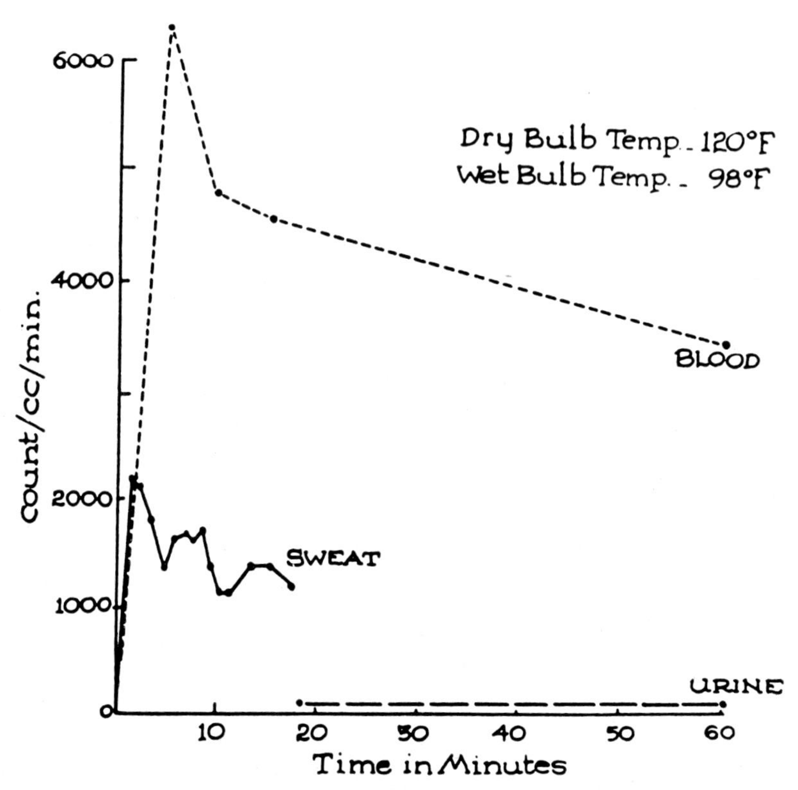

Fig. 54. Variations in concentration of Na^{24} in serum, sweat and urine in a normal subject who was sweating profusely (thermal) when the Na^{24} was suddenly injected intravenously. The Na^{24} appeared in the sweat within 75 seconds after intravenous injection of the isotope. (From *J. Lab. & Clin. Med., 32:*1169, 1947.)

clined slightly during periods of collection of thermally induced sweat (Fig. 51). The ratio of the sweat "specific activity" (Rb^{86}/K^{39}) to serum "specific activity" increased as sweating progressed to reach a value of approximately 1.5 and then remained relatively constant. Thus, Rb^{86} quickly entered the sweat from the blood, and the concentration of Rb^{86} in the sweat reflected changes in concentration of this isotope in the serum. In spite of the rapid transfer of Rb^{86} from blood to sweat, when sweating was rapid there were differences in the concentration-time courses of Rb^{86} for the blood and sweat.

Although the concentration time — course curves of Rb^{86} and K^{42} were similar in configuration, they were quantitatively different (Fig. 52). The concentration of K^{42} in serum and in sweat and the specific activity of K^{42} (K^{42}/K^{39}) were consistently higher than those with Rb^{86} as the tracer of K^{39}. A linear relationship between rubidium and potassium with similar slopes for the specific activities in sweat and serum indicated a constant and orderly transport of the two different elements from blood to sweat (Fig. 53). However, the fact that the specific activity of K^{42} was consistently higher than that of Rb^{86} indicated a more rapid transport of K^{42} than of Rb^{86}. This is probably a manifestation of kinetic differences between potassium and rubidium.

Rate of Excretion of Na^{24}. Na^{24} appeared in the sweat of one forearm within 75 seconds after intravenous injection into the opposite arm. The concentration of this isotope was highest in the blood and lowest in the urine. The concentration in sweat tended to follow very closely that in blood (Fig. 54). When correction was made for circulation time, sodium was found to transfer from the plasma into the interstitial spaces, enter the cells of the glomerulus of the sweat glands and appear in the sweat on the surface of the body in less than 60 seconds (6).

PATHOPHYSIOLOGIC INTERPRETATIONS

Hyperhidrosis The eccrine glands secrete excessive quantities of sweat in hyperhidrosis. This physiologic disturbance may be generalized or localized to the palms, soles of the feet and axillae. Generalized hyperhidrosis may be the result of thermal stimulation or may accompany such systemic disorders as hyperthyroidism, fever or anemia. Also, patients with disturbances which result in "overinsulation," such as obesity or hypermetabolism as in acromegaly, may be hyperhidrotic. Both localized and generalized hyperhidrosis may be associated with lesions of the central nervous system.

Hypohidrosis. This condition may occur after spinal cord injury, damage to postganglionic sympathetic fibers, atropine or atabrine administration and in certain systemic diseases such as gout, Addison's disease, myxedema, diabetes insipidus and profuse diarrhea. Because of the low rate of sweating there is difficulty in eliminating body heat in a hot and humid environment.

Ectodermal Dysplasia. This defect may be associated with complete aplasia of the sweat glands. It appears more often in males than in females and may be generalized or localized. The disorder is usually associated with other ectodermal defects such as anodontia, hypotrichosis, cataracts and depression of the bridge of the nose. The inability to sweat adequately causes heat intolerance. In neutral environments there is usually no difficulty in eliminating body heat unless the patient exercises, making sweating necessary for thermal regulation. However, when the environmental temperature and humidity reach levels at which radiation and convection are no longer adequate for heat loss, the body accumulates heat and fever results since these patients cannot sweat. If the environmental conditions are not altered to allow adequate heat loss by radiation and convection, death results.

Miliaria. After periods of intense sweat gland activity, obstruction to the sweat duct in the corneum may result with development of a vesicle of retained sweat localized to the corneum. This is usually associated with intense pruritus, and in some instances secondary infection may occur.

Fibrocystic Disease (Mucoviscoidosis). The secretion of all of the exocrine glands of the body is abnormal in composition in fibrocystic disease. The sweat of patients with this disease contains sodium and chloride in greater amounts than normal (7). Patients with this malady suffer from heat intolerance. Marked sweating results in considerable losses of sodium and chloride in the sweat, and vomiting, lassitude, dehydration, hyponatremia and eventually circulatory collapse ensue. This problem is most serious in infants because children under two years of age characteristically have higher rates of sweating than adults. The pathophysiologic problem in cystic fibrosis is not exactly analogous to heat exhaustion or heat pyrexia since the peripheral vascular collapse is not due primarily to loss of vasomotor control (heat exhaustion) or to failure to produce sweat (heat stroke). The pathophysiologic difficulty is more closely analogous to adrenal insufficiency with a failure to conserve salt, the peripheral vascular collapse being due in large part to hyponatremia. However, unacclimatized individuals subjected to continuous thermal stimulation also produce sweat high in electrolyte concentration. In fact, even acclimatized individuals may lose the ability to produce sweat with low salt concentration when subjected to prolonged thermal stimulation. Both of the latter situations may reflect a disturbance in adrenocortical function. These remarks are not introduced to suggest that the adrenal gland is at fault in cystic fibrosis, for the disease is a genetic one, probably transmitted by an autosomal dominant gene of high penetrance. These comments merely indicate that the basic physiologic disturbance in cystic fibrosis is different from that of either heat exhaustion or heat stroke. The term "heat prostration" seems best suited to describe the disturbance in cystic fibrosis.

Although a study of the sweat should be made in the diagnosis of cystic fibrosis, the test can be confirmatory rather than diagnostic because of the marked variations in sodium and chloride concentration in normal sweat. It is difficult to decide whether or not the sodium or chloride concentration in the sweat is abnormally elevated. Many factors influence the electrolyte concentration of sweat. Because of wide variations in the normal sodium and chloride concentrations of sweat, the diagnosis of cystic fibrosis on the basis of a single sweat analysis without clinical support can be misleading. In the pediatric literature various investigators have indicated that the upper limits of normal for sweat chloride vary from 60 to 80 mEq./L.

In a study of 50 normal adults di Sant' Agnese found the sweat chloride levels to be below 50 mEq./L in every instance (8). Again, season, geographic location, diet, acclimatization and methods of sweat collection may contribute to the variability in the levels of sweat chloride published by different investigators. These levels have been exceeded in normal subjects studied in this laboratory. There is no doubt that the mean concentrations of sodium and chloride for a group of patients with cystic fibrosis and for a group of normal subjects are widely separated. Nevertheless, because of overlapping these values represent little more than a guide in the study of individual patients.

Ischemia. Ischemia results in a decrease in the activity of the sweat glands during thermal sweating, the most striking effect being a reduction in the rate of sweating. However, since the majority of ischemic diseases involve the lower extremities and since the rate of thermal sweating in this region of the body is not marked, there are usually no thermoregulatory difficulties associated with peripheral vascular disease. Similarly, the sweat glands degenerate after postganglionic sympathectomy, but there is usually no associated thermal difficulty unless there is extensive sympathectomy. The adequacy of postganglionic sympathectomy may be determined by observing the response of the sweat glands in the involved area to either local acetylcholine injection or thermal stimulation.

ACCLIMATIZATION

Acclimatization refers to the sum of all physiologic alterations which develop to insure thermal balance in an organism exposed to stressful environmental conditions. Acclimatization to a hot and humid environment in man requires from several days to several weeks depending upon the state of health of the individual and his activity and is associated with a reduction of the metabolic rate. If an unacclimatized man is exposed to a hot and humid environment, the body's ability to dissipate heat may not be adequate to maintain thermal balance, especially if physical activity is performed. Under such circumstances a variety of pathologic states may develop, including heat cramps, heat exhaustion and heat stroke. The development of any of these states is probably more frequent in temperate climatic regions of the world than in the tropics. This is because an individual living in a cool climate has an increased rate of body heat production (increased metabolic rate) as part of the acclimatization process to cold. Housing, clothing and habits of living are also geared for cold weather and keeping warm. If during the early summer a heat wave develops suddenly, adaptive mechanisms and habits must suddenly be reversed and directed toward lowering the metabolic rate. These changes may not occur rapidly enough to insure thermal balance and, therefore, heat retention results. Depending upon the state of health of the individual, the intensity and duration of the thermal stress and the degree of physical activity as well as other unknown factors, one of the three pathologic conditions mentioned may develop. These clinical states occur frequently in people who migrate from the temperate to the tropical climatic zone.

HEAT CRAMPS, HEAT EXHAUSTION AND HEAT STROKE

Heat cramps result from excessive loss of sodium and chloride in sweat. Drinking large amounts of water without electrolyte replacement may precipitate this condition by reducing the electrolyte concentration of the blood by dilution.

Heat exhaustion involves primarily the dermal circulation and is probably due to loss of vasomotor control. Exposure to high environmental temperature is followed by excessive dilatation of the peripheral blood vessels. The pooling of blood in the dilated vascular spaces is associated with a compensatory increase in cardiac output (Chapter 11). The cardiac output cannot be raised sufficiently to meet body requirements in individuals with disease of the cardiovascular system. Tachycardia and hypotension follow and the symptoms of heat exhaustion develop.

Heat stroke involves failure of both the thermoregulatory system and the cardiovascular system. When man is subjected to prolonged intense sweating, the metabolic and physiologic processes involved with the elaboration of sweat may fail and sweating cease. If the atmospheric temperature and humidity remain elevated, the only pathway remaining for the dissipation of heat is the oral and respiratory tract. The amount of heat that can be dissipated by the respiratory tract is not sufficient to maintain thermal equilibrium, and, as a result, heat gain exceeds heat loss and fever develops. When the temperature and humidity are extremely high, heat may even be gained from the atmosphere by the respiratory tract. The body temperature rises with alarming rapidity and if measures are not instituted promptly to lower body temperature, death inevitably ensues. The hyperpyrexia may irreversibly damage the central nervous system.

It is possible that the ultimate failure of the sweat glands is the result of failure of thermoregulatory hypothalamic mechanisms. However, the fact that denervated sweat glands in the normal subject can be activated by a rise in skin temperature supports the concept of localized failure of the sweat apparatus. The skin of patients with heat stroke may be flushed and pink due to extensive cutaneous vasodilatation. However, in the later stages when the splanchnic vessels are also dilated, the skin appears ashen or even cyanotic.

The distinction between heat exhaustion and heat stroke can easily be made by feeling the axillary and groin areas of the patient. In heat exhaustion these regions are moist with perspiration, whereas with heat pyrexia they are dry. Recovery from heat stroke is dependent upon prompt reduction of body temperature.

The clinical syndromes associated with heat cramps, heat exhaustion and heat stroke are described in detail in the final chapter of this monograph.

THE ROLE OF THE SWEAT GLANDS IN ACCLIMATIZATION TO HEAT

With prolonged sweating the sodium and chloride concentrations in the sweat increase and the total loss of these electrolytes may be considerable. Acclimatization is associated with an effort on the part of the sweat glands to conserve electrolytes and at the same time insure adequate heat dissipation through evaporation of water. This is accomplished by the production of large amounts of sweat containing minimal amounts of sodium and chloride. The finding of higher rates of sweating and lower concentrations of Na^{23} and Cl^{35} in sweat in the summer than in the winter in the same individual is most probably an expression of acclimatization to season.

In unacclimatized individuals subjected to hot and humid environments, several days are usually required for significant reductions in the electrolyte concentration of the sweat to develop (9, 10). Once acclimatization is achieved, subjects in a hot and humid environment experience relatively little difficulty even on a salt-restricted diet. Under these circumstances the sodium concentration of the sweat has been observed to be as low as 5 mEq./L. It is probable that the greater the concentration gradient for sodium and chloride between the serum and the sweat, the greater the osmotic work performed by the sweat glands. Although it has not been proven, it is reasonable that the glomerulus of the sweat gland and the sweat tubule behave in a manner similar to the glomerulus and tubule of the kidney. This implies that electrolytes can be reabsorbed in the tubules. The stimulus for the reabsorption of sodium and chloride in the tubule may be salt depletion and associated changes, such as an increase in the rate of secretion of adrenal cortical hormones (11). Acclimatization to heat may involve alterations in sweat gland tubular function as well as glomerular function. Extreme physical exertion in severe heat for several hours may be associated with a decline in the rate of sweating (12).

The extremely rich vascular plexus which surrounds the glomerulus of the sweat gland seems to support the concept that the sweat gland performs osmotic work. In addition, the great length and helical course of the duct would appear unnecessary if it functioned merely as a passive conducting tubule. The cells of the secretory duct abound with glycogen which is utilized during active sweating. Since the sweat has already been formed in the secretory coil, there would be no need for the energy released from glycogen metabolism if the secretory duct were merely a passive structure. On the other hand, a reabsorptive process in the sweat duct could explain the utilization of glycogen by the tubular cells.

CLINICAL APPLICATIONS

The loss of large quantities of electrolytes in sweat can result in serious illness. In normal man difficulty can be avoided by supplementing the usual sodium chloride intake either by salting the drinking water or by the ingestion of salt tablets. However, in patients with cardiovascular-renal disease with associated disturbances in urinary excretion of electrolytes it is difficult to estimate properly the daily requirements of electrolytes. Diuretic therapy may complicate the problem even more. The elimination of sweating in such patients by providing a comfortable air-conditioned environment represents the surest means of eliminating error in the estimation of electrolyte losses since only urinary losses which can be measured accurately need be considered.

Patients with fibrocystic disease should be protected from environments which stimulate sweating. Since the threshold for sweating is decreased by physical activity, patients with fibrocystic disease should be warned against physical effort during hot and humid weather. Electrolyte depletion develops easily in these patients.

Therapeutic agents containing atropine should be used cautiously in hypohidrotic infants who develop intercurrent infection associated with pyrexia. Atropinization in the presence of poorly functioning sweat glands may make thermal regulation difficult if not impossible.

It should always be remembered that whenever the temperature of the ambient air exceeds skin temperature the only effective means of eliminating body heat is sweating (evaporative cooling). Therefore, under these environmental conditions no drugs should be administered which poison or depress the sweat glands.

Sweating may exacerbate or promote a number of dermatologic diseases. Keratin, one of the more abundant constituents of the corneum, is readily hygroscopic. With much sweating the corneum becomes softened and even mascerated due to the absorption of water by keratin. In addition, the protective fatty acids of the skin (acid mantle) are neutralized by excessive sweating. The softened corneum under these conditions can be easily penetrated by a number of infectious organisms, particularly the dermatophytes (Microsporum, Trichophyton and Epidermophyton). These fungi are responsible for such diseases as "athlete's foot" and "ring worm." Patients with these infections should be instructed to keep their skin dry by avoiding excessive sweating and by using an antiseptic absorbent powder. The use of atropine to reduce sweating has been advocated. However, since this may interfere with heat dissipation, it is probably best to avoid atropine therapy in hot climates and in people who perform heavy physical work. The use of air-conditioning can be extremely beneficial even if available for only part of the day.

Miliaria (prickly heat) can be prevented by a cool atmosphere. The skin should be kept dry as well as cool. This is best accomplished by air-conditioning the environment. Cool baths with corn starch are also helpful. Since the sweat pores are usually blocked with keratinous plugs, a hydrophilic ointment should be used in an effort to dissolve the plug.

The Sweat Retention Syndrome. Sulzberger (13) has described a "sweat retention syndrome" due to plugging of the sweat pores. The syndrome is produced by a rapid elevation of environmental temperature associated with high relative humidity. Under such environmental conditions, susceptible individuals may develop signs and symptoms of poral closure including papules, papulovesicles, stinging and pruritus. The failure to sweat may produce heat asthenia or heat exhaustion. Since the acini of the sweat glands continue to produce sweat when thermally stimulated, they become dilated by increased pressure. The constituents of the sweat escape into the periductal tissue producing inflammatory changes. Treatment consists of eliminating thermal stimulation by cooling and applying agents to the skin which remove the material plugging the sweat pores.

Sweat urticaria may be due to an allergic reaction to the extravasation of material from the sweat ducts into the surrounding tissues. If this is so, this represents another disease associated with autointoxication, a clinical entity which is becoming more and more accepted.

Since patients with ectodermal dysplasia have some degree of impairment of sweating, they should be warned against physical exertion in hot weather. If complete aplasia of the sweat glands exists, they should be encouraged to live in a cool climate or an air-condition environment.

Patients with abnormal sweat patterns, patients with diseases associated with electrolyte disturbances, acutely ill or chronically debilitated patients and patients with cardiovascular disease should avoid environmental conditions which promote sweating.

REFERENCES

1. Montagna, W.: *The Structure and Function of Skin.* New York, Academic Press, 1956.
2. Kuno, Y.: *Human Perspiration.* Springfield, Ill.: Charles C Thomas, 1956.
3. Thompson, N.: Tubular resorption of secretion in human eccrine sweat glands. *Clin. Sc., 19:*95, 1960.
4. Berenson, G. S. and Burch, G. E.: A study of the sodium, potassium and chloride content of thermal sweat of man collected from small isolated areas of skin. *J. Lab. & Clin. Med., 42:*58, 1953.
5. Berenson, G. S. and Burch, G. E.: A study of the excretion of Rb^{86}, K^{42}, and K^{39} in thermal sweating. *J. Lab. & Clin. Med., 49:*401, 1957.
6. Burch, G. E., Reaser, P. B. and Cronvich, J.: Rates of sodium turnover in normal subjects and in patients with congestive heart failure. *J. Lab. & Clin. Med., 32:*1169, 1947.
7. di Sant' Agnese, P. A., Darling, R. C., Perera, G. A. and Shea, E.: Sweat electrolyte disturbances associated with childhood pancreatic disease. *Am. J. Med., 15:*777, 1953.
8. di Sant' Agnese, P. A.: Recent observations on pathogenesis of cystic fibrosis of the pancreas. *Pediatrics, 24:*313, 1959.
9. Robinson, S. and Robinson, A. H.: Chemical composition of sweat. *Physiol. Rev., 34:*202, 1954.
10. Dill, D. B., Jones, B. F., Edwards, H. T. and Oberg, S. A.: Salt economy in extreme dry heat. *J. Biol. Chem., 100:* 755, 1933.
11. Conn, J. W.: In: Dock, W. and Snapper, I.: *Advances in Internal Medicine.* New York, Interscience, 1949.
12. Gerking, S. D. and Robinson, S.: Decline in rates of sweating of men working in severe heat. *Am. J. Physiol., 147:*370, 1946.
13. Sulzberger, M. B. and Herrmann, F.: *The Clinical Significance of Disturbances in the Delivery of Sweat.* Springfield, Thomas, 1954.

VII

PERIPHERAL CIRCULATION

THERMAL regulation depends upon a successful balance, at an optimal thermal level, between heat production and heat loss. Man, a homeothermic animal, maintains a relatively uniform level of body temperature in spite of wide variations in heat production and environmental temperature and humidity. Body temperature is regulated in large measure by varying the rate of heat loss through the body surface.

When the temperature of the body surface exceeds ambient temperature, heat is lost from the body by radiation, convection and conduction. It is estimated that under basal conditions 60% of the total heat loss occurs through radiation and 15% through convection with negligible losses due to conduction. As the environmental temperature approaches body temperature, a greater proportion of heat is lost by the evaporation of water from the skin (about 0.59 Calorie per gram of water vaporized), so that when ambient temperature equals or exceeds skin temperature almost all of the heat is lost by the evaporation of water.

Whether heat is lost by radiation, conduction, convection or evaporation, the heat must be carried by the blood from the musculature and viscera to the body surface. Man is insulated against heat loss by an immediate envelope of the surrounding air and by the subcutaneous tissues. Vasodilatation with the delivery of warm blood to the surface of the skin increases the temperature difference (thermal gradient) between the body surface and the ambient air. This also diminishes the effect of tissue insulation so that heat loss can occur. Vasoconstriction, on the other hand, reduces the rate of heat loss by reducing the thermal gradient and increasing the "effective" tissue insulation. In order to increase surface temperature of the body there must be an increase in deep body temperature and/or a reduction in the thermal insulation of the tissues. Either or both of these factors may initiate the reflexes which ultimately result in vasodilatation.

To increase heat loss there must be an increase in dermal circulation (vasodilatation), and to decrease heat loss there must be a decrease in dermal circulation (vasoconstriction). Thus, the rate of dermal blood flow is important in thermal regulation. Since digital circulation is physiologically similar in many ways to dermal circulation, digital blood flow reflects dermal blood flow. This does not imply that heat loss is uniform for all parts of the body. Indeed, there are wide variations in the

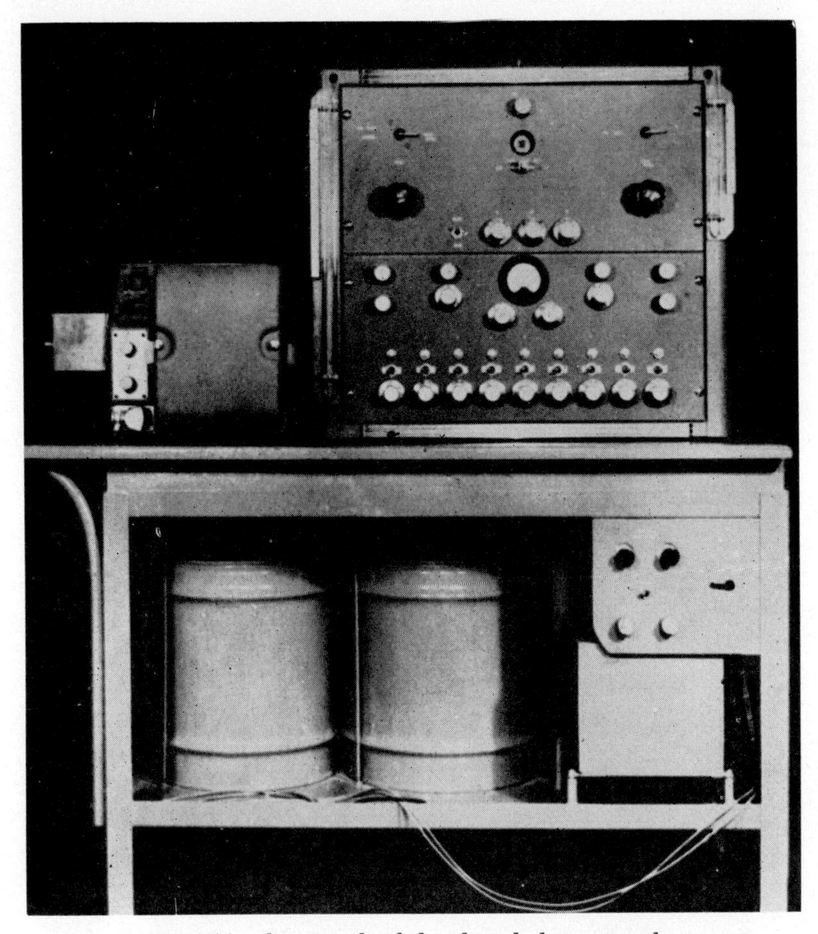

Fig. 55. Photograph of the rheoplethysmograph.

rates of local blood flow and heat loss. Differences in contour influence the effective insulation by the air, being less for cylinders and spheres than for flat surfaces. Thus, a rise in the skin temperature of the fingers is more effective in promoting heat loss than a similar rise in some other body areas. At high temperatures the hands and feet may be warmer than more proximal portions of the body surface, whereas at cool temperatures the skin becomes progressively cooler from central to peripheral areas (1).

Because of the facts noted above, the digital circulation of man was studied rheoplethysmographically to learn aspects of the response of the dermal circulation of man to various environmental temperatures and humidities.

THE RHEOPLETHYSMOGRAPHIC METHOD

The Rheoplethysmograph. The electronic rheoplethysmograph (RPG) (Fig. 55) employed in this laboratory is sensitive to a volume change of less than 0.1 mm.[3] It is so designed as to record automatically, continuously and simultaneously the volumes and rates of digital inflow, outflow and differences between inflow and outflow during a single pulse cycle and for any preselected portion of a pulse cycle (2, 3).

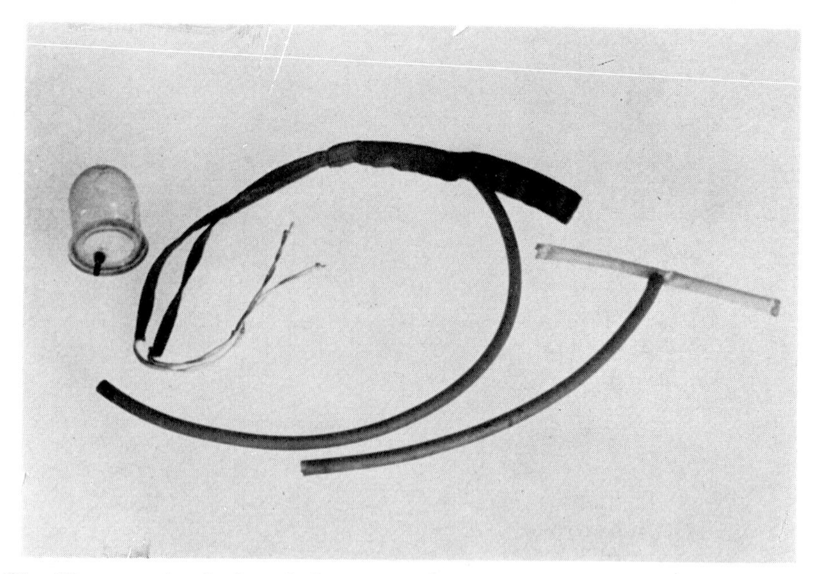

Fig. 56. Photograph of the plethysmographic cup on the left and the collecting pneumatic cuff on the right which is enclosed within an inelastic cloth shown in the center of the photograph.

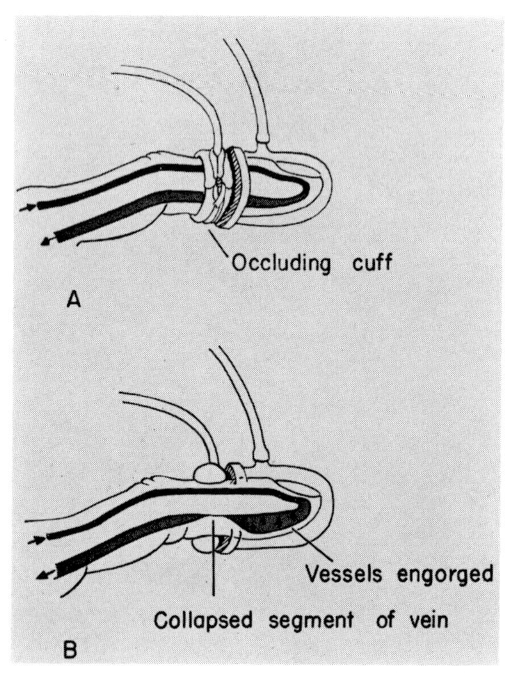

Fig. 57. Diagram of a finger tip in a plethysmographic cup. A. The plastic transparent, lightweight plethysmographic cup and collecting cuff mounted to the terminal portion of the index finger. B. Inflation of the collecting cuff traps inflowing blood in the collecting vessels where it is measured by the plethysmograph.

The Rheoplethysmographic Cup and Collecting Cuff. The finger tip* is enclosed in a lightweight, loosely-fitted plastic plethysmographic cup connected to a sensitive recorder with suitable physical characteristics. A pneumatic collecting cuff is wrapped loosely around the digit just proximal to the cup (Figs. 56, 57). The collecting cuff is suddenly inflated automatically by electronically controlled solenoids to a preselected pressure, usually 60 mm. Hg, in order to obstruct venous outflow without disturbing arterial inflow and to collect the inflowing blood in the collecting vessels in the portion of the digit enclosed in the plethysmographic cup. The rheoplethysmograph is equipped with circuits which are triggered by the digital pulse so that the collecting cuff can be inflated at any preselected moment in the pulse cycle for any interval of time.

* The finger or toe tip is defined as the portion of the digit distal to a plane in which lie the major dorsal and palmar or plantar creases in the region of the distal interphalangeal articulation.

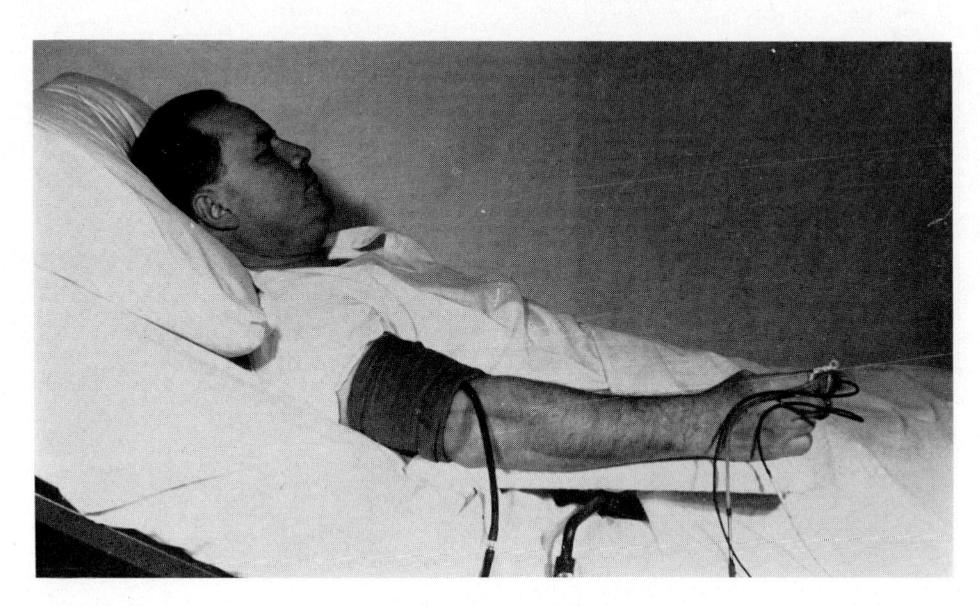

Fig. 58. Position of the subject during the recording of blood flow into the finger tip. The rheoplethysmographic cup and collecting cuff are in place and the digits are supported comfortably at heart level. The pneumatic cuff around the brachium occludes the circulation to the arm for recording the volume curve of the artifact.

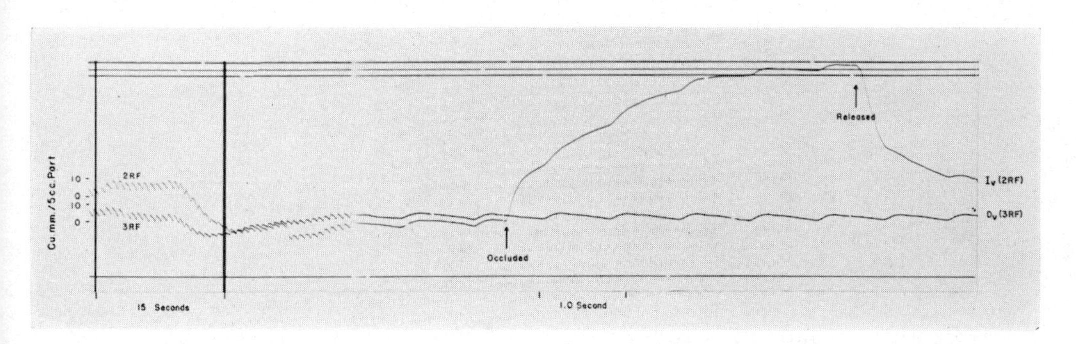

Fig. 59. An original rheoplethysmogram showing the simultaneous volume time-course curves for the second right finger tip (2RF) and the third right finger tip (3RF) of a normal subject resting in bed in a comfortable atmosphere with the digits at heart level. The recordings are shown at slow and fast camera speeds. The collecting cuff was suddenly inflated to a pressure of 60 mm. Hg at the point indicated by the arrow. The inflowing blood was collected in the vessels distal to the occluded digital veins causing 2RF to increase in volume as indicated by the trace. This I_V curve includes the volume artifact (A_V) (Fig. 62) plus the volume of blood flowing into the finger tip. The collecting cuff was deflated at the arrow labeled released.

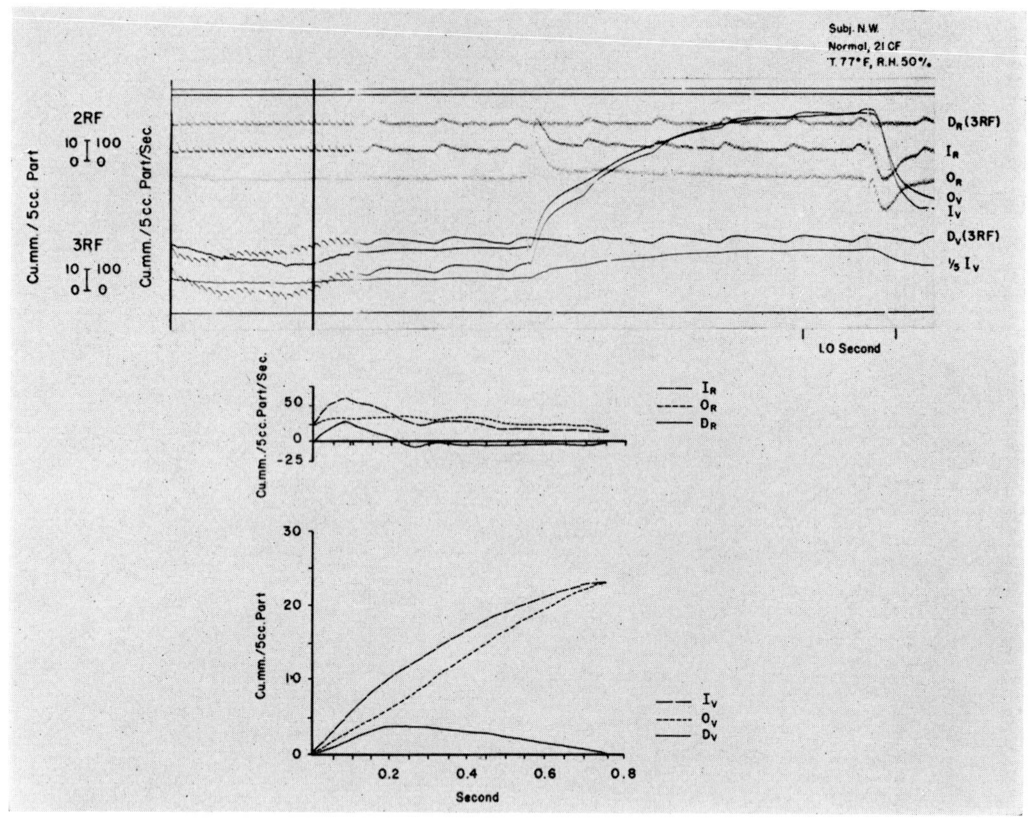

Fig. 60. The completed rheoplethysmogram for a normal subject. The volume and rate curves and changes in the total volumes of the two digits are recorded automatically and simultaneously. The simultaneous curves of rate are the first derivatives of the volume curves. The scale for the volume and rate curves are shown at the left. The ordinate values of rates are ten times the ordinate values of volume. The ordinate values of the traces of total volume of the digits are one-fifth those of the volume pulse traces. By proper standardization of the recording galvanometers to correct for volume of the part, the linear deflection represents changes in volume directly in cu. mm./5 cc. of part and changes in rate directly in cu. mm./5 cc. of part/sec. Consult text for details.

The Rheoplethysmographic Concept. The digit to be studied is supported comfortably at heart level (Fig. 58). The effect of sudden inflation of the collecting cuff upon digital volume is shown in Figure 59. The resultant time course curve is produced by the accumulation of inflowing blood (I_V) trapped in the collecting vessels (mainly veins) of the digit enclosed in the plethysmographic cup. The volume pulse wave of the digit recorded just prior to venous occlusion, or simultaneously for an adjacent digit, represents the time course of the difference (D_V) between the volume of inflow (I_V) and the volume of outflow (O_V) (Fig. 59) (3, 4, 5).

Thus,

$$D_V = I_V - O_V. \qquad (3)$$

Since D_V and I_V are recorded directly from the digit, the time course of the outflow volume (O_V) can be obtained from these curves either manually by

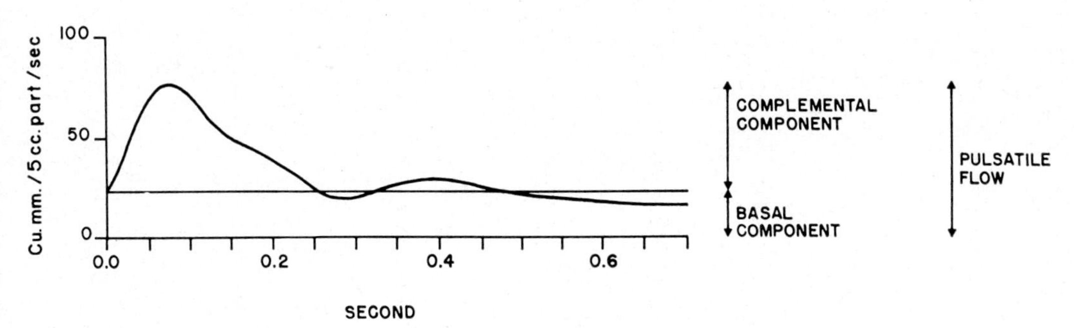

Fig. 61. The inflow rate curve (I_R) shown reflects the pulsatile flow which consists of two components, the basal pulsatile flow and the complemental pulsatile flow as indicated.

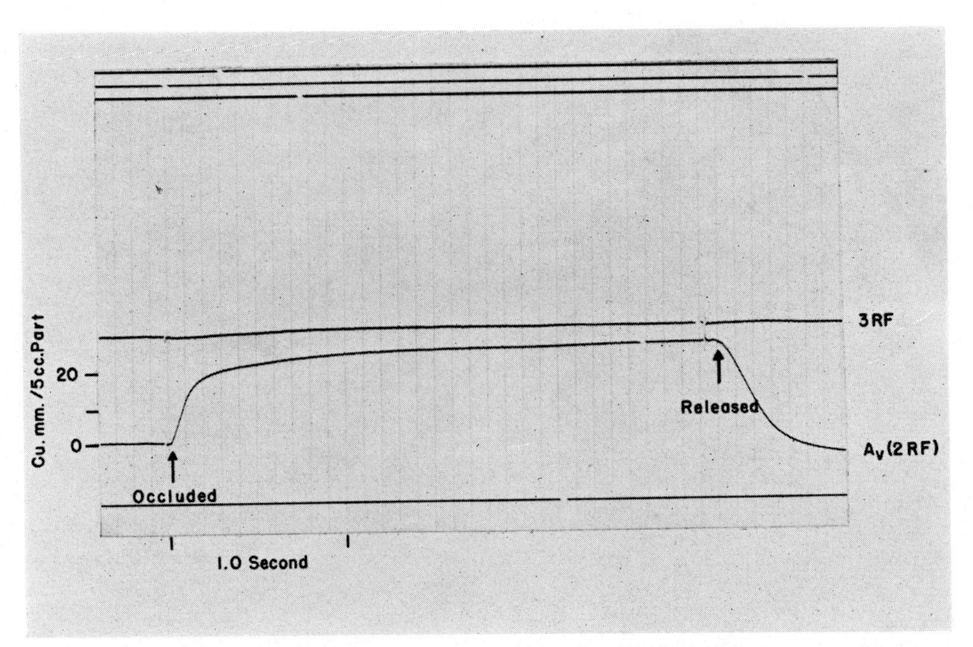

Fig. 62. The artifact volume curve (A_V). The arrows indicate the moment of inflation and deflation of the digital collecting cuff.

substraction or electronically by means of difference circuits, for

$$O_V = I_V - D_V. \tag{4}$$

By means of differentiating circuits the rheoplethysmograph automatically differentiates the volume curves to record simultaneously with each other and with the volume curves the rate of inflow (I_R), the difference between the rates of inflow and outflow (D_R) and the rate of outflow (O_R) (Fig. 60). Thus, the time-course curves of rate are the time courses of the first derivatives

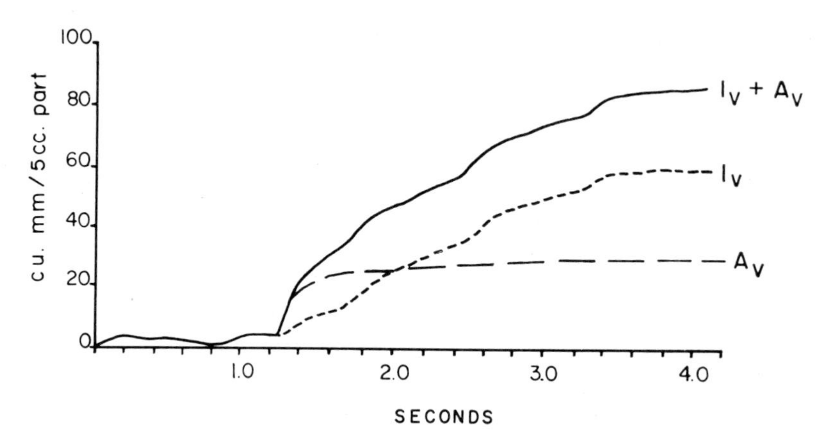

Fig. 63. Method for manually correcting the recorded rheoplethysmographic curve of the volume time course of 2RF, which consists of I_V and A_V, to volume inflow (I_V) by subtracting from it the volume artifact curve (A_V).

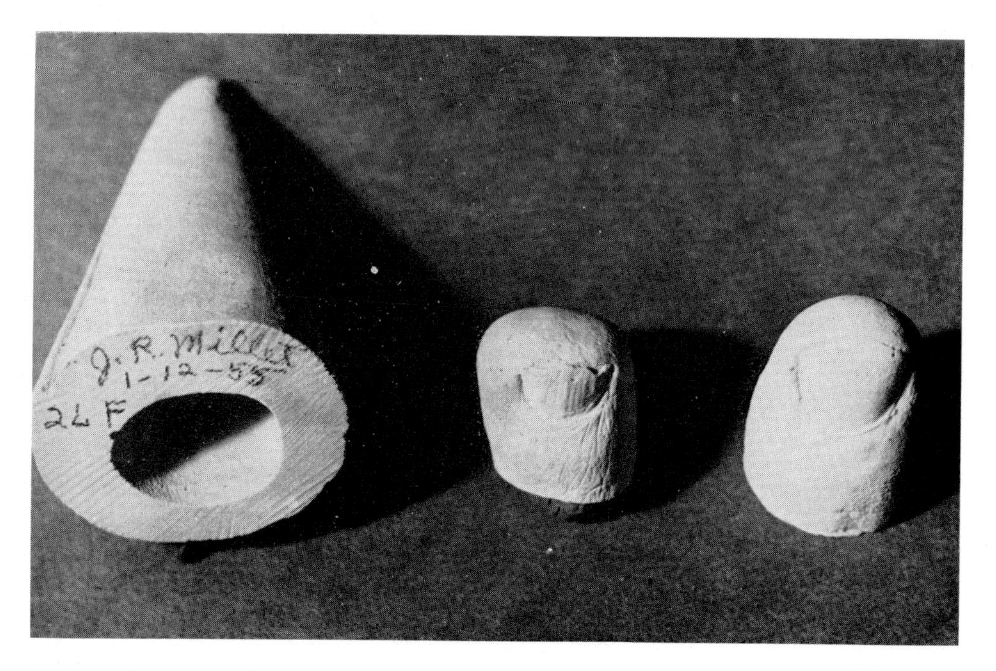

Fig. 64. Positive and negative casts of finger and toe tips used to measure the volume of the part studied. The volume is determined from the negative cast shown on the left by weighing mercury necessary to just fill the cast. The volume is determined from positive casts shown to the right by weighing mercury displaced by the cast.

of the respective volume curves (3, 5). As with the volume curves (Equations 3 and 4),

$$D_R = I_R - O_R \quad \text{and} \qquad (5)$$
$$O_R = I_R - D_R. \qquad (6)$$

Basal and Complemental Pulsatile Flow. The curve of the rate of digital inflow, which is pulsatile, has been divided into basal and complemental components (Fig. 61). The basal component is equal to the rate of blood flow at the end of diastole, whereas the complemental component which is superimposed upon the basal component is the increase in the rate of inflow due to systolic ejection (Fig. 61). Together, the basal and complemental components comprise the pulsatile flow (3, 5). The maximal rate of pulsatile flow refers to the peak of the curve of pulsatile flow which, of course, is identical to the peak of the curve of complemental flow.

The Rheoplethysmogram. In Figure 60 a completed original rheoplethysmogram (RPG) is shown for the second (2RF) and third (3RF) right finger tips. The sudden rise in the volume trace for 2RF was produced by the accumulation of inflowing blood (I_V) within collecting vessels of the digit and the volume artifact (A_V). In order to obtain the true inflow volume curve (I_V), the curve of the artifact (A_V) must be subtracted from the recorded volume trace. The curve of the artifact is recorded by inflating the collecting cuff while the circulation to the arm is arrested at the brachium (or calf, when studying the toe) by sudden inflation of a blood pressure cuff to a level greater than systemic arterial blood pressure (Fig. 62). After the artifact curve (A_V) is subtracted from the volume trace for 2RF, the resultant curve represents the time course of the volume of inflowing blood (Fig. 63). However, after 0.20 second following inflation of the collecting cuff, the volume artifact usually becomes insignificant and can be ignored (3, 5).

Correction for Size of Part. In order to express the digital blood flow in quantitative terms, the volume of the part studied must be known. This volume is obtained from measurements of positive and negative casts made of dental stone (Fig. 64) (5, 6, 7). The volume

TABLE 6

CALIBRATION FACTORS TO CORRECT FOR DIGITAL SIZE SO THAT 1 mm. OF DEFLECTION ON THE RECORDED TRACE REPRESENTS 1 cu. mm. VOLUME CHANGE FOR 5 cc. OF PART

Volume of Part cc.	*Deflection of Galvanometer* mm.	*Volume of Part* cc.	*Deflection of Galvanometer* mm.
1.0	50.0	5.2	9.6
1.4	35.7	5.6	8.9
1.8	27.8	6.0	8.3
2.2	22.7	6.4	7.8
2.6	19.2	6.8	7.4
3.0	16.7	7.2	6.9
3.4	14.7	7.6	6.6
3.8	13.2	8.0	6.3
4.2	11.9	8.4	6.0
4.6	10.9	8.8	5.7
5.0	10.0		

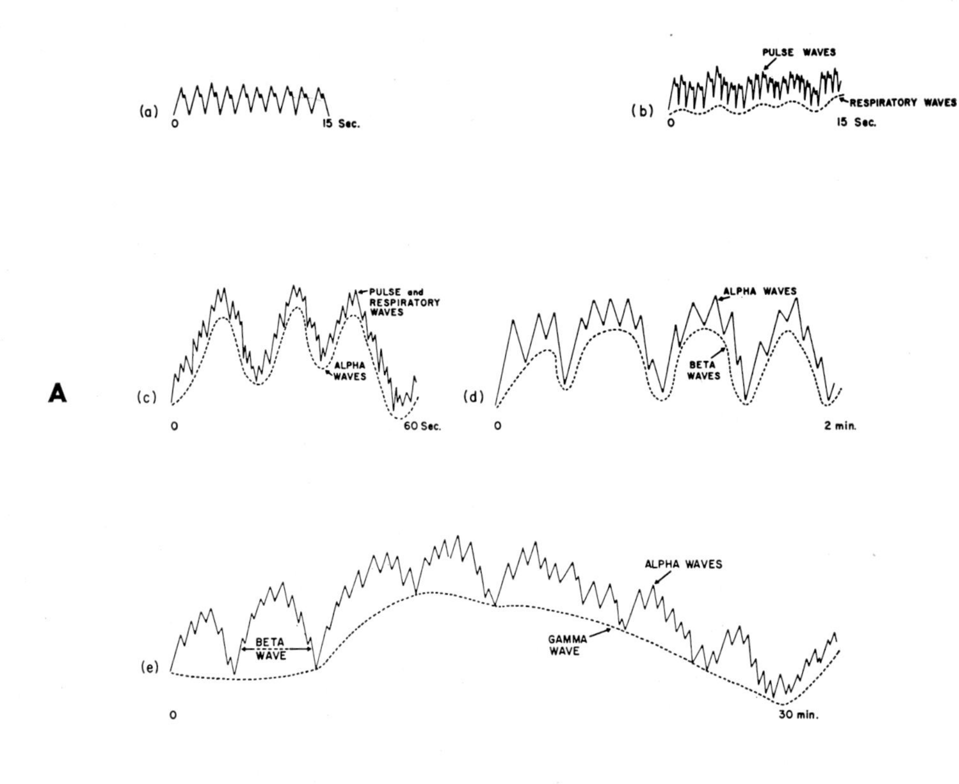

B

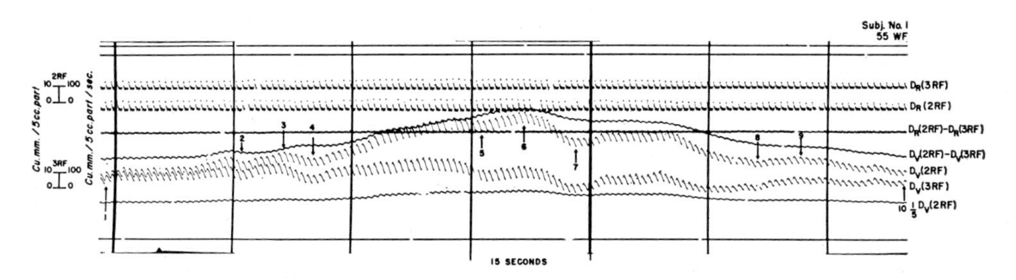

Fig. 65. A. Schematic representation of the 5 types of deflections due to spontaneous variations in digital volume; a, pulse waves; b, pulse and respiratory waves; c. pulse, respiratory and alpha waves; d, alpha and beta waves (pulse and respiratory waves not shown); e, alpha, beta and gamma waves. B. Original RPG showing pulse waves (D_V), alpha deflections (arrows 2 to 4 and 5 to 7) and a beta deflection (arrows 1 to 6 and 6 to 10). Note an alpha deflection is descending, arrows 3 to 4, on an ascending beta deflection, arrows 1 to 6, and an alpha deflection is ascending, arrows 8 to 9, on a descending beta reflection, arrows 6 to 10.

of the positive cast is measured indirectly by displacement of mercury which is weighed on an analytical balance to 0.1 mg. The volume of the negative cast is obtained from the weight of the mercury required to fill the cast.

Calibration of the Rheoplethysmograph. The sensitivity of the RPG is adjusted for each digit so that 10 mm. of deflection on the completed record is equal to 10 $mm.^3$ volume change per 5 cc. of part (Table 6). The volume of the part is reduced to 5cc. for reference because 2RF (tip of the right index finger) of man averages 5 cc. in size. This correction for size of the part permits quantitative comparison of data from subject to subject and part to part. The differentiating circuits used to record the rate curves automatically on the rheoplethysmogram were so designed that there is a 10:1 ratio between the rate and volume curves. Therefore, the scale for the rate curves in cu. mm./ 5 cc. part/sec. is obtained by merely multiplying the ordinate scale of the volume trace by ten.

Conversion Factor in Plethysmography. The unit of measurement employed in other laboratories to express blood flow is cc./100 cc. of part. By multiplying the numerical values obtained in the present studies by 1.2 it is possible to convert cu. mm./5 cc. part to cc./100 cc. of part.

THE NORMAL PERIPHERAL BLOOD FLOW

An average normal subject resting quietly in a neutral environment has a volume pulse curve (D_V) and a digital inflow curve (I_V) which are generally of good amplitude. For example, in a representative normal subject the average maximal value for D_V was 4 cu. mm./5 cc. part, and for I_V, 22.7 cu. mm./5 cc. part for a pulse cycle, and the mean rates of basal pulsatile flow and maximal pulsatile flow were 25 and 60 cu. mm./5 cc. part/sec., respectively (Fig. 60).

The Five Spontaneous Digital Volume Deflections. There are constant spontaneous variations in the digital volume of normal subjects, which have been classified into five separate rhythms (Fig. 65) (8, 9) as follows:

(1) pulse waves
(2) respiratory waves
(3) alpha deflections
(4) beta deflections
(5) gamma deflections.

The alpha, beta and gamma deflections have been shown to be independent of the pulse and respiratory waves (8, 10). The *alpha deflections* have a mean frequency of 7.9 per minute and a mean magnitude of 14.5 $mm.^3$ per 5 cc. of part. *Beta deflections* occur at a mean rate of 1.3 per minute with a mean magnitude of 30 $mm.^3$ per 5 cc. of part. Thus, the relatively short alpha deflections are superimposed upon the longer beta deflections. *Gamma deflections* have a mean frequency of four per hour and have a mean magnitude of 150 $mm.^3$ per 5 cc. of part. Extreme vasoconstriction or vasodilatation diminishes the magnitude and frequency of the alpha, beta and gamma deflections.

These spontaneous variations in volume are associated with changes in digital volume and reflect pre- and postcapillary activity. It has been found that when an alpha deflection ascends on a descending beta deflection, the rate of inflow is increasing as the total digital volume decreases, reflecting precapillary dilatation and postcapillary constriction

RPG, ALPHA DEFLECTION ASCENDING, BETA DEFLECTION DESCENDING

Subject at Rest, 2RF

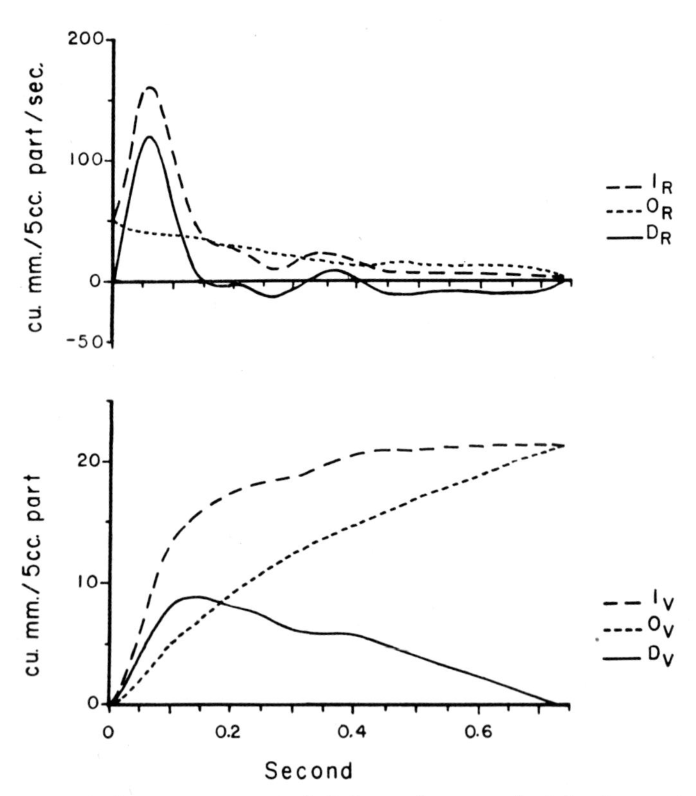

Fig. 66. Rheoplethysmogram recorded from the second right finger tip (2RF) for a pulse cycle while an alpha deflection was ascending and a beta deflection descending. The I_V curve shows a rapid leveling-off due to leakage of blood past the collecting cuff as a result of "overfilling" by only 20 cu. mm. of inflowing blood. The small capacity of the collecting vessels indicates high tone in these vessels as would be expected with postcapillary constriction. The relatively high rate of digital inflow is indicated by the peak rate of flow of 160 cu. mm./5 cc. part/sec. Compare with curves in Figure 67. (From *Proc. Soc. Exper. Biol. & Med., 102*:400, 1959.)

(Figs. 65, 66). On the other hand, when an alpha deflection descends on an ascending beta deflection, the rate of inflow is decreasing while the total digital volume increases, reflecting precapillary constriction and postcapillary dilatation (Figs. 65, 67) (11). These deflections are known to be independent of the Traube-Hering pressure waves, to reflect fluctuations in vascular volume and blood flow and are considered to play a role in thermal regulation. These waves are probably also concerned with the transcapillary exchange of fluid and electrolytes and the flow of intercellular fluid and lymph. Analysis of these spontaneous variations has led to the concept that the blood flow to the finger behaves in a manner similar to the blood flow to the glomerulus of the kidney in

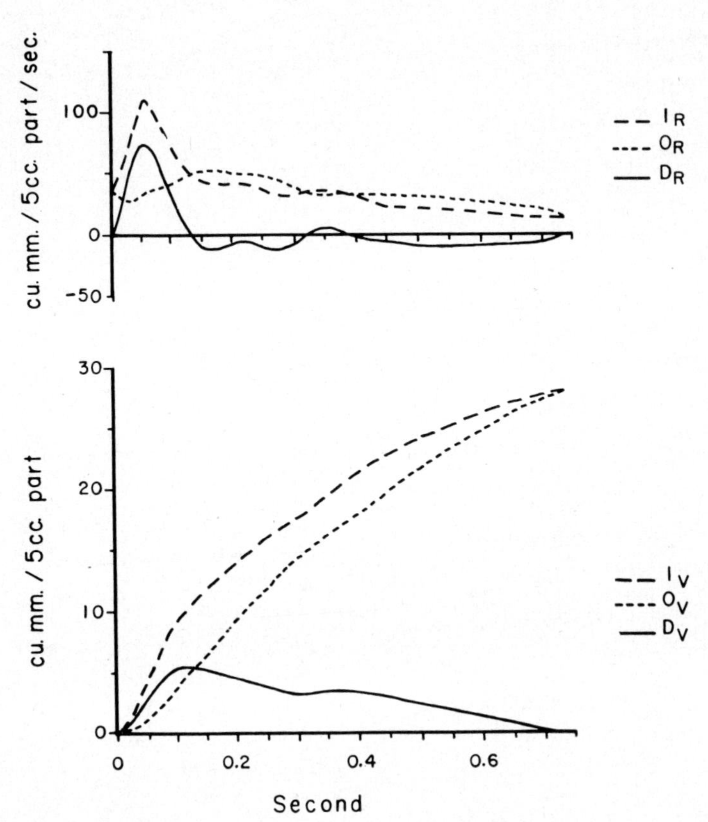

Fig. 67. Rheoplethysmogram recorded seconds later for the same digit as shown in Figure 66. In this instance the alpha deflection was descending while the beta deflection was ascending. Note the filling of the collecting vessels during both the systolic and diastolic phase of the pulse cycle. The collecting vessels were not "overfilled" even by 30 cu. mm. of inflowing blood. This situation would be anticipated for a loose postcapillary vascular system associated with postcapillary dilatation. (From *Proc. Soc. Exper. Biol. & Med., 102:*400, 1959.)

that there may be discordant pre- and postcapillary constriction and dilatation depending upon moment-to-moment body requirements. The alpha deflection reflects variations in caliber of the precapillary vessels and the beta deflection reflects variations in caliber of the postcapillary vessels.

ENVIRONMENTAL TEMPERATURES AND DIGITAL BLOOD FLOW

The Influence of a Hot and Humid Environment on Digital Blood Flow. When a subject was exposed to a hot and humid environment, D_V, I_V and O_V increased considerably in magnitude. Figure 68 shows the effect of a hot environment

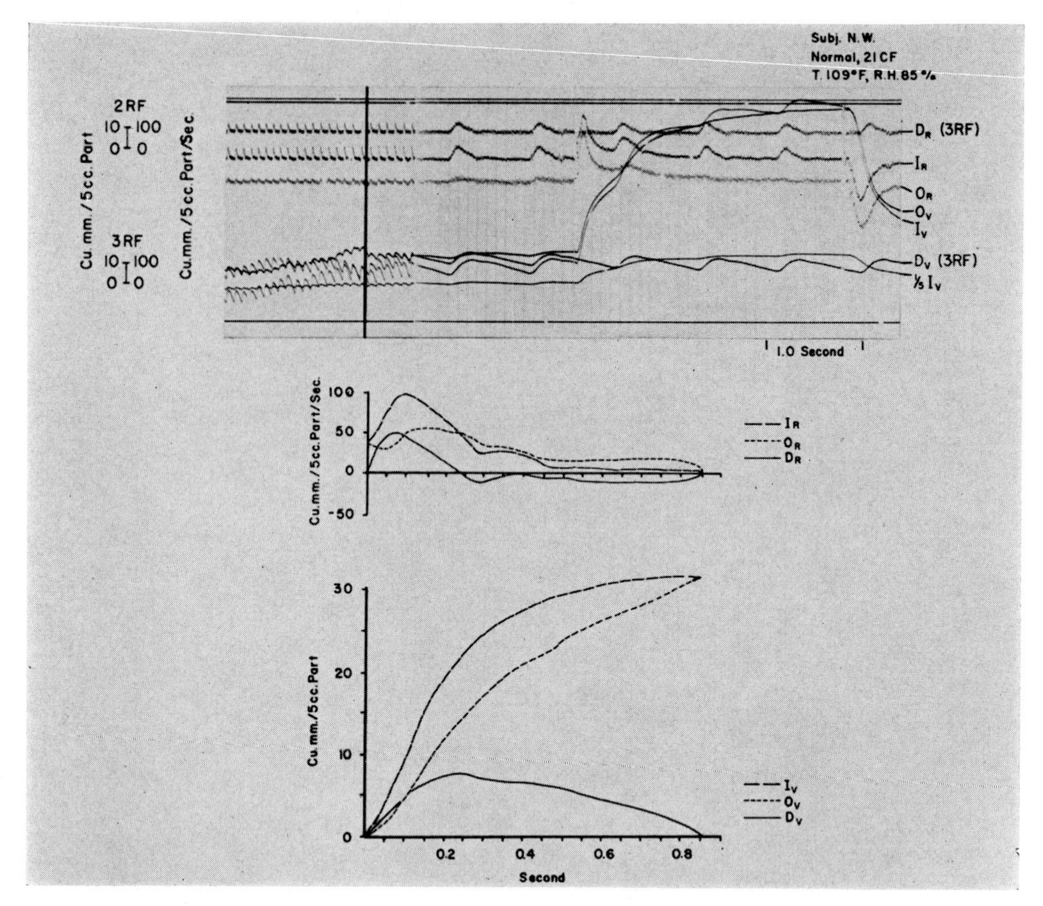

Fig. 68. Rheoplethysmogram recorded for a subject exposed to a hot and humid environment. Note the rapid rate of digital inflow with early leveling-off of the I_V curve during diastole. This leveling-off is due to "overfilling" of the venous reservoirs or collecting vessels resulting in leakage of blood beneath the collecting cuff.

on the digital blood flow for the same subject shown in Figure 60. D_V increased to 7.8 cu. mm./5 cc. part; I_V increased to 31.4 cu. mm./5 cc. part for the pulse cycle, and the basal pulsatile and maximal pulsatile rates of flow were 39 and 97 cu. mm./5 cc. part/sec., respectively. The magnitude of the alpha and beta deflections was decreased considerably by the hot environment.

In a hot and humid environment digital blood flow was so rapid that the collecting vessels of the digit quickly overfilled and leakage past the collecting cuff occurred early in the first pulse cycle following inflation of the cuff (Fig. 68). When leakage occurs past the collecting cuff, a satisfactory inflow curve, I_V, cannot be obtained for a whole pulse cycle. In order to construct an average RPG for a complete pulse cycle under circumstances of high rates of digital flow, the curves of volume and rate can be plotted from values obtained for short intervals of time (fractions of a pulse cycle) at various moments in the pulse cycle, as illustrated in Figure 69.

The digital inflow curves (I_V and I_R) tend to reflect the behavior of the arterial or precapillary vessels and the digi-

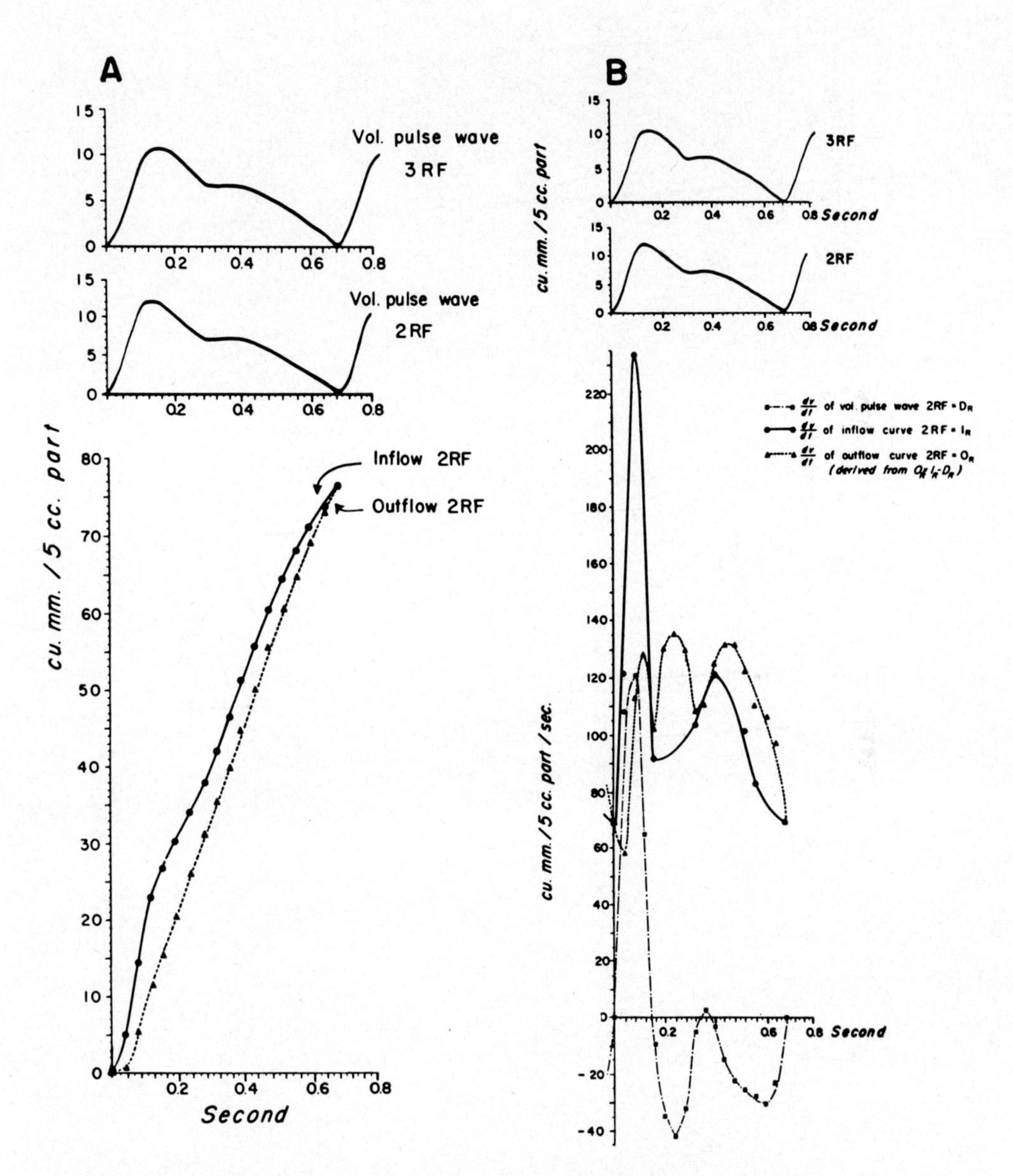

Fig. 69. In order to correct for the error due to rapid overfilling of the collecting vessels and leakage of blood beneath the collecting cuff, average inflow volume curves (A) and rate curves (B) were constructed from many inflow curves recorded for successive pulse cycles at different moments along the pulse wave. (From *Digital Plethysmography.* New York, Grune & Stratton, 1954.)

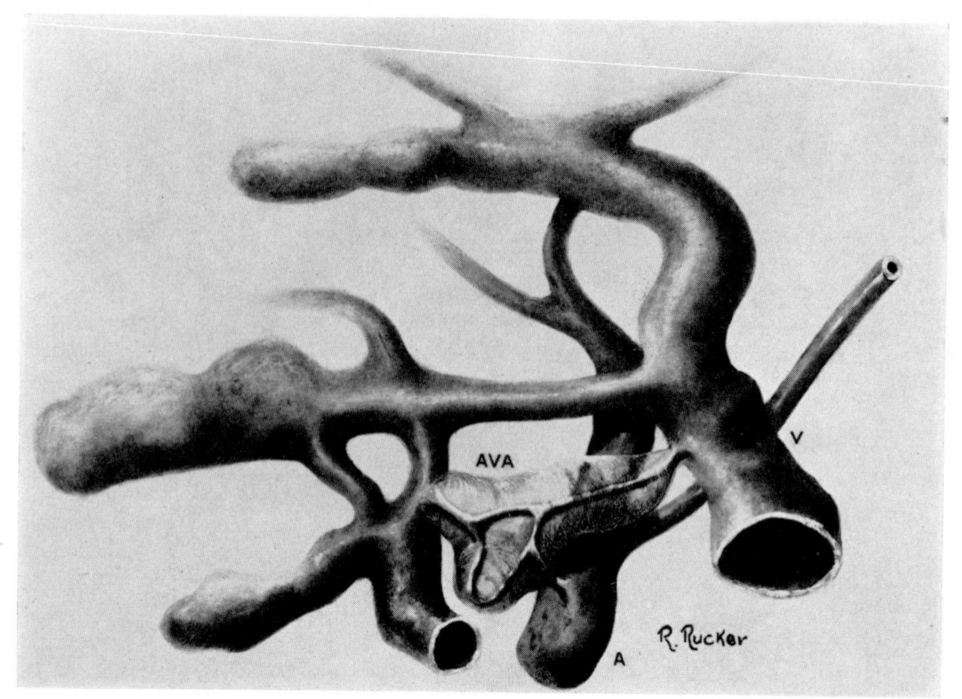

Fig. 70. Stereogram drawn from reconstructed spatial sections of a sub-ungual arterio-venous anastomosis (AVA) of a human finger tip. A and V indicate an artery and vein, respectively.

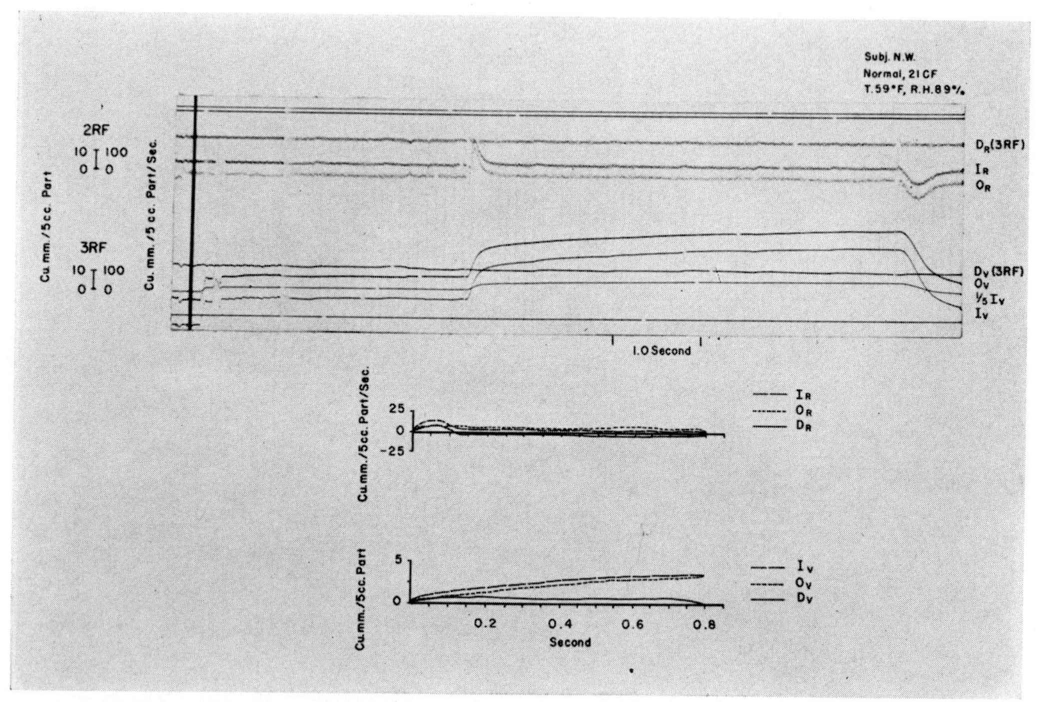

Fig. 71. The digital rheoplethysmogram for the same patient as shown in Figures 60 and 68 studied in a cold environment. Compare the curves with those of Figures 60 and 68.

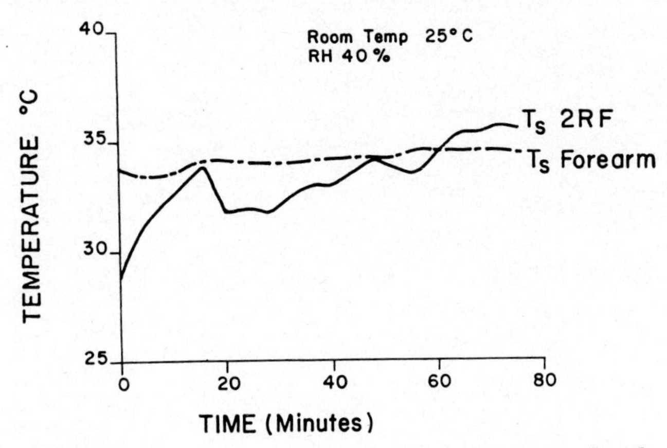

Fig. 72. Skin temperatures recorded simultaneously for the second right finger tip and forearm of a subject in a comfortable environment. Note the marked fluctuations in the skin temperature of the finger tip while that of the forearm remained relatively constant.

tal outflow curves (O_V and O_R) tend to reflect the behavior of the postcapillary vessels. The pre- and postcapillary vessels are under the control of the autonomic nervous system and are undoubtedly influenced by reflexes originating in the higher heat-regulating centers such as the hypothalamus as well as all connecting links in the psychoneurogenic centers and pathways of the peripheral and central nervous systems. The A-V anastomoses must also be involved in thermoregulatory and other reflexes. These anastomoses are abundant in the finger tip and must serve some important function in the regulation of the peripheral blood flow (Fig. 70). In addition, humoral factors of local and distant origin must also contribute to the regulation of the peripheral circulation.

Thus, a hot and humid environment increases greatly the rate of digital blood flow. All of the digital vessels are markedly dilated, including the A-V anastomoses. The vessels of the finger tip which are representative of the circulation to the skin are converted to a functional state similar to that of an A-V aneurysm or shunt.

The Influence of a Hot and Humid Environment on the Digital Veins. As already indicated, the digital veins are dilated in a hot and humid environment. Furthermore, the pressure in these veins is elevated. The increased digital venous pressure is partly responsible for the leakage that occurs beneath the collecting cuff during venous occlusion in a hot and humid environment. Leakage takes place when the venous pressure distal to the collecting cuff exceeds the pressure in the collecting cuff.

The Influence of a Cold Environment on Peripheral Blood Flow. In a cold environment the magnitudes of D_V and I_V are small. The RPG for the same subject illustrated in Figures 60 and 68 shows D_V to be reduced to 0.9 cu. mm./5 cc. part, I_V to 3.2 cu. mm./5 cc. part for the pulse cycle, and the basal and maximal pulsatile rates of flow reduced to 5 and 12 cu. mm./5 cc. part /sec., respectively (Fig. 71). The alpha and beta deflections were also greatly reduced. The magnitudes of D_V, I_V and

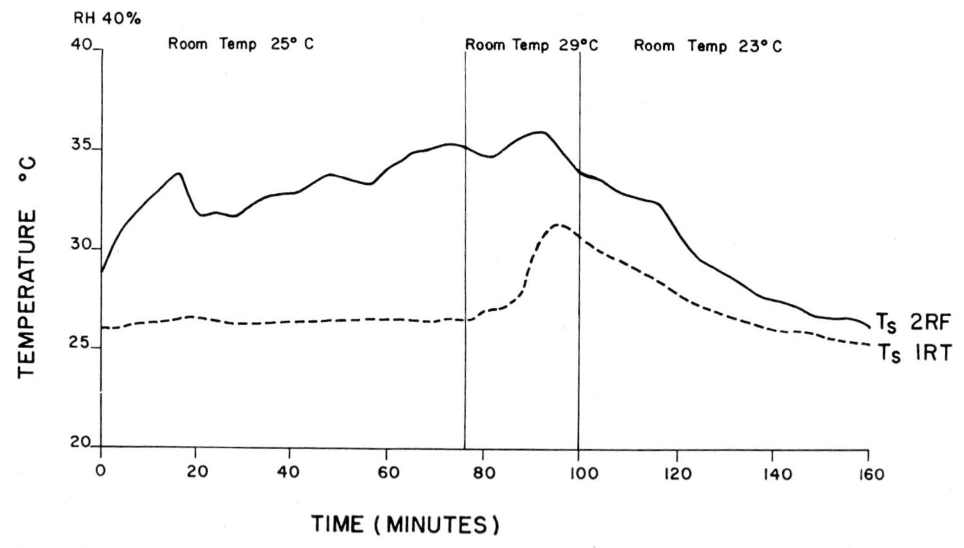

Fig. 73. Skin temperature of the second right finger tip (2RF) and the first right toe tip (1RT) recorded simultaneously in a neutral environment, in a warm environment and in a cool environment. In the neutral environment the temperature of the finger tip fluctuated markedly while that of the toe tip was relatively constant. Upon increasing the room temperature to 29° C. the temperature of the toe tip increased greatly. Lowering the room temperature to 23° C. produced a decrease in temperature for both finger and toe tips.

O_V as well as the rates of basal and maximal pulsatile flow were reduced so much that they could not be measured accurately when subjects were exposed to a cold environment for prolonged periods of time. All digital vessels including A-V anastomoses are markedly constricted and digital flow is reduced to almost zero except for variations in flow due to the hunting phenomenon (12).

The Influence of a Cold Environment on the Digital Veins. The digital veins are constricted in a cold environment. High venous tone was indicated by the low rates of digital blood flow when the environment was cooled (Fig. 71). Many studies performed in this laboratory have shown that in a cold environment digital inflow takes place primarily during systole when arterial pressure is highest (13). The low rates of digital flow during systole have been found to be due to a decline in the A-V pressure gradient after the first pulse beat, with the rate of leakage past the collecting cuff equal to the rate of inflow so that there was no net change in digital volume.

The Influence of Environmental Temperature on Skin Temperature. Lightly clothed subjects were studied while resting in a hospital-type bed in an air-conditioned climatic room to learn the relationship of digital skin temperature to digital flow. The temperature of the skin of the finger tip was found to vary directly with digital blood flow, i.e., as the blood flow increased the skin temperature increased and vice versa. There was a marked lag in time, however, between an increase or decrease in digital blood flow and a corresponding increase or decrease in skin temperature. In a

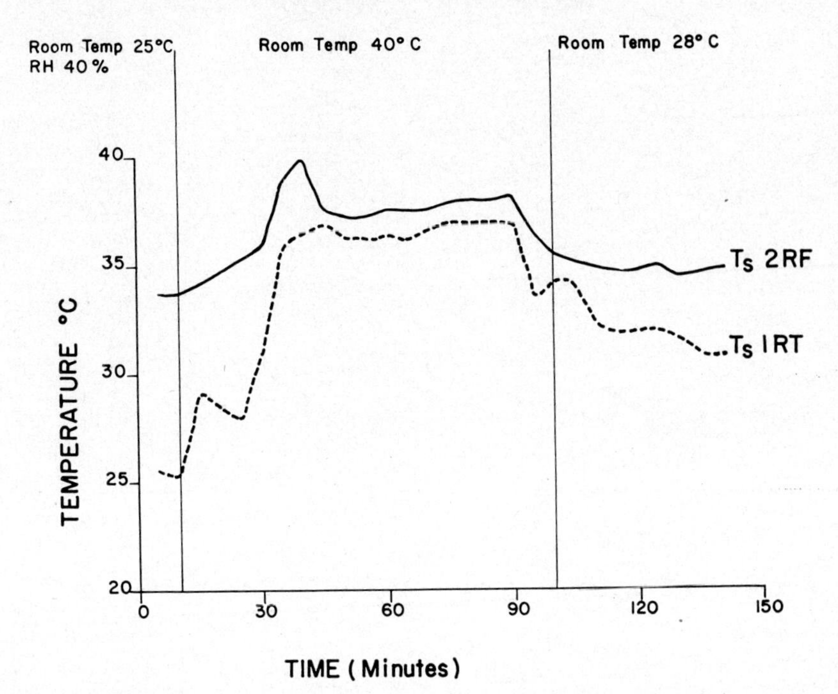

Fig. 74. Warming the climatic room to 40° C. resulted in a rise in the temperature of the toe tip essentially to that of the finger tip.

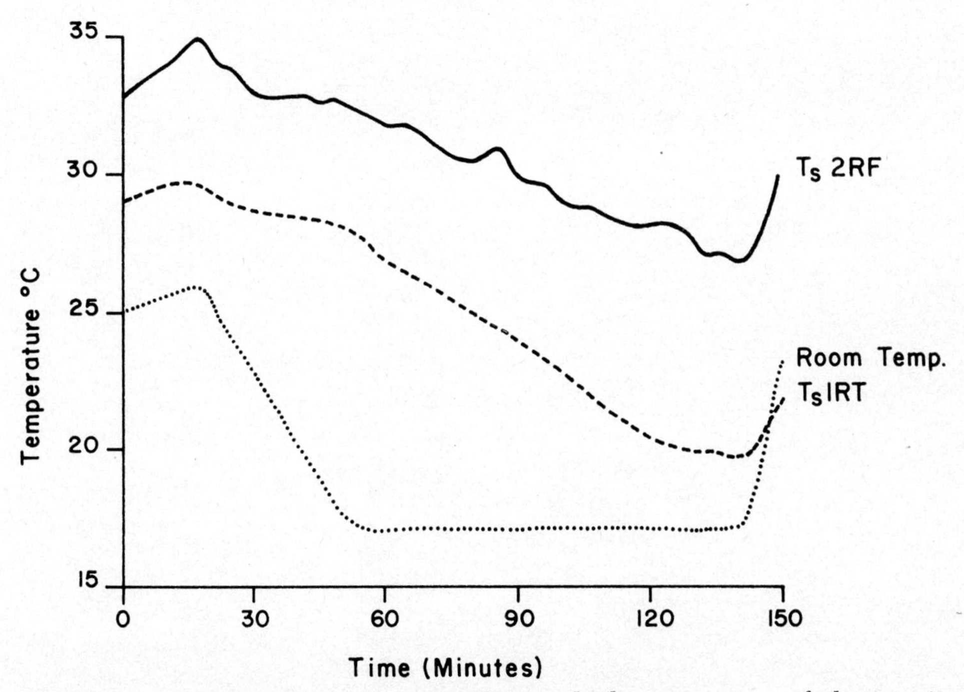

Fig. 75. As the room temperature was decreased, the temperature of the toe tip decreased to a lower level than that of the finger tip. Experiments have shown that the temperature of the toe tip would eventually have reached the environmental temperature while that of the finger tip would have remained low but still higher than that of the toe tip.

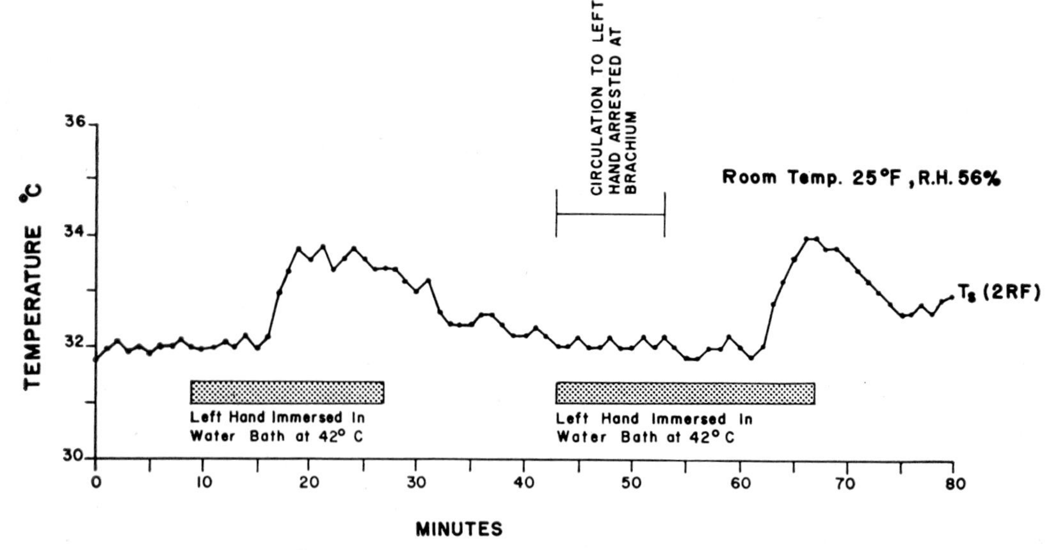

Fig. 76. Immersion of the left hand in a water bath at 42° C. produced an increase in skin temperature of the finger tip on the contralateral side. The circulation to the left hand was then arrested at the brachium and the hand again immersed in a water bath at 42° C. There was no increase in skin temperature of the contralateral finger tip until the circulation was restored to the hand immersed in the hot water bath.

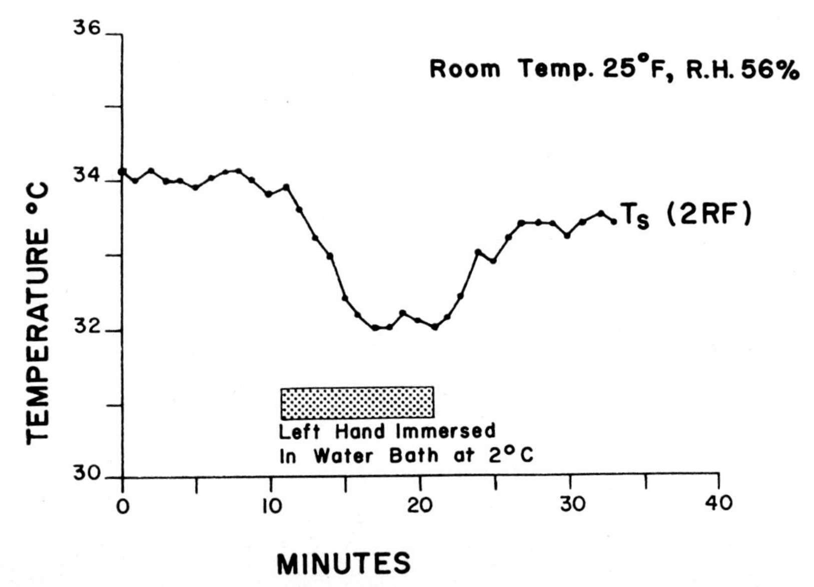

Fig. 77. The left hand was immersed in a water bath at 2° C. which produced a decrease in skin temperature in the second right finger tip (2RF). The latent period was extremely short.

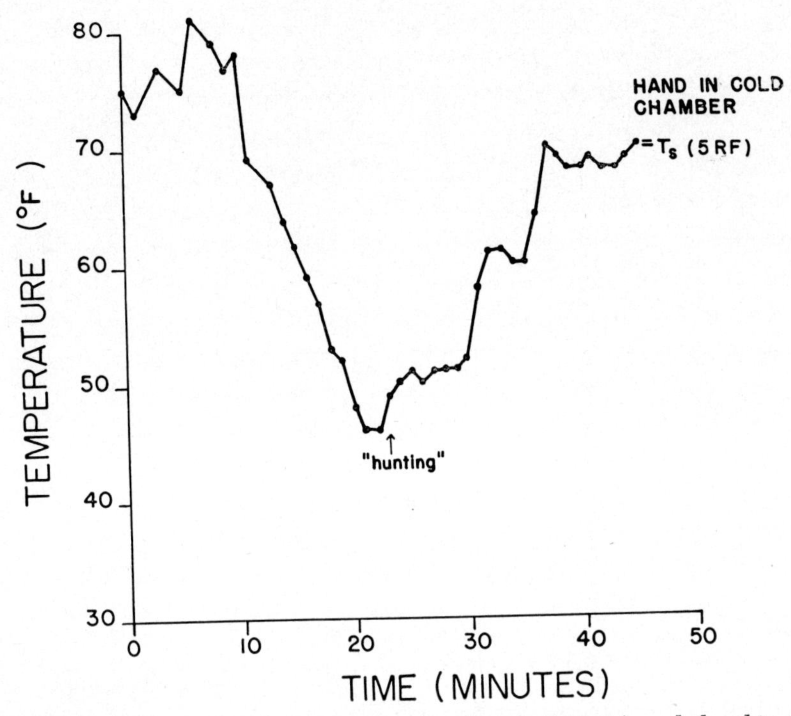

Fig. 78. The hand was placed in an arctic chamber (−18° C.) and the skin temperature from the fifth right finger tip was measured. The temperature of the finger tip decreased, but the decline in the skin temperature of the fifth right finger tip was interrupted by an increase in the skin temperature. In time the temperature of the skin again decreased and after a period of time it rose again. This is a reflection of the "hunting phenomenon" of Sir Thomas Lewis.

comfortable environment (25° C., 40% R.H.) the skin temperature of the forearm and toes was relatively uniform, whereas that of the finger tip fluctuated markedly (Figs 72, 73). This suggests that at comfortable environmental temperatures the hands play a greater role in thermal regulation than either the toes or forearm. When the room was made slightly warmer (29° C.), the temperature of the toes increased (Fig. 73), and at high environmental temperatures (40° C.) the skin temperature of the toes was essentially the same as that of the finger tips (Fig. 74). When the environmental temperature was lowered (18° C.), the skin temperature of the toes decreased to a lower temperature than that of the finger tips (Fig. 75).

The vasomotor responses important in thermal regulation were studied by observing reflex changes in skin temperature of one limb while the opposite limb was immersed in cold or warm water (12). When the left hand was immersed in a water bath at 42° C., the skin temperature of the finger tip of the right hand increased after a variable latent period of five to ten minutes (Fig. 76). When the circulation to the hand *immersed* in the warm water was arrested at the brachium by means of a pneumatic cuff, there was no increase in the temperature of the opposite limb until the circulation was re-established,

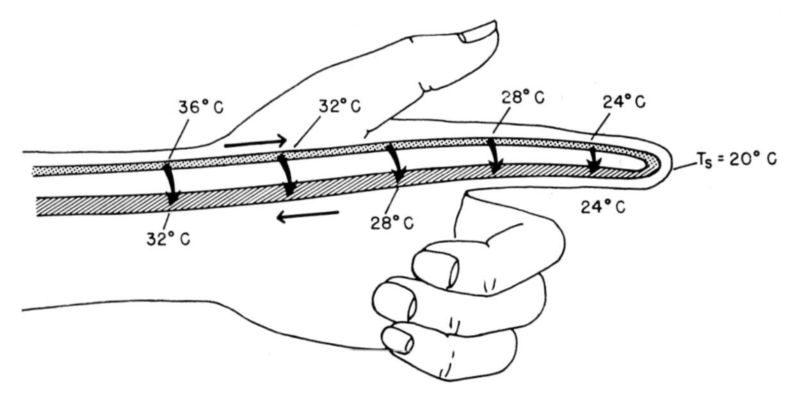

Fig. 79. Diagrammatic representation of the concept of thermal countercurrent flow. See text for details.

and, again, only after a latent period of several minutes (Fig. 76). The response in the opposite limb could be blocked by procaine. These observations suggest that warm blood bathing the hypothalamus initiates afferent impulses in a reflex arc in which the cervical sympathetic nervous system is the efferent limb and is responsible for the vasodilatation observed in a hot and humid environment.

Digital reflex vasoconstriction in response to immersion of the opposite hand in cold water was prompt (Fig. 77) and could be blocked by procaine. Apparently, both the afferent and efferent components of the reflex vasoconstriction are mediated over nervous pathways.

PATHOPHYSIOLOGIC INTERPRETATIONS

Vasoconstriction develops rapidly with exposure to a cool or cold environment and is eventually followed by paresthesia or numbness. The vasoconstriction produced by reducing the amount of heat transported by the blood vessels to the skin is concerned with the conservation of body heat. Occasionally, in an attempt to meet the more general body priorities of thermal regulation, the vasoconstriction may reduce digital blood supply sufficiently to cause a disturbance of local tactile sensory function.

The "Hunting Phenomenon." With continued exposure to cold, the "hunting phenomenon" described by Sir Thomas Lewis develops (Fig. 78). This consists of short periods of vasodilatation superimposed upon an over-all vasoconstriction. This local oscillation in the rate of digital blood flow with exposure to cold tends to prevent severe damage and death of the tactile sensory organs and other digital tissues in the presence of an over-all vasoconstrictive state necessary to reduce heat loss.

Thermal Countercurrent Flow. In a subject exposed to a cool environment, heat conservation takes place not only through vasoconstriction but also through arteriovenous heat exchange, i.e., thermal countercurrent flow (14). Under conditions of body cooling, warm blood entering the arm transfers heat to the cool venous blood returning from the extremity. This precooling of outgoing arterial blood by the blood returning through the veins serves to minimize heat loss and takes place not only in the

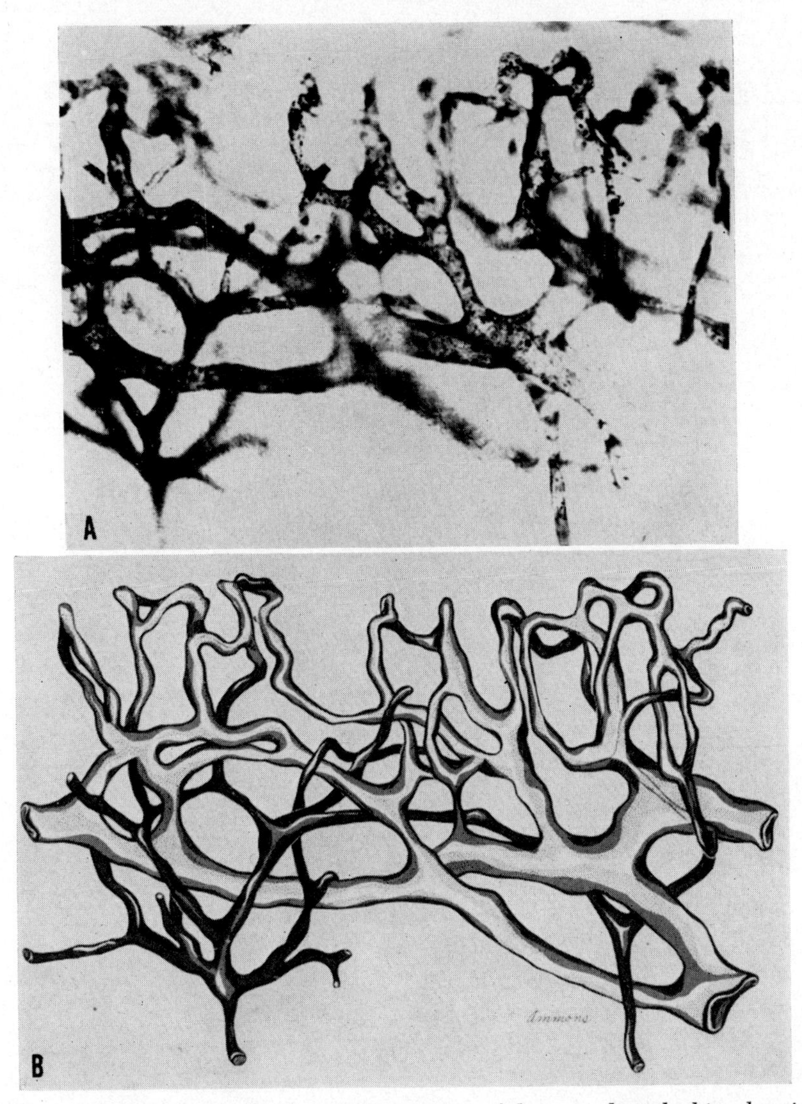

Fig. 80. A. Photomicrograph of a thick section of human digital skin showing the arterial and venous system injected with India ink. B. Drawing of photomicrograph shown in A. It can be seen that the relatively narrow arterial vessels intertwine among the larger digital veins. Warm blood going to the skin can readily lose heat to the counterflowing cooler blood returning from the skin. Thus, instead of heat being lost to the cool atmosphere, the heat is returned to the body.

arm but also in the fingers, toes and skin, where a rich network of venae comites are ideally suited for arterio-venous heat exchange (Figs. 79, 80).

The Australian aborigine can sleep nude through a cold eight-hour night on the ground with relatively little metabolic compensation (15). Obviously, he must be admirably protected from loss of body heat. It has been stated that these aborigines are able to achieve marked peripheral vasoconstriction, thus keeping cutaneous and subcutaneous tissue insulation high. Although it has

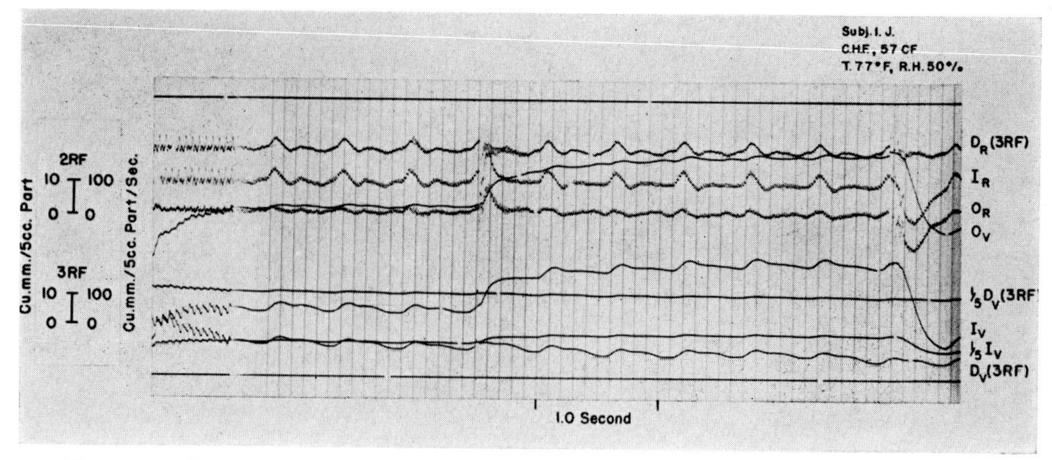

Fig. 81. The digital rheoplethysmogram from a patient in congestive heart failure showing marked digital vasoconstriction. The I_V curve decreased during diastole due to high venous tone and reduced digital blood flow.

not been studied, it may be that these natives possess a highly developed system of venae comites and thermal countercurrent exchange to allow for more complete arteriovenous heat exchange.

Tissue Injury Due to Cold. Associated with the vasoconstriction and pallor of the skin produced by exposure to cold, there is a contraction of smooth muscle in the skin causing "goose flesh." When the skin temperature decreases below 25° C., the small blood vessels of the skin open, whereas those of larger caliber remain constricted and the skin appears cyanotic (16). As the skin temperature decreases below 15° C., the skin color changes to bright pink because tissue metabolism is greatly diminished and there is incomplete dissociation of oxyhemoglobin. At 7° to 8° C. "goose flesh" disappears. With chronic exposure to cold, the skin becomes thickened and stiff and the tissues swell due to edema which is probably inflammatory in origin. Prior to freezing of the tissues the capillaries tend to become stiff and sludging of the formed elements of the blood develops.

Selectivity of Dermal Blood Flow. When the environmental temperature is increased and the relative humidity of the ambient air is high, the rate of blood flow increases. The dermal circulation adjusts rapidly to extremes in environmental temperature by means of wide variations in blood flow. The increase in blood flow to the skin of man subjected to a warm and humid environment is selective rather than uniform throughout the body. The rate of blood flow is greater to the fingers, ear lobe and toes than to the face and forearm. The blood flow to the hands and feet is primarily concerned with heat loss, whereas the blood flow to the arms and legs is concerned more with metabolic requirements of the extremital muscles.

Dermal Blood Flow in Diseased States. Diseased states modify the circulatory response to environment. The rate of digital blood flow is low in congestive heart failure because of vasoconstriction (17) (Fig. 81). This impairs heat loss. The reduction in the rate of heat loss by radiation and convection with accumulation of heat tends to stimulate sweating in an attempt to maintain thermal balance. Patients with congestive heart failure tolerate a hot and humid environment poorly, especially when the temperature is so high that they accumulate heat from the environment, imposing a burden upon the heart in addition to that already present in association with the underlying cardiac disease. In patients with serious cardiac disease and myocardial insufficiency or in patients with cardiac decompensation, acute exacerbation of the congestive failure with pulmonary edema may be precipitated by a warm and humid environment. The factor primarily responsible for the development of acute congestive heart failure is the increased cardiac work and effort produced by the hot and humid environment (18).

Patients with *Raynaud's disease* may or may not respond to a hot environment with vasodilatation. Those patients who develop increased digital blood flow in response to environmental heat can take advantage of the reflex vasodilatation by wearing warm clothing. Patients who fail to increase blood flow when exposed to a warm environment may be injured by the application of heat locally. Application of heat to an ischemic part may cause necrosis if the heat increases tissue metabolism beyond the capacity of the circulation to deliver oxygen to the tissues. It is simple to distinguish between patients with Raynaud's phenomenon with organic obstructive arterial disease and patients with functional peripheral vasoconstriction by noting the response of the digital circulation to a warm environment.

Patients with *myxedema* have difficulty with thermal regulation, particularly in maintaining a normal skin temperature. This is due not only to the low metabolic rate but also to an increase in thermal insulation produced by the myxedematous fluid and thickened skin and the poor peripheral circulation.

Certain individuals are *hypersensitive to heat or cold. Urticaria* is the most frequent manifestation of hypersensitivity to heat or cold. Hence, thermal sensitivity has been considered an "allergic" state. The changes are associated with dilatation of the dermal blood vessels considered to be due to the release of histamine.

Normal subjects unacclimatized to heat may develop orthostatic hypotension upon standing erect in a hot environment for long periods of time partly because of cutaneous vasodilatation. This vasodilatation, in addition to pooling of blood in the legs, is probably the mechanism responsible for collapse of soldiers standing at attention for long periods of time in hot and humid climates.

The marked dilatation associated with exposure to heat requires a great deal of blood to fill the dilated dermal vessels. If acclimatization has not occurred and the blood volume is not increased, the blood must be made available by compensatory vasoconstriction in other areas. Marked compensatory constriction of the splanchnic vessels establishes a potentially dangerous and somewhat unreliable hemodynamic situation. Should the splanchnic system suddenly dilate, syncope would follow.

CLINICAL APPLICATIONS

Patients with cardiac disease should be protected from environments which require a high rate of dermal blood flow since increased flow is associated with an increase in cardiac output which burdens the heart. Such patients should be placed in an air-conditioned environment during periods of hot and humid weather. If possible, patients with cardiac disease living in tropical or subtropical climates should be advised to vacation in cooler regions during the hot seasons. When advising patients it should be remembered that sudden heat waves may produce even greater thermal stress in temperate zones.

Patients with peripheral vascular insufficiency should avoid exposure to cold. To exploit the benefits of reflex vasodilatation, patients with peripheral vascular disease should be advised to wear warm clothing during cool or cold weather. The patient with Raynaud's disease of the upper extremities will develop some vasodilatation in the upper extremities in response to keeping the feet and body as well as the arms and hands warm and dry. The use of loose-fitting, warm gloves is especially important. Even in subtropical climates thin cotton gloves should be worn in the cool evenings and during cool days. Patients with peripheral vascular insufficiency should be placed in a comfortably warm environment. Not infrequently, patients with vasospastic or occlusive vascular diseases are seen in a chilly, drafty hospital room or in a ward bed next to an open window.

The response of the dermal blood vessels to local warming of remote regions of the body is useful in the diagnosis of vascular insufficiency. Thus, if both feet are warmed while the temperature of the second right finger tip is measured, failure of the temperature of the finger tip to increase suggests organic occlusive vascular disease in the vessels to the right arm and/or hand and finger. This test is dependent upon reflex release of vasoconstrictor tone. The test must be interpreted with caution, however, since the failure to eliminate vasoconstrictor impulses may not always indicate organic vascular disease.

REFERENCES

1. Newburg, L. H.: *Physiology of Heat Regulation and the Science of Clothing.* Philadelphia, Saunders, 1949.
2. Burch, G. E.: Method for recording simultaneously the time course of digital rate and of digital volume of inflow, outflow and the difference between inflow and outflow during a single pulse cycle in man. *J. Appl. Physiol., 7:*99, 1954.
3. Burch, G. E.: Selected quantitative applications of digital rheoplethysmography. *Am. Heart J., 52:*388, 1956.
4. Burch, G. E.: *Digital Plethysmography.* New York, Grune & Stratton, 1954.
5. Burch, G. E.: George Brown Lecture: digital rheoplethysmography. *Circulation, 13:*641, 1956.
6. Burch, G. E. and Sodeman, W. A.: The correlation of bone volume and soft tissue volume in the human finger tip. *Human Biol., 10:*295, 1938.
7. Burch, G. E., Cohn, A. E. and Neumann, C.: A study of the total volume of the human finger tip and toe tip. *Human Biol., 13:*526, 1941.
8. Neumann, C., Cohn, A. E. and Burch, G. E.: A study of the relationship between the pulse and alpha waves of the tips of the fingers and toes of 5 adults. *Am. J. Physiol., 136:*448, 1942.
9. Neumann, C., Cohn, A. E. and Burch, G. E.: A study by quantitative methods of the spontaneous variations in volume of the tips of the fingers and toes and postero-superior portion of the pinna of hypertensive patients and senile subjects. *Am. J. Physiol., 136:* 451, 1942.
10. Burch, G. E. and DePasquale, N.: Relation of arterial pressure to spontaneous variations in digital volume. *J. Appl. Physiol., 15:*23, 1960.

11. Burch, G. E.: Digital pre- and postcapillary vasoconstriction and vasodilatation resembling pre- and postglomerular arteriolar function in kidney. *Proc. Soc. Exper. Biol. & Med., 102:*400, 1959.

12. Lewis, T.: *Vascular Disorders of the Limbs.* London: Macmillan & Co., 1949.

13. Burch, G. E.: Rheoplethysmographic studies of digital venous tone and venous activity. *J. Lab. & Clin. Med., 55:*342, 1960.

14. Scholander, P. F.: Evolution of climatic adaptation in homeotherms. *Evolution, 9:*15, 1955.

15. Hammell, H. T., Elsner, R. W., Le Messurier, D. H., Anderson, H. T. and Milan, F. A.: Thermal and metabolic responses of the Australian aborigine exposed to moderate cold in summer. *J. Appl. Physiol., 14:*605, 1959.

16. Kreyberg, L.: Development of acute tissue damage due to cold. *Physiol. Rev., 29:*156, 1949.

17. Burch, G. E.: Evidence for increased venous tone in chronic congestive heart failure. *Arch. Int. Med., 98:*750, 1956.

18. Burch, G. E. and Hyman, A.: Influence of a hot and humid environment upon cardiac output and work in normal man and in patients with chronic congestive heart failure at rest. *Am. Heart J., 53:*665, 1957.

VIII

WATER AND HEAT LOSS FROM THE LUNGS: METHODS AND THEORETIC CONSIDERATIONS

APPROXIMATELY 52% of insensible water loss from the body takes place through the lungs (1). That water is lost from the lungs can be appreciated by recalling the vapor cloud that forms with expiration on a frosty day. The surface area of the respiratory tract of a 70-kilogram man is approximately 70 m^2 with a parenchymal respiratory surface of about 50 m^2* (2), whereas the dermal surface is only about 1.73 m^2. Thus, the amount of water lost by diffusion through the wet surface of the respiratory tract with 50 times more surface area than the skin is essentially the same as the amount lost by diffusion through the skin. Man is protected from desiccation through the respiratory tract by a functional barrier and through the skin by a specialized layer which inhibits water loss. The ratio of respiratory surface area to body weight is much less in man than in small animals such as the dog. The relatively large respiratory surface area in the dog is an advantage because this animal depends upon the oral and respiratory tracts for thermal regulation.

In man resting quietly in a comfortable environment only about 10% of the total *heat loss* from the body occurs across the 70 m^2 of the respiratory tract, whereas about 90% is lost across the 1.73 m^2 of the dermal surface. The proportion of heat lost through the lungs decreases further for a man in a hot and humid environment, whereas that lost through the skin increases.

In Chapter 3, a method for measuring water loss from the lungs using a sensitive human balance was described. The technique involved either an indirect measurement of respiratory water loss or a direct measurement of water loss with the subject sealed in a large vapor-proof tank. However, these types of measurement are not applicable to certain studies and are relatively less sensitive than the one to be described. Furthermore, previously used methods, such as chemical absorption of respiratory water, are inaccurate and impractical (4, 5, 6). Therefore, in order to determine with greater accuracy water and heat loss from the lungs, it became necessary to develop an accurate, dependable and practical method by which both water loss and heat loss from the lungs could be measured simultaneously and in such a manner that ambulatory and hospital

---

* von Hayek of Vienna estimates that there are between 300 million and 400 million alveoli in the lungs and that the respiratory surface is about 30 m^2 in expiration and 100 m^2 in deep inspiration (3).

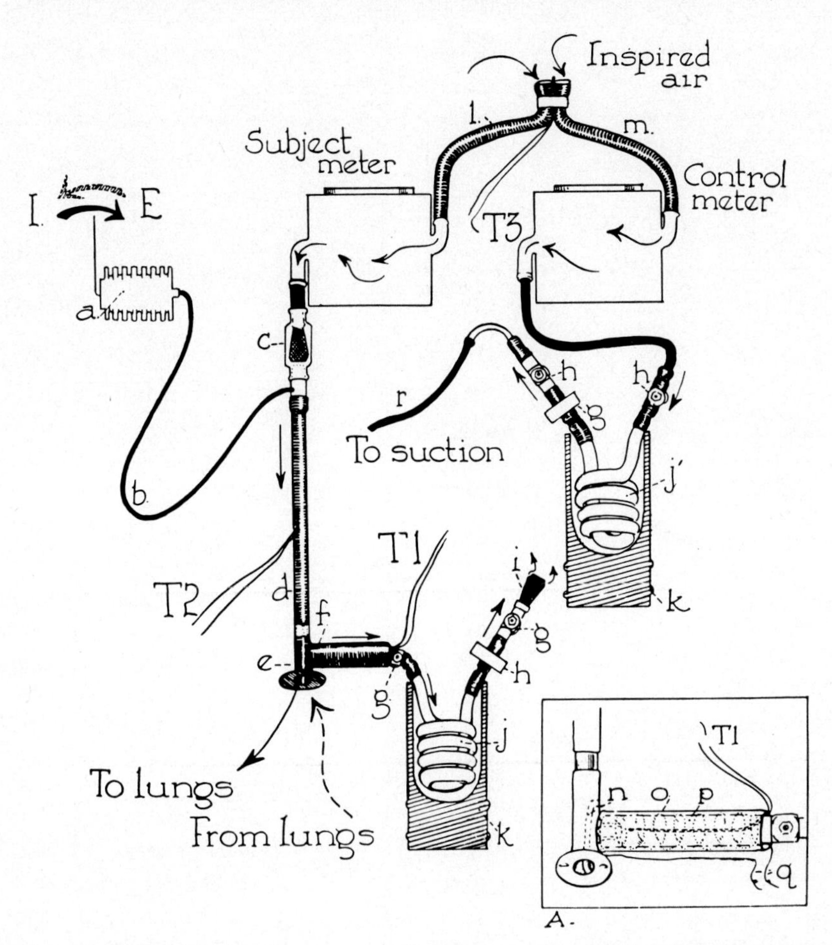

Fig. 82. A schematic representation of the apparatus employed to measure the rate of water loss from the respiratory tract. The mouthpiece (e) is inserted and the subject's nose is closed with a clip. Upon breathing he inspires room air through tubing (1). The air passes through the "subject meter" where its volume is recorded. It then passes through the flutter valve and housing (c) and through rubber tube (d) into his lungs. On expiration the air passes out through the side tubing in the mouthpiece through the heated efferent rubber tube (Insert A) into aluminum coil (j) and out through the trap (h), stopcock (g) and flutter valve (i) into the atmosphere. Consult text for other details. (From *Arch. Int. Med.*, *76*:308, 1945.)

patients could be studied in large numbers and at frequent intervals.

A *gravimetric method* for the measurement of the rate of water loss as well as a quantitative method for the measurement of the rate of heat loss from the lungs was developed and is described below. The techniques are accurate, practical and relatively simple (7).

A GRAVIMETRIC METHOD FOR THE MEASUREMENT OF EXPIRED WATER

The apparatus developed to measure quantitatively the expired water is shown in Figure 82. The apparatus consists essentially of three parts: (1) two meters for measuring the volume of air circulated through the lungs and collecting coils, (2) aluminum col-

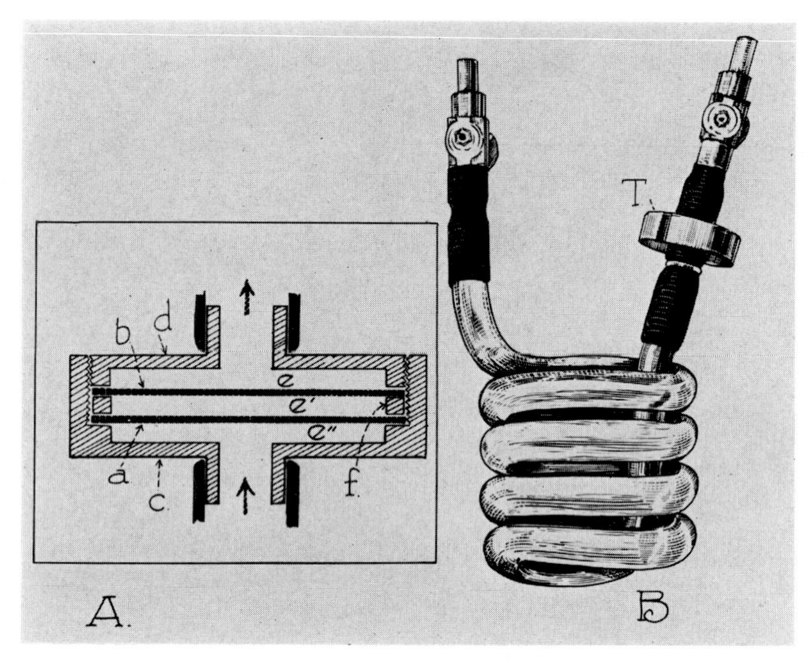

Fig. 83. A schematic representation of the aluminum collecting coils. Insert A shows details of the construction of the trap (T) used to prevent the escape of frozen water upon expiration. Parts a and b are fine-meshed brass filters; e, e′ and e″ are air spaces between the filters which allow free circulation of the expired air. (From *Arch. Int. Med., 76*:308, 1945.)

lecting coils and (3) a system of rubber tubing with necessary heater, thermocouples, flutter valves and mouthpiece to direct the flow of air.

The meters are ordinary commercial test gas meters which can measure the volume of air flow under low pressure to an accuracy of about 30 cc. All air that circulates through the lungs and coils passes through the meters so that the volume and rate of circulation of air may be measured.

The aluminum coils, which were constructed and employed in essentially the same manner as those used for measuring water loss from the skin (Chapter 3), were made to weigh less than 200 gm. so that they could be weighed on an ordinary analytic balance. The internal diameter of the coils was about 16 mm. and the wall thickness about 0.7 mm. The length of tubing in each coil was about 160 cm. A finished coil is shown in Figure 83. Each open end of the coil was connected by rubber tubing to an aluminum stopcock in order to isolate the lumen of the collecting coil from the atmosphere. By carefully varying the amount of rubber tubing and aluminum tubing, all coils were made to weigh about the same (within a few milligrams) to facilitate repeated weighings.

A metal filter (Insert A, Fig. 83) was placed just proximal to the stopcock guarding the exit from the coils to prevent any of the condensed frozen expired water from being blown out of the coils. This filter consisted of a short, broad, thin-walled, cylindrical aluminum housing which enclosed two layers of 100 mesh per square inch brass screen. The two layers of screen filter were kept apart by means of a metal ring (f, Insert A, Fig. 83). The diameter of the housing was 4.0 cm. and the length, 1.0 cm. The large diameter reduced the resistance to the flow of air through the housing, and the double layer of filter insured complete trapping of the snow.

The rubber tubing, flutter valves and mouthpiece were connected as shown in Figure 82. A nichrome heater (o, Insert A, Fig. 82) surrounded the efferent tube (p) leading from the mouthpiece to the subject collecting coil* to maintain the walls of this efferent tubing at a temperature of 92°F. (33.4° C.) so as to prevent condensation of expired water along its walls. A rheostat connected in series with the heater permitted the heater temperature to be adjusted whenever the environmental temperature was changed.

The collecting coils were dried prior to use by fanning and by wiping the external surface and drawing room air through the interior. The dried coils were then weighed and placed in a thermos jar and iced with chips of solid carbon dioxide (Fig. 82). This procedure cooled the coils to —70° C. The coils were then connected to the meters, the patient and the air suction, as indicated in Figure 82. The physiologic studies were conducted in an air-conditioned room.

After resting for at least 60 minutes the subject inserted the mouthpiece (such as is used for ordinary clinical measurements of metabolic rate) and adjusted his chair and the apparatus so that he was comfortable and relaxed. He was instructed to breathe through his nose while all stopcocks were opened and the air lines through the subject coil made patent. The nose was then closed with a clip, and timing with a stopwatch was started simultaneously. The subject inhaled air from the room through the subject meter and exhaled through the warm efferent tube (f) and through the subject coil (j), where the expired water condensed and the dried air escaped into the atmosphere. This procedure was continued for a period of five to ten minutes.

Simultaneously with the collection of the expired water from the subject, an equal volume of room air is drawn through the room meter and through the room coil (j′), where the water in the room air is condensed, the dried room air escaping into the vacuum system providing the suction. The intake openings for the subject meter and the room meter are placed adjacent to each other so that similar samples of air enter both systems, i.e., the subject system and the control, or room-air, system. After a known period of study the stopcocks guarding the collecting coils are closed. The coils are dried by fanning and wiping and are weighed again. The gain in weight represents the quantity of water collected after known volumes of air have irrigated the respiratory tract over known periods of time. From these known quantities, the subject's weight and height, and the grams of water collected, the rate of water loss from the lungs is calculated. This quantity is expressed in *grams per square meter of body surface per ten minutes.*

The grams of water collected in the subject coil represent both the water in the inspired room air and the water lost from the respiratory tract. The water

* The term "subject coil" indicates the aluminum collecting coil used to trap the expired water and "room coil" indicates the collecting coil used to measure the water content of an equal volume of room air.

collected in the room coil represents the water contained in the inspired room air. Therefore, the difference between the amount of water collected in the subject coil and that collected in the room coil represents the quantity of water lost from the respiratory tract.

Method of Testing and Calibrating the Apparatus. To determine the accuracy of the method, a Kjeldahl connection bulb containing a known amount of water was placed in the air line with the subject coil and meter in a position relative to that occupied by the subject. Air was drawn through the subject meter, through the connection bulb and then through the subject coil. Simultaneously, an equal volume of room air was drawn through the room meter and coil. By weighing the coils and connection bulb before and after this procedure, it was possible to determine the accuracy of the method for collecting expired water. It was possible to vary the quantity of water lost from the connection bulb by heating the bulb. The results are shown in Table 7. The mean error was —0.27% with extremes of +1.25 and —1.27%. Neither the quantity of water collected nor variations in the rate of air flow, within the limits encountered when studying subjects, influenced the accuracy of the method.

In order to determine the completeness with which the water was trapped by the subject coil, two coils were connected in series and iced with solid carbon dioxide. Room air was drawn through the coils, or a subject expired through the coils. It was found that the first coil through which the moisture-laden room air or expired air passed trapped the moisture almost completely. For example, when the quantity of water trapped by the first coil was about 400 mg., the maximum amount of water collected by the second coil in the series did not exceed 4 mg. When the first coil collected 1,500 mg. of water, the second coil collected a maximum of 17 mg. These data show that when quantities of water collected are near 1 gm. or less

TABLE 7

ACCURACY OF THE METHOD FOR MEASURING THE RATE OF WATER LOSS FROM THE RESPIRATORY TRACT

Test No.	*Known Water Loss Gm.*	*Water Collected Gm.*	*Error Gm.*	*Error %*
1	0.7943	0.7899	−0.0044	−0.55
2	1.0578	1.0553	−0.0025	−0.24
3	0.7657	0.7646	−0.0011	−0.14
4	0.7653	0.7602	−0.0051	−0.67
5	0.7064	0.7152	+0.0088	+1.25
6	0.8163	0.8112	−0.0051	−0.62
7	0.8596	0.8656	+0.0060	+0.70
8	1.0781	1.0730	−0.0051	−0.47
9	1.0821	1.0743	−0.0078	−0.72
10	0.8337	0.8231	−0.0106	−1.27
Mean	0.87593	0.87324	−0.0027	−0.27
Maximum	1.0821	1.0743	+0.0088	+1.25
Minimum	0.7064	0.7152	−0.0106	−1.27

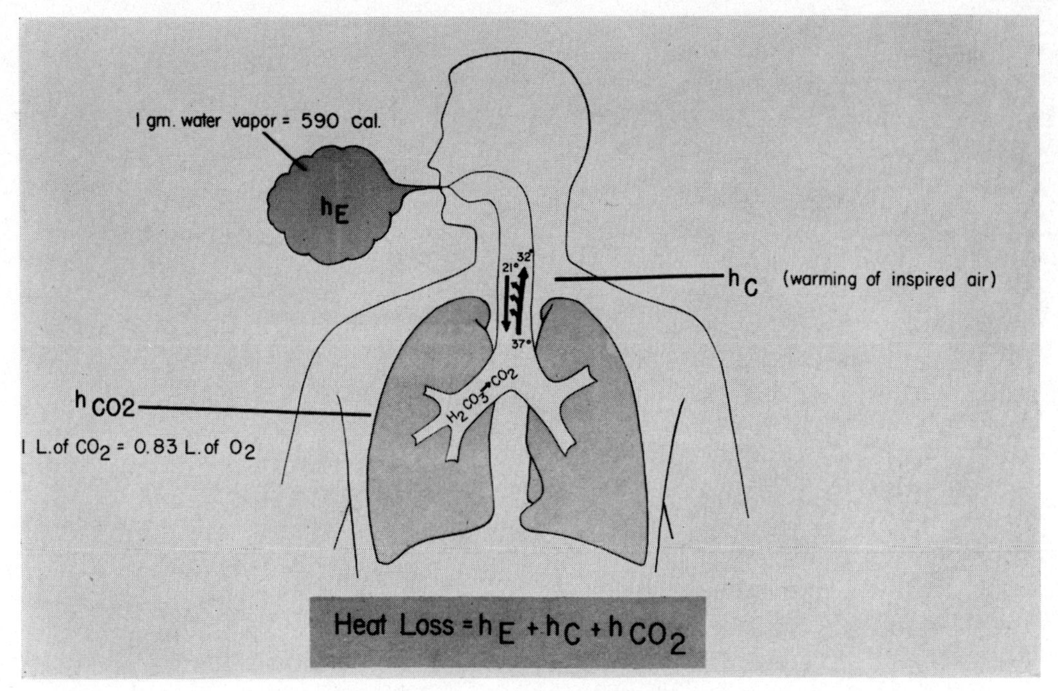

Fig. 84. Diagram showing the three ways in which heat is lost from the lungs, i.e., by the evaporation of water, by the warming of inspired air and by the conversion of H_2CO_3 to CO_2 and H_2O.

the error due to incomplete removal of water from the expired air is less than 1%. In the following chapter it will be shown that the water collected in any one collecting coil rarely exceeded 1 gm.

The accuracy of the method depends a great deal upon the accuracy with which the water in the room air is measured. Since room air is drawn through the two meters and the collecting coils simultaneously as well as through the orifices of two rubber tubes placed adjacent to each other (Fig. 82), it is not likely that the water content of air entering the two systems differs. However, to determine if a difference exists, room air of equal volume was drawn simultaneously through the room meter and coil and through a separate meter and coil. In a typical experiment, one coil collected 0.4686 gm. of moisture from the room air while the other collected 0.4685 gm. from an equal volume of room air. This indicates that the method employed for measuring the moisture in the room air was satisfactory.

The process of drying the outside of the coils by wiping and fanning, and of weighing the coils, icing them, drying them again by wiping and fanning and reweighing them must entail certain errors. As a test, several coils were put through the process outlined. The results showed an error usually less than 1 mg. and not exceeding 2 mg., a surprisingly small error considering the surface area of the coils, the method of drying and the accuracy of the balance ($\pm$0.1 mg.).

The length and diameter of the aluminum tubing of the coils increase the friction to the flow of air on expiration.

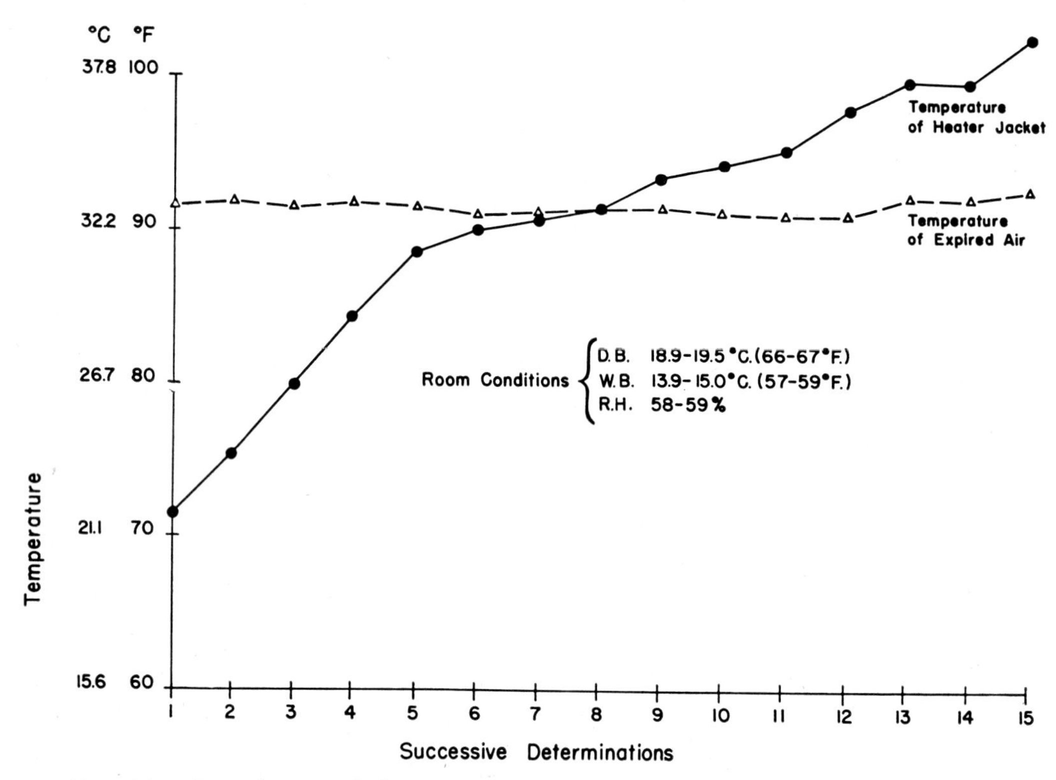

Fig. 85. The influence of the temperature of the heater jacket and efferent tube (Fig. 82, Insert A) on the temperature of the expired air. The conditions of the room (temperatures by dry bulb and wet bulb thermometers and relative humidity) are shown. (From *Arch. Int. Med., 76*:308, 1945.)

By placing a T tube in the system of tubing near the mouthpiece and connecting this to a mercury manometer, it was found that the pressure on expiration during quiet respiration averaged +36 mm. water (2.6 mm. Hg), the extremes being 30 and 40 mm. water. The pressure on inspiration was essentially of the same magnitude but negative.

There was no appreciable loss of water by condensation in the system other than in the collecting coils. This is obvious from the data presented in Table 7. The heater around the efferent tubing prevented such a loss. By means of a thermocouple placed within the efferent tube it was possible to be sure that the efferent tube prior to the start of a study was sufficiently warm to prevent condensation on its walls. In addition, segments of glass tubing were inserted in various places within the system for observing condensation. Failure of the walls of the glass tubes to become clouded after prolonged breathing through the system indicated that no large quantities of water were lost by condensation within the tubing.

A METHOD FOR MEASURING THE RATE OF HEAT LOSS FROM THE RESPIRATORY TRACT

With relatively minor modifications, the method just described for the determination of water loss from the lungs may also be used to measure the heat loss simultaneously with the water loss.

Heat is lost from the lungs by (Fig. 84):

(1) evaporation of water
(2) warming of inspired air (convection)
(3) decomposition of carbonic acid in solution to carbon dioxide gas with expiration.

The *evaporation of water* was measured by the method described above. To measure the *heat loss by warming of inspired air*, thermocouples (T_1, T_2 and T_3) were placed in the efferent tube (f), in the afferent tube (d) and at the site of entry of the room air into the subject meter (Fig. 82). These made it possible to determine with a potentiometer, accurate to 0.1°C., the temperatures of the inspired and expired air. The subject meter recorded the volume of inspired air for a known period of time. From the temperature of the expired air and from the grams of water removed from the expired air, it was possible to determine the mass of air expired as well as its specific heat. With these factors known, it was possible to calculate the rate of heat loss by convection (Equation 9, p. 110).

The fine wire (copper-constantan) used for the thermocouples made it possible to record the temperature of the expired air as it passed over the thermocouple junction. The heat from the nichrome heater surrounding the efferent tube did not interfere with the accuracy with which the temperature of the expired air was recorded because the heater was outside a thick-walled rubber tubing, the thermocouple was of fine wire and the heater was set at a temperature very near the temperature of the expired air (0° to 1° C. variation). Figure 85 shows that the temperature of the heater did not influence the recorded temperature of the expired air unless the temperature of the heater exceeded 36° C. (about 96° F.).

The temperatures of the inspired and expired air were recorded from two to four minutes after the subject began to respire through the water-collecting apparatus. Although it does not require two minutes to reach a state of equilibrium, it was preferable to wait at least two minutes to avoid errors.

The *excretion of carbon dioxide* was measured by having the subject breathe into a Benedict-Roth type of clinical machine for measuring the basal metabolic rate immediately after collecting the expired water and measuring the temperatures of the inspired and expired air. This was done without allowing the subject to move from his previous sitting position for which the expired water was measured. The rate of liberation of carbon dioxide was calculated from the rate of absorption of oxygen recorded by the BMR machine, using a respiratory quotient of 0.83.

The metabolic rate rather than the basal metabolic rate was recorded. Since the subjects rested from 30 to 60 minutes in the observation room before the metabolic rate was recorded, it was safe to assume that the body was in thermal equilibrium with the environment and that, therefore, the total body heat produced (determined from the metabolic rate) was equal to the total heat lost. From this measured heat loss, it was possible to express heat loss by any or all of the three previously mentioned components of respiratory heat loss as percent of total body heat loss.

By measuring the subject's height and weight, it was possible to correct for body size. This was done by expressing all heat loss in units of kilogram calories per square meter of surface area per ten minutes.

MATHEMATIC CONSIDERATION OF HEAT LOSS FROM THE RESPIRATORY TRACT

Heat loss from the lungs consists of three components which do not include conduction or radiation. The total loss of heat from the respiratory tract, H, may be expressed as

$$H = h_E + h_C + h_{CO_2}, \quad (7)$$

where

h_E = Heat loss by evaporation of water from the membranes of the respiratory tract,
h_C = Heat loss by warming inspired air (convection); this may be a positive value if air warmer than body temperature is inspired, and
h_{CO_2} = Heat loss by the decomposition of H_2CO_3 in solution to CO_2 gas which is expired.

The heat loss by evaporation of water may be expressed as

$$h_E = \frac{0.59W}{A} \quad (8)$$

where

h_E = Kilogram calories per square meter of surface area per ten minutes,
W = Grams of water lost from the respiratory tract per ten minutes, and
A = Surface area of the subject in square meters. The factor 0.59 is the part of a kilogram calorie necessary to vaporize 1 gm. of water at a temperature of 37.25° C.

The heat loss by convection (heating of inspired air) may be expressed as

$$h_C = \frac{M(t' - t)S}{A}, \quad (9)$$

where

h_C = Kilogram calories per square meter of body surface per ten minutes,
M = Mass of air expired (in grams) in ten minutes,
t' = Temperature of the expired air in degrees centigrade,
t = Temperature of the inspired air in degrees centigrade,
S = Specific heat of air, and
A = Surface area of the subject's body in square meters.

Equation (9) for dry air becomes

$$h_C = \frac{0.2404M(t' - t)}{1000A}$$

$$= \frac{2404M(t' - t)}{10^7A}. \quad (10)$$

The heat loss by excretion of CO_2 under standard conditions may be expressed as

$$h_{CO_2} = \frac{Lh_V}{22.4A}, \quad (11)$$

where

h_{CO_2} = Kilogram calories per square meter of surface area per ten minutes,
L = Liters of CO_2 expired in ten minutes,
h_V = Kilogram calories of heat absorbed per mole of CO_2 gas liberated when H_2CO_3 in solution is decomposed,
A = Surface area of the subject's body in square meters, and
22.4 = Volume of a mole of gas under standard conditions.

Since from the thermochemical equations the decomposition of an infinite dilution of carbonic acid into water and carbon dioxide is associated with the absorption of 4.7 kilogram calories for each mole of carbon dioxide liberated, Equation (11) becomes

$$h_{CO_2} = \frac{4.7L}{22.4A}. \quad (12)$$

Although the blood in the lungs is not a truly infinite dilution of carbonic acid, for practical purposes it may be considered as such.

From Equations (8), (10) and (12), Equation (7) becomes

$$H = \frac{0.59W}{A} + \frac{2404M(t' - t)}{10^7 A} + \frac{4.7L}{22.4A}. \quad (13)$$

The techniques used to measure the various factors which determine the amount and rate of heat loss from the lungs will be discussed in the next chapter.

REFERENCES

1. Burch, G. E. and Winsor, T.: The relation of total insensible loss of weight to water loss from the skin and lungs of human subjects in a subtropical climate. *Am. J. M. Sc., 209:*226, 1945.
2. Willson, H. G.: The terminals of the human bronchiole. *Am. J. Anat., 30:*267, 1922.
3. von Hayek, H.: *The Human Lung.* New York, Hafner Publishing Co., 1960.
4. Galeotti, G. and Signorelli, E.: Uber die Wasserbilanz während der Ruhe und bei der Anstrengung im Hochgebirge. *Biochem. Ztschr., 41:*268, 1912.
5. Weyrich, W.: *Beobachtungen über die unmerkliche - wasserausscheidung der Lungen und ihr Verhältniss zur Haut perspiration.* Dorpat, E. J. Karow, 1865.
6. Benedict, F. G. and Benedict, C. G.: Perspiratio insensibilis. Ihr Wesen und ihre Ursachen. *Biochem. Ztschr., 186:* 278, 1927.
7. Burch, G. E.: Study of water and heat loss from the respiratory tract of man. *Arch. Int. Med., 76:*308, 1945.

IX

RATES OF WATER AND HEAT LOSS FROM THE LUNGS

THE RATE OF WATER LOSS FROM THE RESPIRATORY TRACT

THE mean rate of water loss from the respiratory tract of 56 normal subjects studied in New Orleans during two hot summer months (August and September) was 0.842 gm. per square meter of body surface per ten minutes, the extremes being 0.527 and 1.172 (1). There were no significant differences due to sex or race (Fig. 86).

The influence of season on the rate of water loss from the lungs was negligible, whereas the rate of water loss from the skin was significantly influenced by season.

In five normal adults mild exercise increased the rate of water loss from the respiratory tract by a mean value of 36% (Fig. 87).

Since most normal adults breathe through the nose rather than through the mouth, the difference in the rate of water loss from the respiratory tract while breathing through the mouth and the nose was studied. Under identical conditions subjects breathing through the nose and then through the mouth demonstrated no differences in the rates of water loss.

In studying the rate of water loss from the respiratory tract, the nature and state of the subject's respiration must be considered. Rapid and shallow breathing greatly increased the rate of water loss from the lungs. Deep breathing also increased the rate of water loss, but to a lesser degree. However, more water was lost from the lungs per unit volume of air inspired with deep, slow breathing than with rapid and shallow breathing (Fig. 88). This is probably due to the fact that the air remains in the lungs for a longer time with deep breathing, thus allowing more time for the water on the surface of the respiratory tract to saturate the inspired air before it is expired.

Influence of Environment on the Rate of Water Loss from the Respiratory Tract. The rate of water loss from the respiratory tract was influenced by environmental conditions. In cool and dry, cool and foggy, comfortable, and hot and dry environments the rate of water loss remained relatively unchanged (Fig. 89). However, in a hot and wet environment there was a definite decrease in the rate of water loss from the lungs (Fig. 89). The temperature and humidity of the air under which the various experiments were conducted are shown in Figure 89. That the rate of water loss from the respiratory tract was not significantly different when an at-

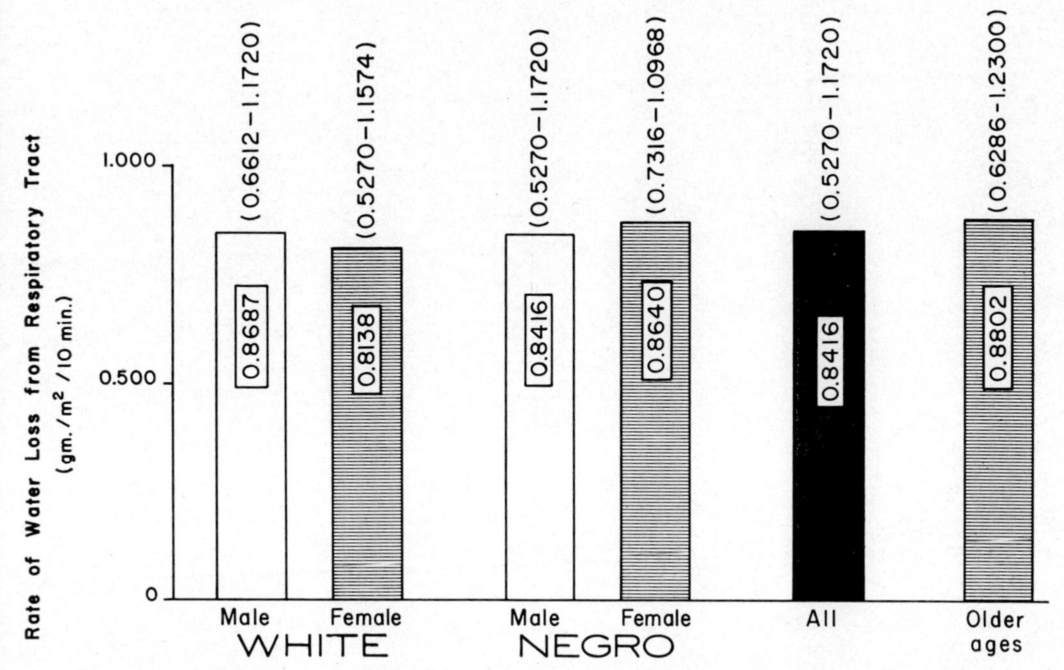

Fig. 86. The rate of water loss from the respiratory tract of 56 normal young adults from a subtropical climate sitting in a comfortable environment. The older age group shown on the right consisted of 8 normal subjects varying from 50 to 60 years of age. (From *Arch. Int. Med.*, *76*:315, 1945.)

mosphere of cool dry, cool foggy or comfortable air was breathed was expected, since the absolute quantities of water vapor per unit volume of air at 15° C. and 60% relative humidity, 15° C. and 94% relative humidity, and 20° C. and 52% relative humidity are not very different, the values being 7.9, 12.4 and 12.7 mg. per liter, respectively. Since expired air has a temperature of about 33° C. and a relative humidity of about 88% and, therefore, contains 31.6 mg. of water vapor per liter, large and essentially equal amounts of water can be and are added to the inspired air under the three room conditions before it is expired.

However, when air which is hot and much above body temperature is breathed, the situation is different. For example, when hot, dry air (50° C., 18% R.H.) containing 13.3 mg. of water vapor per liter is inspired and cooled by the respiratory tract to about 39° C., the relative humidity of the inspired air suddenly increases to about 38%, but the air still contains 13.3 mg. of water vapor per liter. This air is capable of taking on more water than cool air, but its dryness and its ability to remove water from the respiratory tract are not as great as might be expected since cooling of the inspired air by the respiratory tract decreases its capacity to take up water. The effect of cooling the inspired air is even more pronounced when hot and humid air is inspired. When inspired air of 50° C. and 49% relative humidity containing 37.1 mg. of water per liter is cooled by the respiratory tract to 39° C., its relative humidity is raised to 80%, but it still contains the same 37.1 mg. of water per liter of air,

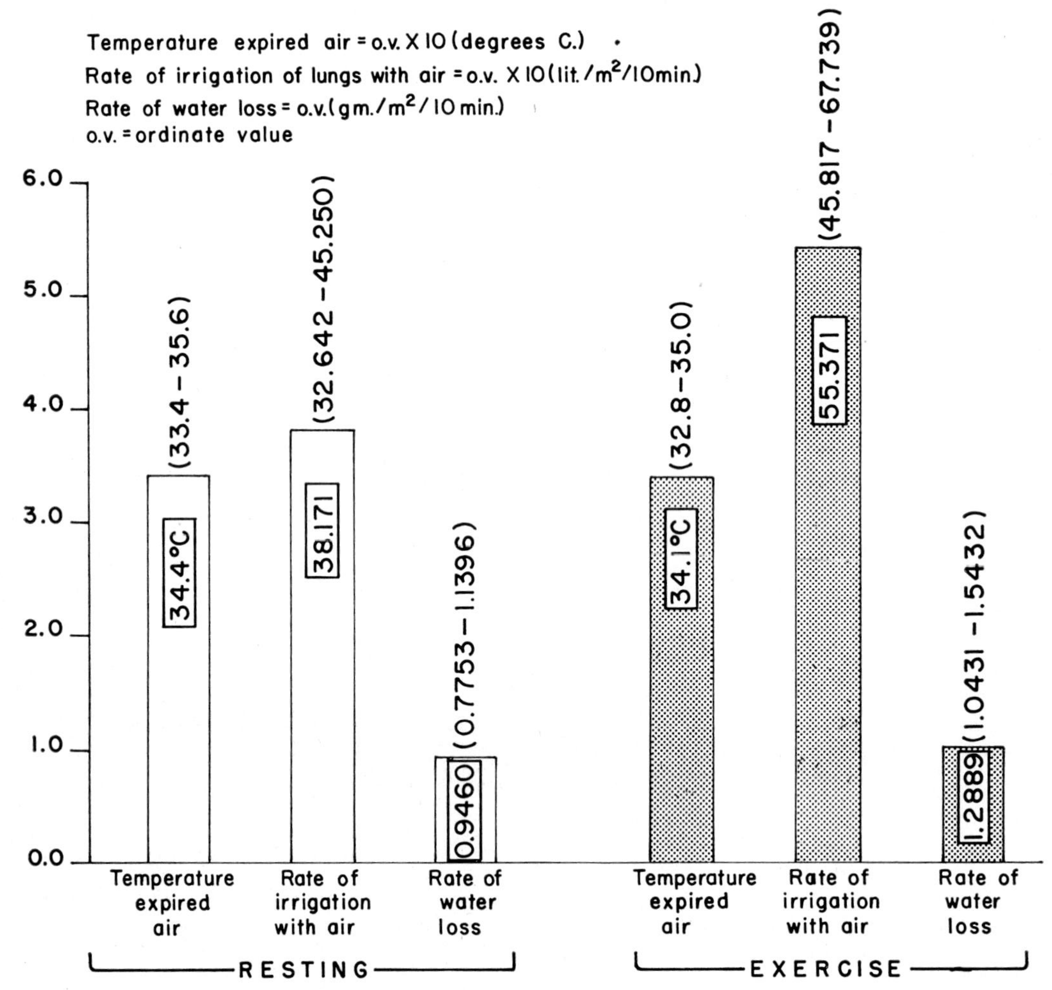

Fig. 87. The effect of mild exercise on the temperature of the expired air, rate of irrigation of the respiratory tract with air and rate of water loss in 5 normal young adults. (From *Arch. Int. Med.*, 76:315, 1945.)

so that little water can be added to this hot and humid air by the respiratory tract. It is impossible to reach 100% relative humidity in expired air because the water on the surface of the membranes of the respiratory tract is not chemically pure. Furthermore, the vapor pressure of air at 39° C. and 80% relative humidity is extremely high and the water vapor would be forced out of the nose or mouth into the atmosphere of much lower vapor pressure before high values of relative humidity could be reached. Therefore, in a hot and humid environment the rate of water loss from the respiratory tract would be expected to decrease, whereas in cool and foggy air (relative humidity high and absolute water content relatively low) the rate of water loss would be expected to be essentially the same as that in a comfortable environment.

Rate of Water Loss from the Respiratory Tract in Congestive Heart Failure. The mean rate of water loss from the respiratory tract in patients with func-

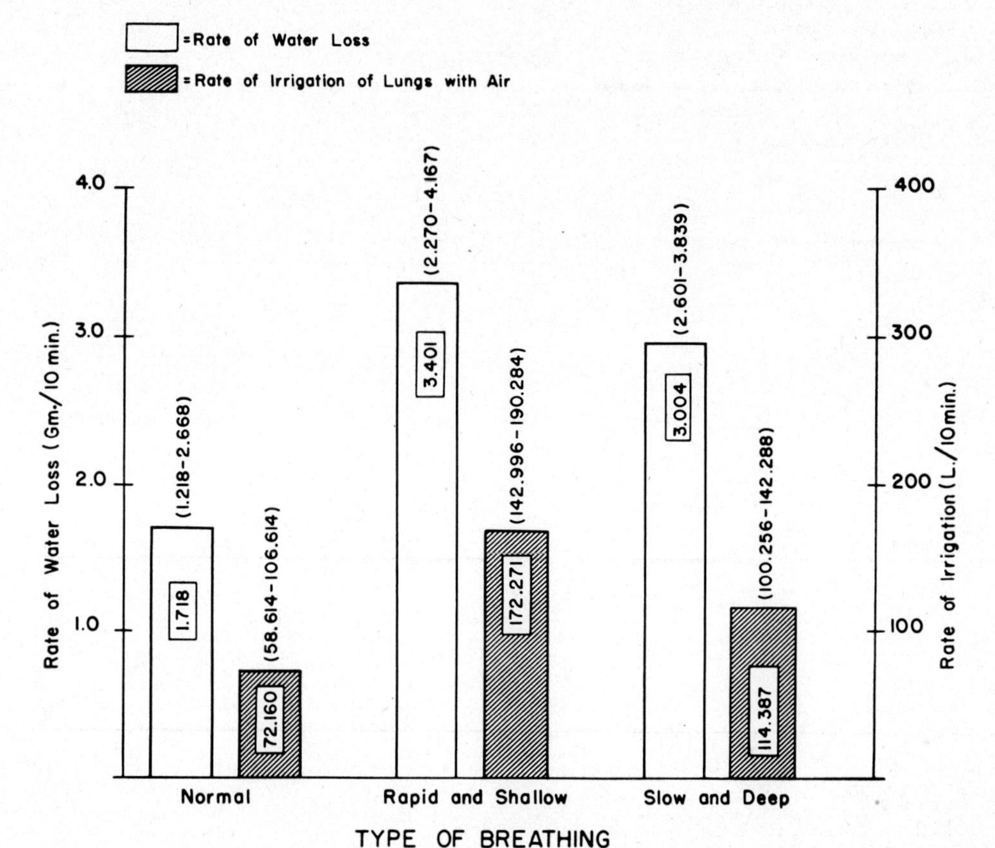

Fig. 88. The influence of rate and depth of respiration on the rate of water loss. The rate of water loss is directly related to the rate of irrigation of the respiratory tract by air. (From *Arch. Int. Med.*, *76:*315, 1945.)

tional class IV uncomplicated right and left congestive heart failure was 0.946 gm. per square meter of body surface per ten minutes, the extremes being 0.497 and 1.482 (2). Thus, the rate of water loss from the respiratory tract of patients with congestive heart failure was greater than that of normal subjects studied under similar environmental conditions (Fig. 90). Patients with congestive heart failure were not studied in hot and dry or hot and humid environments because of their inability to withstand such atmospheric conditions without untoward effects. However, when the environmental temperature was raised only slightly (from 20.3° to 35.7° C.), there was no significant change in the rate of water loss from the lungs (3).

Rate of Irrigation of the Respiratory Tract with Air. The rate of water loss from the lungs is intimately related to the rate of irrigation of the respiratory tract with air. In a comfortable environment there is a linear relationship between these two parameters (Fig. 91). The mean rate of irrigation of the respiratory tract with air for 56 subjects was 38.286 liters per square meter of body surface per ten minutes, the extremes being 28.316 and 53.250. There was no significant difference due to sex or race.

During exercise there was a mean increase of 45.1% in the rate of irriga-

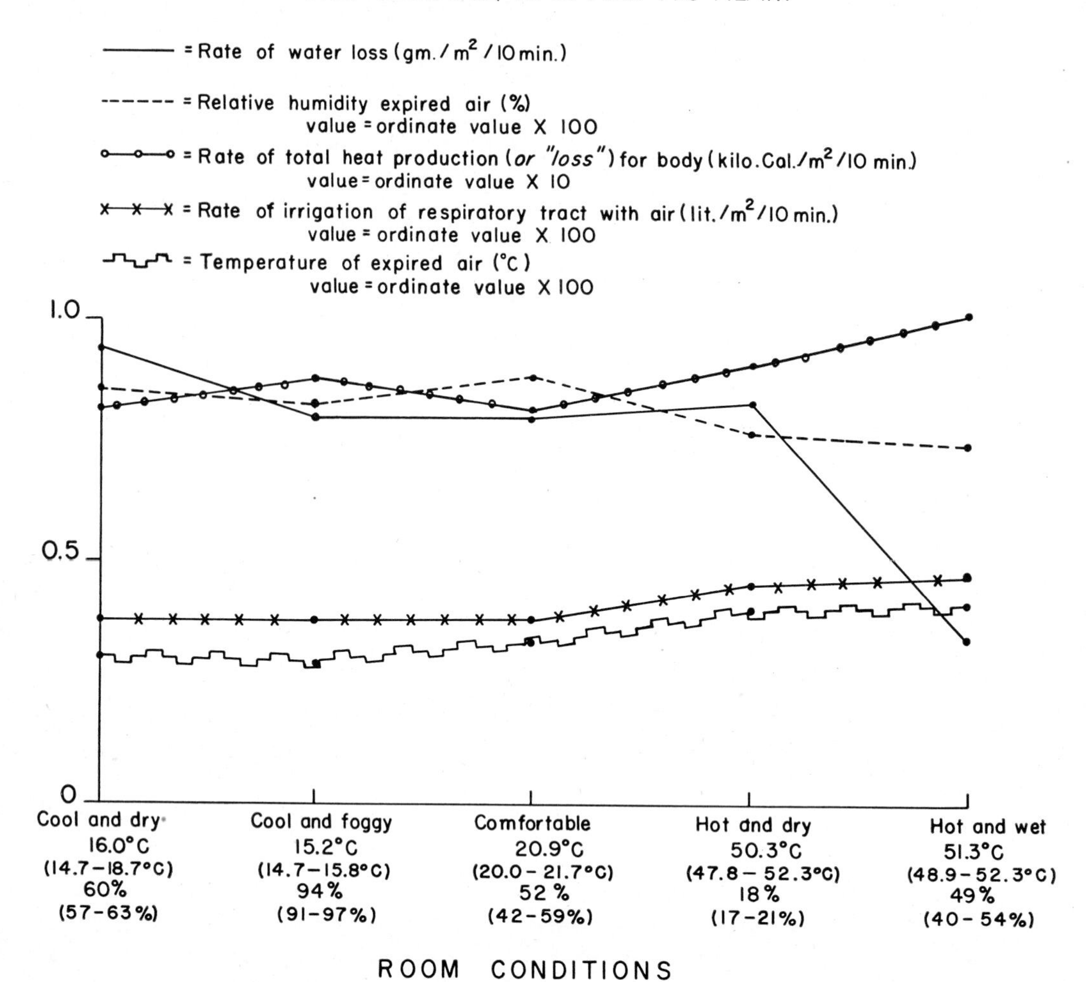

Fig. 89. A graphic representation of the influence of room temperature and humidity on rate of water loss, temperature of expired air, rate of irrigation of the lungs with air, relative humidity of the expired air and total heat production. (From *Arch. Int. Med.*, *76*:315, 1945.)

tion of the respiratory tract with air. The increase in the rate of water loss from the lungs during exercise is a result of the increase in the rate of irrigation of the lungs with air. Similarly, differences in the rates of water loss from the respiratory tract during different types of breathing were related more to the quantity of air irrigating the respiratory tract than to the nature of the breathing. The rate of water loss from the respiratory tract in congestive heart failure is greater than in the normal subject because of the greater rate of irrigation of the respiratory tract with air due to the dyspnea. The patients with congestive heart failure had a mean rate of water loss that was 12% greater than that for normal subjects. The rate of irrigation of the respiratory tract of these patients with air was 17% greater than that for the normal (Table 8).

TEMPERATURE OF EXPIRED AIR

The mean temperature of the expired air of 27 normal young adults sitting

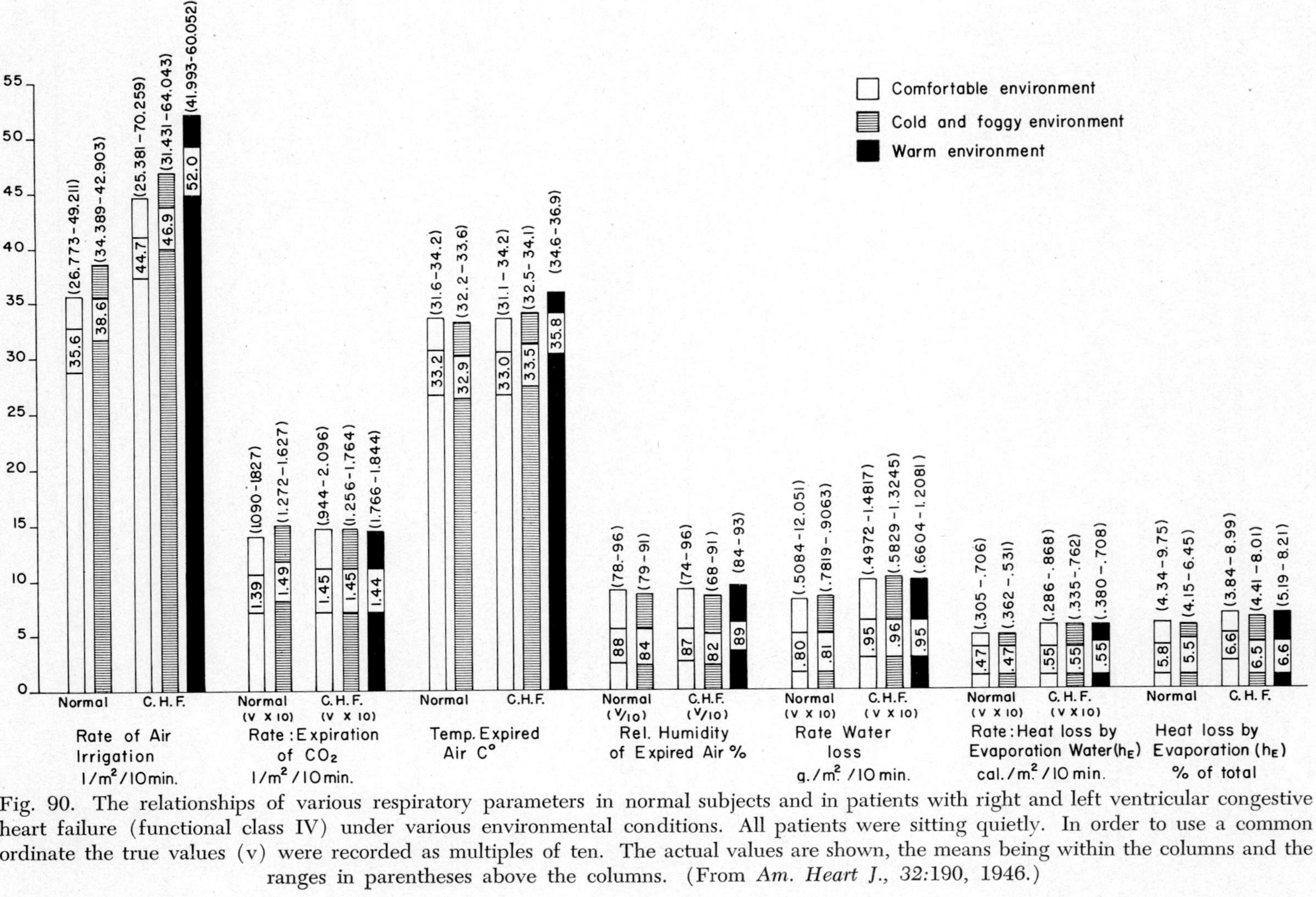

Fig. 90. The relationships of various respiratory parameters in normal subjects and in patients with right and left ventricular congestive heart failure (functional class IV) under various environmental conditions. All patients were sitting quietly. In order to use a common ordinate the true values (v) were recorded as multiples of ten. The actual values are shown, the means being within the columns and the ranges in parentheses above the columns. (From *Am. Heart J.*, *32*:190, 1946.)

TABLE 8

COMPARISON OF RATES OF WATER AND HEAT LOSS FROM THE RESPIRATORY TRACT OF NORMAL SUBJECTS AND PATIENTS WITH CONGESTIVE HEART FAILURE

Parameter Studied	*Normal*	*Congestive Heart Failure*	*% Difference*
Rate of Irrigation (L./m²/10 min.)	38.286	44.688	+16.7
Water Loss (gm./m²/10 min.)	0.842	0.946	+12.3
h_E (kg-cal./m²/10 min.)	0.505	0.552	+ 9.3
h_C (kg-cal./m²/10 min.)	0.122	0.157	+28.6
h_{CO_2} (kg-cal./m²/10 min.)	0.291	0.303	+ 4.1
H (kg-cal./m²/10 min.)	0.883	1.013	+14.7
Total Body Heat Loss (kg-cal./m²/10 min.)	8.08	8.65	+ 6.9

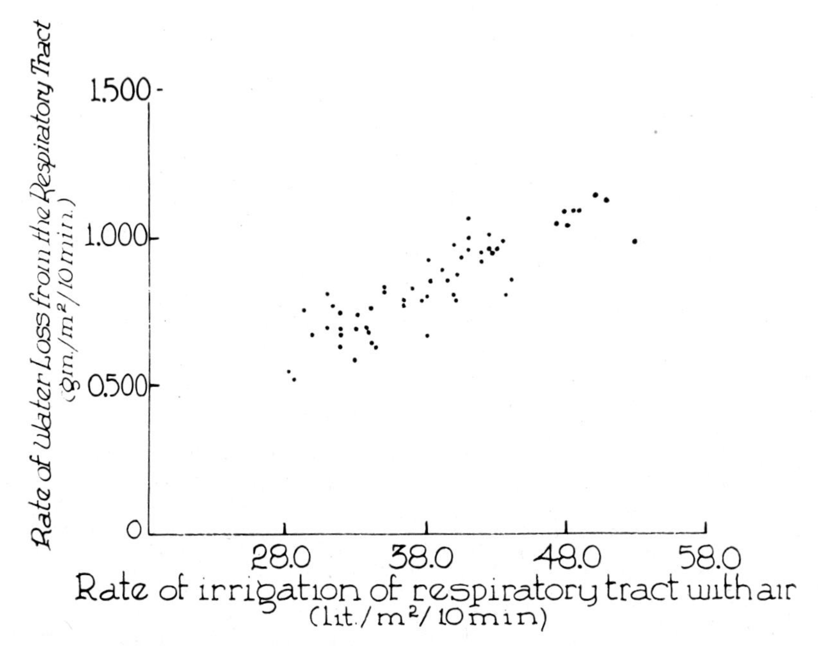

Fig. 91. The influence of the rate of irrigation of the respiratory tract with air on the rate of water loss from the respiratory tract in 56 normal young adults sitting in a comfortable environment. Note that the relationship is essentially linear. The correlation coefficient for the rate of irrigation of the respiratory tract with air and the rate of water loss from the respiratory tract was +0.914. (From *Arch. Int. Med.*, 76:315, 1945.)

relaxed was 33.2° C., with a range of 31.6° to 34.2° C., when the inspired air had a mean temperature of 20.5° C. (extremes, 19.5° and 21.4° C.) and a mean relative humidity of 57.2% (extremes, 54% and 61%) (Fig. 90).

The temperature of the expired air did not vary significantly with the temperature of the inspired air when the latter ranged from 20° to 36° C. However, when air of temperatures higher than 36° C. was inspired, the temperature of the expired air increased (Fig. 89). When subjects inspired cool, dry air, the mean temperature of the expired air was 33.1° C. (31.7° to 34.2° C.). When they inspired cool, foggy air, the mean temperature of the expired air was 32.9° C. (32.2° to 33.6° C.). When hot and dry or hot and moist air was inspired, the mean temperature of the expired air was 39.6° C. (38.1° to 40.6° C.) and 42.1° C. (40.6° to 43.4° C.), respectively.

The temperatures of the expired air of patients with congestive heart failure in a comfortable environment and a cold, foggy environment were essentially similar to those of normal subjects (Fig. 90).

RELATIVE HUMIDITY OF THE EXPIRED AIR

The relative humidity of the expired air can be calculated if the temperature of the expired air and total quantity of water in the expired air are known. In 27 normal young adults in a sitting position breathing room air at 20.5° C. (19.5° to 21.4° C.) with a relative humidity of 57.2% (54% to 61%), the mean relative humidity of the expired air was 88.2% (78% to 96%) (Fig. 90).

The relative humidity of the expired air was influenced by the temperature and relative humidity of the inspired air (Fig. 89). When cool and dry or cool and foggy air was inspired, the mean relative humidity of the expired air was 86.1% (83% to 94%) and 83.0% (79% to 91%), respectively. When hot and dry or hot and moist air was inspired, the mean relative humidity of the expired air was 75.8% (60% to 91%) and 74.4% (71% to 83%), respectively.

The relative humidity of the expired air for patients with congestive heart failure was essentially the same as that for normal subjects (Fig. 90). The mean relative humidity of expired air for 24 patients with functional grade IV congestive heart failure studied in a room with a mean temperature of 20.1° C. and a mean relative humidity of 56% was 87% (74% to 96%).

Although there was evidence of a significant relationship between the rates of water and heat loss from the skin and the basal metabolic rate, there was no significant relationship between the rate of water loss from the lungs and the metabolic rate. A correlation coefficient of —0.26 was found between water loss from the respiratory tract and the rate of metabolism at the same moment for 27 normal adults. Metabolic rate is an expression of the rate of oxygen consumption, whereas water loss is not necessarily dependent upon oxygen consumption but rather depends upon the rate of irrigation of the respiratory tract with air (Fig. 91). Thus, the lack of a significant relationship between water loss from the lungs and the metabolic rate is to be expected. More air is circulated through the lungs than is necessary to meet the demands of the body for oxygen. This statement is supported by the fact that a correlation coefficient

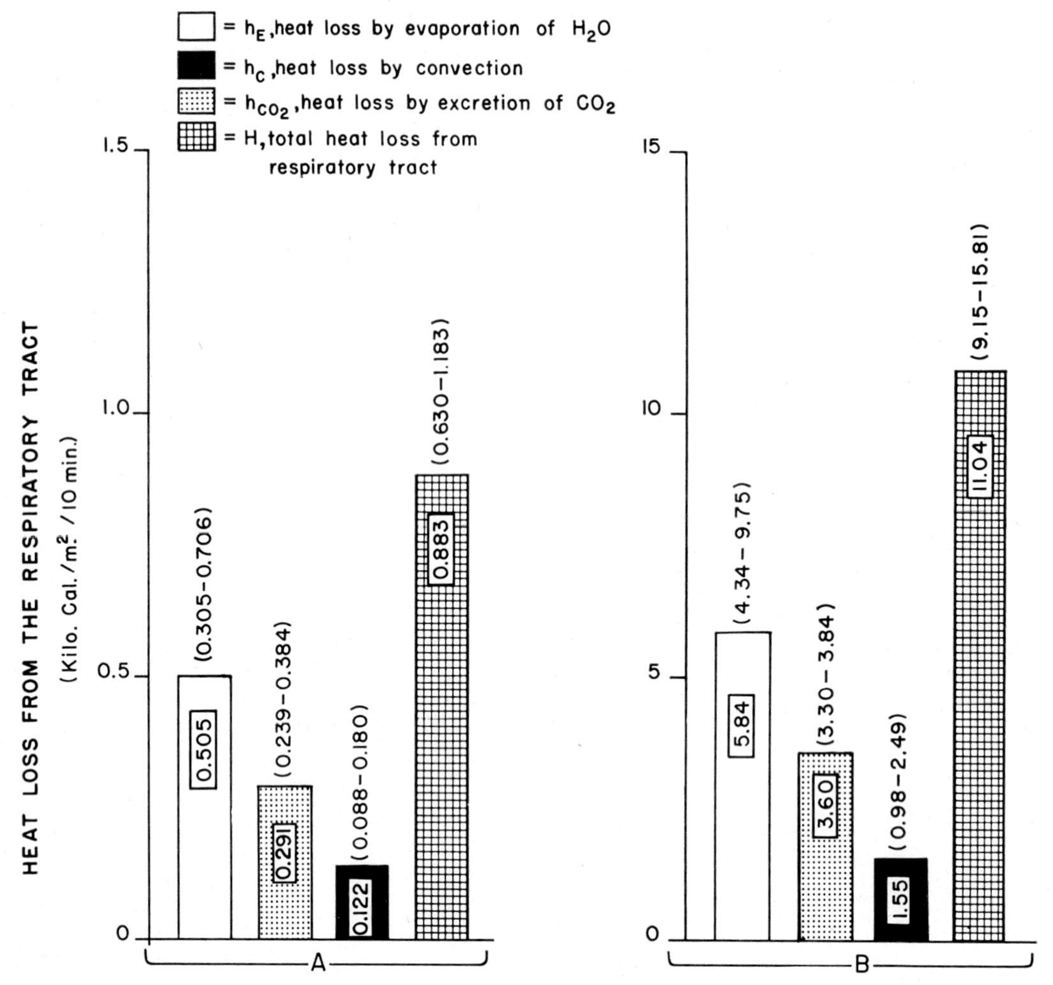

Fig. 92. The rate of heat loss from the respiratory tract through its various components. A shows the rate of heat loss from the lungs in kg-cal./m²/min. and B shows the rate of loss of heat as percent of total body heat loss. (From *Arch. Int. Med.*, *76*:315, 1945.)

of only +0.07 was found between the metabolic rate and the rate of irrigation of the respiratory tract with air.

THE RATE OF HEAT LOSS FROM THE RESPIRATORY TRACT

As already stated, heat loss, H, from the respiratory tract involves three components. These are (1) heat loss by the evaporation of water, h_E, (2) heat loss by convection (warming of inspired air), h_C, and (3) heat loss by decomposition of carbonic acid with expiration of carbon dioxide gas, h_{CO_2}. These three components were measured simultaneously in 27 normal adults. Total heat loss from the body was determined by means of a Benedict-Roth type of BMR apparatus.

Heat Loss by Evaporation of Water (h_E). The rate of heat loss by the evaporation of water (h_E) varied between 0.305 and 0.706 kg. calorie per square meter per ten minutes for the 27 subjects studied, with a mean rate of 0.505 kg. calorie per square meter per ten

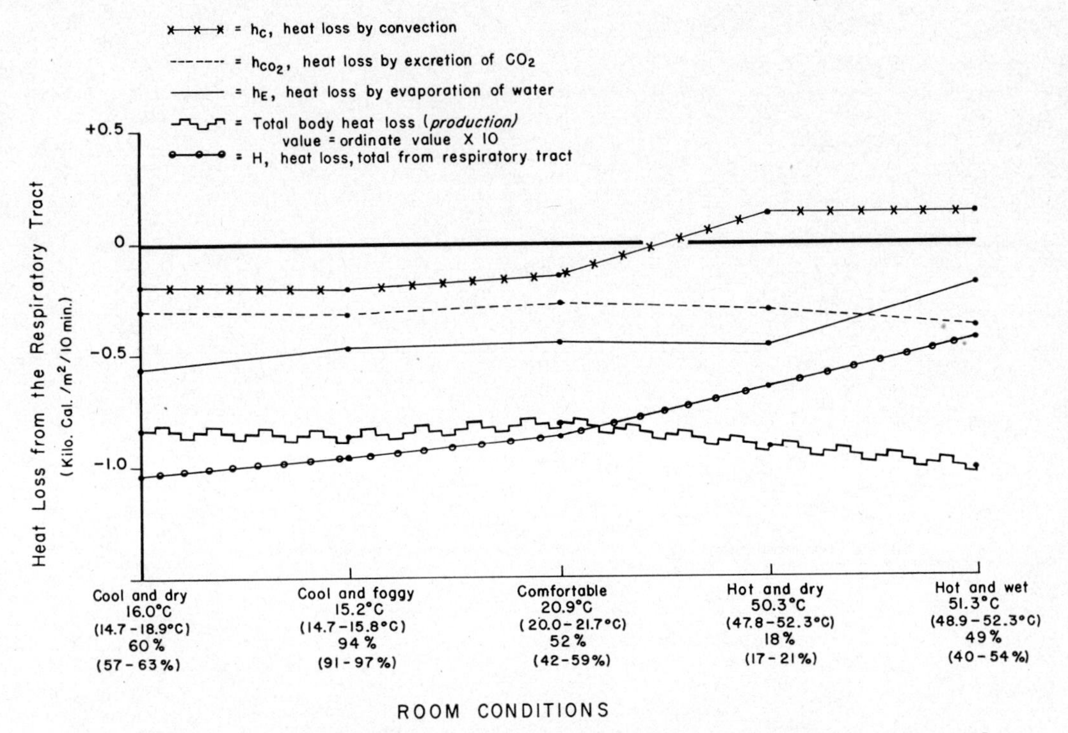

Fig. 93. The mean rate of heat loss from the respiratory tract for various room conditions in 27 normal young adults. The heat loss measured with a Benedict-Roth BMR apparatus was considered to represent the total heat loss from the body since the body was in thermal equilibrium with the environment. This assumption does not apply to the hot room because there probably was storage of heat. The relative loss of heat by the various components and their relationships are evident. (From *Arch. Int. Med.*, *76*:315, 1945.)

minutes. The rate of heat loss from the respiratory tract by evaporation (h_E) represented about 5.8% of total body heat loss and about 53% of total heat loss from the lungs (Fig. 92). Heat loss from the lungs by evaporation is influenced by atmospheric conditions. There were no significant variations in h_E when the atmosphere was cool and dry, cool and wet, hot and dry or comfortable. However, in a hot and moist environment h_E decreased significantly (Fig. 93). Thus, in a hot and humid environment heat loss by evaporation of water from the lungs became insignificant.

The mean rate of heat loss by evaporation of water (h_E) was 0.552 calorie per square meter of body surface per ten minutes (range 0.286 to 0.868) for patients with congestive heart failure studied in a neutral environment (Fig. 90). This represented 6.5% of total body heat loss and was essentially the same as that found for the normal subjects studied in a similar environment. The coefficient of correlation found between the rate of water loss and the rate of irrigation of the respiratory tract with air should be the same as that between h_E and the rate of irrigation of the respiratory tract with air.

Heat Loss by Convection (h_C). The rate of heat loss by warming of inspired air (h_C) varied between 0.088 and 0.180 kg-cal./m^2/10 min., the mean being 0.122 kg-cal./m^2/10 min. for the 27 subjects studied (Fig. 92). Heat loss by convection averaged about 14% of the total heat loss from the lungs and 1.5% of the total body heat loss in a neutral environment. The rate of heat loss from the respiratory tract due to warming of inspired air (h_C) was the same for a cool and dry, cool and foggy and comfortable environment (Fig. 93). The lack of difference was due to the compensatory influence of the rate of irrigation of the respiratory tract with air. The value of h_C should tend to be higher when cool air is inspired; but in a cool environment the amount of air inspired per unit time was less than in the comfortable atmosphere. However, there was a definite change in h_C when the room air was raised above body temperature (Fig. 93). Instead of losing heat by convection the body *gained* heat from the atmosphere, and h_C became a positive value. Except for the effect on the density and specific heat of the expired air, heat loss by convection was affected relatively little by the moisture in the air. Although h_C was not large, it could become important under certain conditions of low or high atmospheric temperature (for example, tropical and subtropical climates).

The mean rate of heat loss due to convection, h_C, was 0.157 kg-cal./m^2/ 10 min. (range, 0.091 to 0.248) in a neutral environment for patients with congestive heart failure (Fig. 94). This represented a mean loss of about 1.8% of the total body heat loss and 15% of the total heat loss from the respiratory tract. The rate of heat loss from the lungs due to h_C in these patients was increased about 29% over that in normal subjects. Again, this was due to the increased rate of irrigation of the respiratory tract with air in patients with dyspnea due to congestive heart failure.

Heat Loss by Decomposition of H_2CO_3 (h_{CO_2}). The rate of heat loss by expiration of carbon dioxide (h_{CO_2}) varied between 0.237 and 0.384 kg-cal./m^2/10 min. with a mean rate of 0.291 kg-cal./m^2/10 min. for the 27 normal subjects studied. The mean loss of heat by h_{CO_2} was about 33% of the total heat loss from the respiratory tract and averaged 3.6% of the total body heat loss.

The value of h_{CO_2} was not influenced a great deal by atmospheric conditions except for factors which increased the rate of irrigation of the respiratory tract with air ("washing" out of carbon dioxide from the blood). Changes in metabolic rate also did not affect the value of h_{CO_2}. In a hot and humid environment the metabolic rate and rate of irrigation of the respiratory tract with air were increased. These were associated with an expected increase in h_{CO_2}.

The mean rate of heat loss due to the excretion of carbon dioxide was 0.303 kg-cal./m^2/10 min. (range, 0.198 to 0.440) for the patients with congestive heart failure (Fig. 94). This mean rate represented an increase of 4.1% over that for the normal. The relatively small increase in h_{CO_2} when compared with the large increase in the rate of water loss from the respiratory tract in congestive heart failure shows that the increases in water and heat loss are mainly the result of dyspnea rather than the result of an increase in the rate of metabolism associated with congestive heart failure.

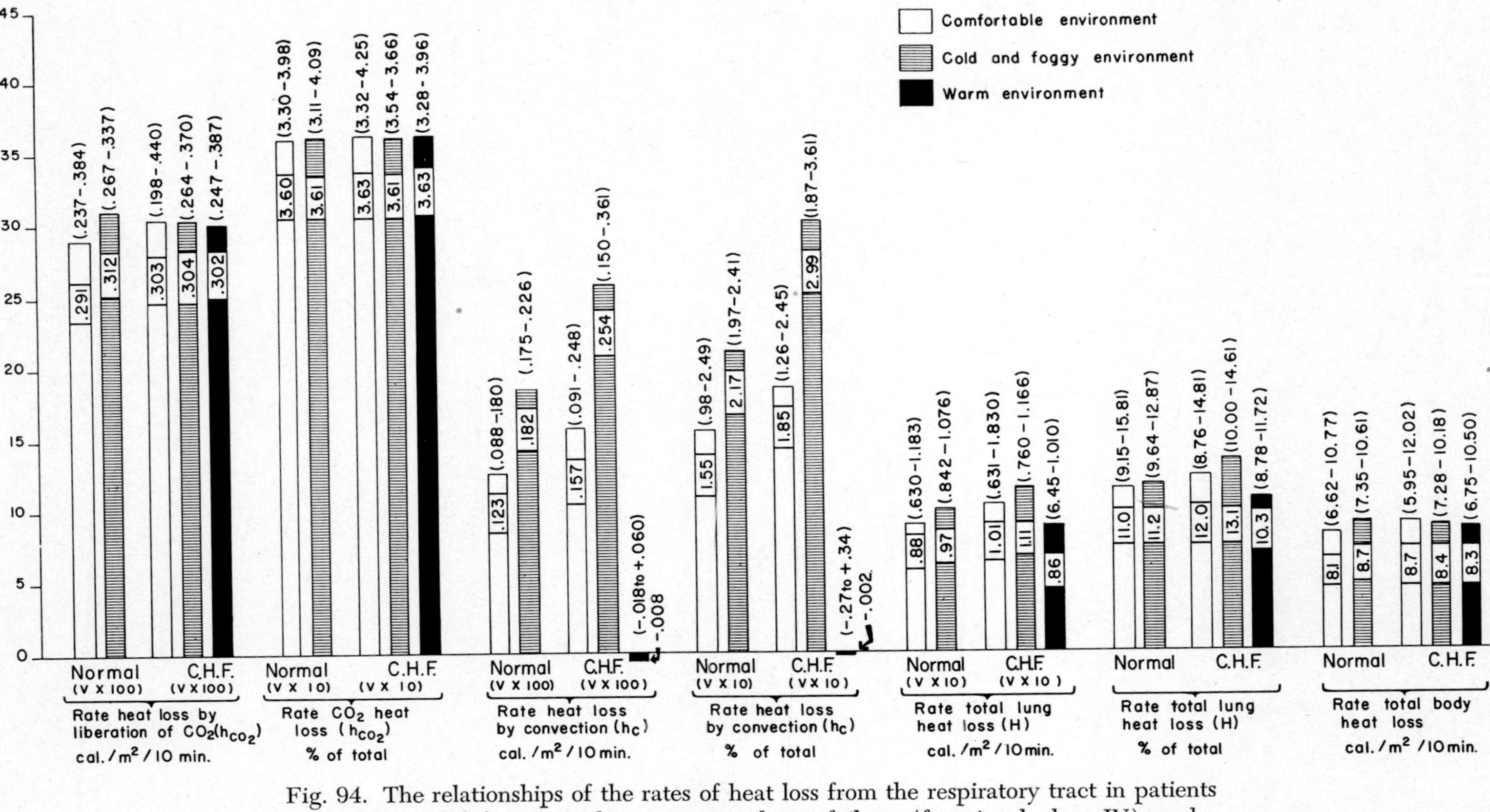

Fig. 94. The relationships of the rates of heat loss from the respiratory tract in patients with right and left ventricular congestive heart failure (functional class IV) under various environmental conditions. (From *Am. Heart J.*, 32:190, 1946.)

Total Heat Loss (H). The rate of total heat loss from the respiratory tract (H) varied from 0.630 to 1.183 kg-cal./m^2/10 min. with a mean rate of 0.883 kg-cal./m^2/10 min. for the normal subjects studied in a neutral environment (Fig. 94). The total heat loss from the respiratory tract averaged about 11% of the total heat loss from the body in a neutral environment but varied with the environmental conditions. H changed very little in a cool environment with a low or high relative humidity, whereas H decreased significantly in a hot, dry environment with a temperature greater than body temperature and decreased markedly for a hot and humid atmosphere (Fig. 93).

Although the rate of total heat loss from the respiratory tract decreased in a hot and humid environment, the rate of heat production increased. The decrease in H in the hot and humid environment was due mainly to the decrease in h_E and the change in h_C. Under these atmospheric conditions h_C became a positive rather than a negative value. Instead of body heat being lost by convection, convection produced a gain in body heat.

Total Body Heat Production. The rate of total heat production was also measured using the Benedict-Roth BMR machine in all the subjects in whom the rates of water and heat loss from the respiratory tract were studied. The mean rate of total body heat loss for the subjects who were considered to be in thermal equilibrium in a neutral environment was 8.08 kg-cal./m^2/10 min.

The mean total body heat loss was found to be 8.65 kg-cal./m^2/10 min. for a group of patients with congestive heart failure (Fig. 94). This represented an increase of 6.9% over the normal. The fact that the rate of irrigation of the respiratory tract with air increased to a greater extent than total body heat production in the patients with congestive heart failure further supports the assumption that the increased rates of heat and water loss in congestive heart failure were due to dyspnea rather than to the increased metabolic rate associated with congestive heart failure (Table 8).

The rate of total body heat production increased in the normal subjects in a hot and dry environment. However, because of heat storage a commensurate increase in total heat loss, as measured by the metabolic rate, did not occur. When the humidity of the hot atmosphere was increased, the rate of total body heat production increased further. When the temperature of the atmsophere was greater than that of the body (50° C.), thermal equilibrium between the subject and his surroundings did not exist, and, therefore, the rates of heat production and heat gain exceeded the rate of heat loss.

PATHOPHYSIOLOGIC INTERPRETATIONS

The surface area of the respiratory tract has been estimated to be about 70 m^2 during quiet breathing and 90 m^2 when the lungs are moderately inflated. The surface area of the alveoli alone is about 55 m^2, an area approximately 30 times the skin area of an average-sized man. In a normal adult sitting in a comforable environment the total heat loss from the respiratory tract accounted for about 11% of the total heat loss from the body. This percentage is too large to be ignored when studying thermal balance. The importance of this factor is even more evident when it is realized that the habits of man render it impossible to vary heat loss from the respiratory tract even under extreme environmental conditions. It is possible to influence the amount of heat lost from the cutaneous surface of the body by the use of clothing. But, in the case of the respiratory tract it is not so easy to vary heat loss. The rate of heat loss from the respiratory tract remained relatively unchanged in a cool or uncomfortably cold environment. Thus, whereas the cutaneous heat loss can be reduced to a minimum in a cool environment, no protective mechanisms are available for the respiratory tract. Furthermore, in a hot and humid environment heat may actually be gained through the respiratory tract because of the change that occurs in h_c and because of condensation of water on the respiratory surface as saturated hot air is inspired and cooled.

Thermal adaptation is much more highly developed for the skin than for the lungs in man. Not only is the rate of heat loss from the lungs relatively low when compared to the rate of heat loss from the skin, but, upon exposure to cold or heat, no adaptive mechanisms intervene to ensure homeostasis. Thus, heat is lost from the respiratory tract when it should be conserved and gained when it should be lost.

Considering the extremely large surface area of the respiratory tract, the influence of cold on blood vessels, and the glandular function of the entire respiratory tract, it is not surprising that there is a great tendency for infections of the respiratory tract to develop during the cold months of the year.

It has been stated that a subject inspiring foggy air will gain water from the atmosphere by a deposition of many small droplets of water on the surface of the epithelium of the respiratory tract. However, this is unlikely, unless the fog is composed of large droplets, since upon inspiration of air at 15° C. and 97% relative humidity (cool, foggy air), the temperature of the air is raised to about 33° C., and the air is no longer foggy. In fact, it is no longer saturated and is even capable of taking on a great deal more water from the surface of the respiratory tract. Water, therefore, is not absorbed from a cool and foggy atmosphere but rather is readily lost to it.

The high correlation between the rate of irrigation of the respiratory tract with air and the rate of water loss from the lungs suggests that within certain environmental limits man may increase the respiratory rate to maintain thermal equilibrium. However, in the studies of the influence of a hot and humid environment on cardiac work (Chapter 11), it was found that, although a hot and humid environment did increase the respiratory rate in healthy subjects, the increase was small when compared to the increase in the pulse rate. Thus, even though the respiratory tract may play some role in cooling the body and maintaining thermal equilibrium, the role is relatively minor.

The presence of free fluid in the lungs of patients with congestive heart failure did not increase the rate of water loss from the lungs. This was probably due to the high vapor tension above the edema fluid. Even in the normal individual the respiratory surfaces are wet. Patients with congestive heart failure could not withstand hot and humid environments satisfactorily for adequate measurements. Attempts to study patients in such an environment had to be terminated before any data could be obtained because of the severe distress the patients experienced. The primary difficulties developed by patients with congestive heart failure in a hot and humid environment were dyspnea and circulatory failure. The dyspnea was not the result of an increased demand for oxygen to meet metabolic requirements, for the rate of oxygen consumption does not increase under warm environmental conditions. The precise mechanisms by which warm environmental air stimulates respiration are unknown. It is possible that psychogenic factors are primarily in-involved, since a hot atmosphere produces marked apprehension and a sense of suffocation even in some normal subjects. Furthermore, patients with congestive heart failure have difficulty dissipating heat through the skin. The gain in heat from a hot and humid atmosphere through h_c adds an additional burden on the already impaired thermoregulatory mechanisms and ultimately on the heart.

It is well known that respiratory infections are most frequently encountered during the cold months of the year and during periods of the year associated with rapidly changing atmospheric fronts. It has been suggested that sudden cooling of the respiratory tract results in constriction of the submucosal blood vessels. The ischemia that results probably renders the mucous membranes vulnerable to attack by microorganisms in the respiratory passages. This theory has been employed widely to explain the precipitation of the common cold by cold weather.

Influenza has a strong meteorotropism. Atmospheric conditions associated with stationary anticyclones and saturated air during the cold months favor infection with influenza. The spread of an influenza epidemic apparently is supported by a succeeding period of cyclonic weather which lowers the resistance of the population (4). It has been claimed that the world-wide spread of influenza epidemics is associated with the migration of high pressure areas. Likewise, meningitis (5), scarlet fever (6) and diphtheria (7) epidemics have been related to changes in atmospheric conditions.

The relationship of respiratory allergy to climate has received a great deal of attention. The literature contains numerous references to the influence of atmospheric conditions on outbreaks of hay fever and asthma (8, 9, 10, 11). The flora of a particular geographic region will determine, of course, the type of allergens (pollen) which reach inhabitants of an area. In large measure, soil and climate determine the type of plant growth in a particular region as well as the time of pollenation. For example, the ragweed district in the United States includes the region east of the Rocky Mountains with the exception of the southern tip of Florida. Hay fever inducing pollens, in addition to ragweeds, which are commonly found in the United States are derived from June grass, timothy, red-top, orchard grass, Bermuda grass and marsh elder. Plant pollens are not the only inhalants which may produce respiratory allergy. House dust, molds, feathers, horse dander and hair from any of the domestic animals are all known to produce respiratory allergy. Furthermore, asthmatic attacks may result from allergens which are ingested, injected, or which merely come into contact with the skin.

Wind movement, rainfall, average summer temperature and humidity influence the annual pollen crop, animal and plant growth and other sources of allergens. The simple fact is that most pollens are air-borne and are, therefore, totally dependent upon atmospheric conditions (weather) for transport and dispersion.

The influence of climate on respiratory allergy goes further than the mere production and dispersion of pollen. Changes in climatic conditions independent of alterations in the pollen count may induce asthmatic attacks. Certain asthmatics will develop severe bronchospasm simply by going from a warm house into the cold night air. A cold wind may also induce an asthmatic attack. Passage of warm or cold fronts may result in large scale outbreaks of asthma. In low-lying areas and in regions surrounded by mountains, calm weather conditions promote air pollution with a subsequent increase in the number of asthmatic attacks. The "smog" that occasionally settles over Los Angeles is a well known example of such a condition. Most if not all large scale outbreaks of asthma can be explained by sudden meteorologic changes.

European climatologists, in particular, have been active in attempting to relate certain diseases to climate. In many cases the associations depend upon weak statistical correlations (12). Also, in some studies all of the possible factors are not considered, and in others the techniques of case finding are poor. Nevertheless, a number of European investigators believe there is an association between pulmonary embolism and climatic change (13, 14, 15, 16). These observers have related the occurrence of pulmonary embolism to passage of warm and cold fronts and, although this relationship cannot be considered proven, the data presented in support of such an association cannot be ignored.

CLINICAL APPLICATIONS

The fact that heat can be gained from the respiratory tract of man makes it necessary to provide a cool environment for all patients experiencing thermal difficulty. Furthermore, acute pulmonary edema may be precipitated in patients with heart disease as a result of exposure to a hot and humid environment.

Individuals with respiratory allergy may be benefited by the installation of an air-conditioning unit in the bedroom. The air-conditioned atmosphere is less humid and may contain fewer allergens than unmodified air. Patients with cardiac asthma may also benefit by the removal of allergens from the ambient air. It has been observed that during large scale outbreaks of bronchial asthma a significant proportion of those affected have cardiac disease. Many of these individuals give no history of respiratory allergy prior to the development of the cardiac disease. Similarly, during periods of air pollution by industrial waste products, most deaths occur in individuals with cardiac disease. Therefore, the treatment of patients with cardiac asthma must include a careful survey of the atmospheric conditions to which the patients are exposed. In severe cases it is probably wise to advise the patient to move to a dry climate. In milder instances the use of air-conditioning, desensitization, bronchodilator and antihistaminic drugs, in addition to the indicated cardiotonic drugs, may reduce the frequency of attacks. Respiratory infection must be treated early and adequately. Furthermore, the physician must be alert to the fact that often patients with cardiac asthma have chronic respiratory tract infection, usually with gram-negative organisms, with few of the signs of infection. In such instances the character of the sputum is a valuable indicator of whether or not infection is present.

Patients with cardiac asthma, as well as patients with bronchial asthma, who develop episodes of bronchospasm upon sudden exposure to cold air may benefit by inhalation of a bronchodilator before going out of doors. It is important to remember that the sudden onset of wheezing is associated with both smooth muscle spasm and edema of the mucous membranes. The subsidence of the edema is relatively slow, so that the physician's attention should be directed toward teaching the patient how to protect himself from factors which are frequently associated with the development of bronchospasm.

Individuals with chronic sinusitis, otitis and bronchitis living in the temperate climatic zone often experience difficulty during the winter months. Antibiotics and bacterial desensitization frequently fail to eliminate the source of infection. In some instances the persistence of infection in the nasal and respiratory passages results in bronchiectasis and emphysema. Such patients profit by a warmer climate.

Patients with chronic pulmonary disease in whom CO_2 retention exists develop apnea when placed in an oxygen-rich environment because the chemoreceptors responsible for breathing are only responsive to anoxia. However, if high fever, congestive heart failure or cardiac asthma exists, use of the oxygen tent simply as a source of air-conditioning without added O_2 may be beneficial.

In a hot and humid environment patients with high fever may lose large amounts of carbon dioxide through the respiratory passages due to the combination of an increased metabolic rate with increased CO_2 formation and hyperpnea due to fever and exposure to heat. The resultant respiratory alkalosis may produce tetany and in some instances even cardiac damage.

REFERENCES

1. Burch, G. E.: Rate of water and heat loss from the respiratory tract of normal subjects in a subtropical climate. *Arch. Int. Med., 76:*315, 1945.
2. Burch, G. E.: The rates of water and heat loss from the respiratory tract of patients with congestive heart failure who were from a subtropical climate and resting in a comfortable atmosphere. *Am. Heart J., 32:*88, 1946.
3. Burch, G. E.: Influence of variations in atmospheric temperature and humidity on the rates of water and heat loss from the respiratory tract of patients with congestive heart failure living in a subtropical climate. *Am. Heart J., 32:*190, 1946.
4. Cordes, H.: Die Grippe und ihre Beziehung zu atmospharischen Einflussen. *Arch. Meteorologic, Geophysik und Bioklimatologie,* Ser. B, *6:*462, 1955.
5. Gowen, G. H.: Onset and cause of epidemic meningitis as related to fluctuations in temperature and barometric pressure. *J. Lab. & Clin. Med., 23:*385, 1938.
6. Warmbt, W.: Zur meteorotropie des Scharlachs. Germany. *Deutscher Wetterdienst in der US-Zone, Berichte,* No. *42:*93, 1952.
7. Mucke, D. and Fieber, S.: Uber die Auslosung der Diphtherie durch meteorologische Einflusse. *Deutsche Gesundheitswesen, 7:*300, 1952.
8. Balyeat, R. M.: Factors which determine the pollen content of the air. *J. Lab. & Clin. Med., 12:*1151, 1927.
9. Durham, O. C.: Comparison of ragweed pollen incidence in the United States for 1929 and 1930. *J. Allergy, 2:*258, 1931.

10. Dingle, A. N.: Meteorological considerations in ragweed hay fever research. *Fed. Proc., 16:*615, 1957.

11. Dingle, A. N.: Meteorologic approach to the hay fever problem. *J. Allergy, 26:* 297, 1955.

12. Berg, H.: Statistisch gewonnene Ergebnisse in der Medizin-meteorologie in Bartels, J. zur Statistisch Methodik. *Annalen der Meteorologie, Medizin-meteorologische Hefte, No. 8:*39, 1953.

13. Berg, H.: Die Auslosung von Krankheiten durch meteorologische und solare Vorgange. *Naturwissenschaftliche Rundschau, 3:*161, 1950.

14. Berg, H.: Zur Meteorotropie der fulminanten Lungenembolie. *Annalen der Meteorologie, Medizin-meteorologische Hefte, No. 9:*60, 1953.

15. Geppert, M.: Zur statistischen Methodik der bioklimatischen Forschung. *Annalen der Meteorologie, Medizin-meteorologische Hefte,* No. *9:*21, 1954.

16. Raettig, H. and Nehls, E.: Die Meteorotropie der Lungenembolie unter besonderer Berucksichtigung der Arbeitsmethode. *Zeitschrift fur Klinische Medizin, 138:*242, 1940.

X

THE EFFECT OF THERMAL STRESS ON THE CARDIOVASCULAR SYSTEM OF MAN: THEORETIC CONSIDERATIONS OF THE ESTIMATION OF CARDIAC WORK

ACCLIMATIZATION to a hot and humid environment and adaptation to thermal stress depend to a great extent upon the heart. The various adjustments of normal man to a hot and humid environment involve the ability of the heart and circulation to perform greater amounts of work. In such an environment the vessels of the skin dilate in an attempt to increase heat loss from the body. However, if the environmental temperature exceeds body temperature and the atmosphere is humid, heat is absorbed rather than lost. This absorption of heat further stimulates the cardiovascular system, so that cardiac output increases, vasodilatation increases and the skin literally becomes an arteriovenous shunt. The rate of blood flow attains extremely high levels as still more heat is absorbed from the atmosphere. Unless this vicious cycle is interrupted, the cardiovascular system will fail.

In addition, the increase in heat loss by evaporation from the skin in response to a hot and humid environment depends upon increased sweat gland activity, which, in turn, requires greater dermal blood flow, an increase in cardiac output and an increase in cardiac work.

As yet there are no methods available by which cardiac work can be measured directly and accurately. In 1952, a method was described (1) by which cardiac work could be estimated indirectly from right heart catheterization and the Fick principle. Certain calculations of cardiac work were made based upon physical principles used in engineering. Certain broad generalizations and assumptions were necessary to apply these principles to the human heart. For example, the time-course curve of volume for the ventricle was considered to vary with time in the manner described by Wiggers (2). Furthermore, the ventricles were treated as spheres. From these and other assumptions as well as from direct measurements, the curves shown in Figure 95 were obtained.

The *pressure* curve for the right ventricle was recorded directly by means of an intracardiac catheter and suitable pressure transducer, electronic amplifiers and recorder. The *volume* curve was derived as follows. From the sum of the stroke volume, obtained by the direct Fick method, and an assumed residual volume of 25 cc. for the normal-sized heart, the volume of the ventricle just before the semilunar valves open was determined and plotted temporally with the corresponding point of the pressure curve. The residual volume (25 cc.) corresponded temporally to the

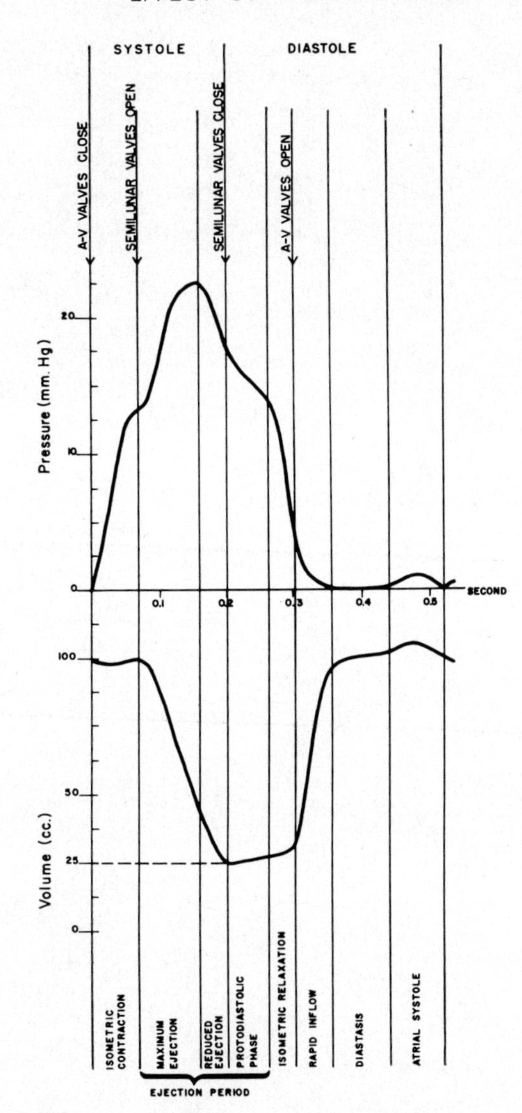

Fig. 95. The time-course curves of pressure and volume for the right ventricle. The pressure curve was recorded directly from the right ventricle through an intracardiac catheter. The volume curve was calculated to conform with curves of Wiggers. See text for details.

point on the pressure curve at which the semilunar valves close. The remainder of the volume curve was constructed by determining the percentage of the volume ejected, according to Wiggers (2), for given points along the pressure curve. The residual volume was assumed to be 150 cc. for patients with congestive heart failure.

To obtain time-course curves of pressure for the left ventricle, the maximal level of pressure recorded directly from the brachial artery was utilized and the pressure curve was assumed to vary with time according to Wiggers. The stroke volume and the volume time-course curve were considered to be the same as those for the right ventricle. The curves obtained are time-course curves of pressure and volume.

To obtain pressure-volume-time course diagrams, the pressure and volume for each time interval of the cardiac cycle were plotted simultaneously. Such a pressure-volume diagram is shown in Figure 96. It is evident from the diagram that during the phase of isometric contraction there is a rapid rise in intra-

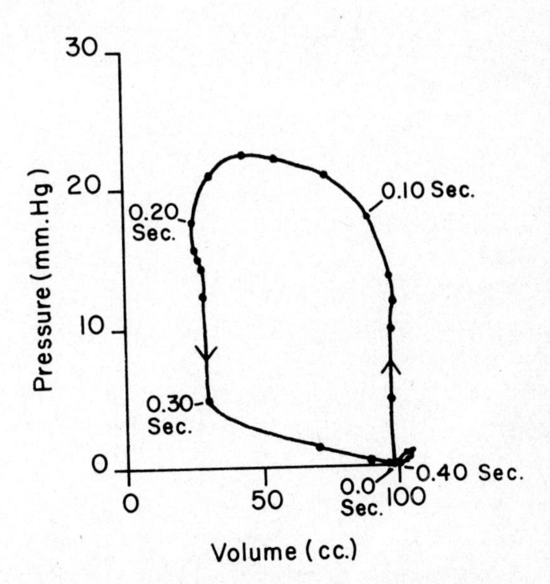

Fig. 96. The time course of the pressure-volume relationship for the right ventricle. This curve was obtained from the pressure and volume curves shown in Figure 95. The area enclosed by the pressure-volume diagram indicates quantitatively the mechanical cardiac work performed by the heart.

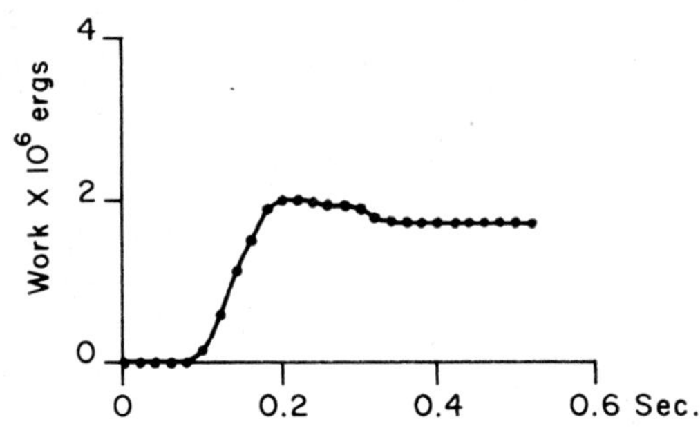

Fig. 97. The time-course of accumulated cardiac work was obtained by integration of the pressure-volume diagram shown in Figure 96.

ventricular pressure without any change in volume, and that during the ejection phase, pressure changed slightly, whereas volume decreased rapidly. Following ejection there was a rapid reduction in pressure with only a slight increase in volume and, finally, there was a rapid increase in volume with continued reduction in pressure as the ventricle filled during diastole. The area enclosed by the pressure-volume-time "loop" is an index of work performed by the ventricle during that cardiac cycle. As will be seen in the following chapter, the characteristics of such a loop are altered considerably by a hot and humid environment in normal subjects and in patients with congestive heart failure.

By integration of the pressure-volume diagram of Figure 96, according to the equation

$$W = \int P\,dV, \qquad (14)$$

the curve of accumulated mechanical work shown in Figure 97 was obtained. The first derivative of the work curve with respect to time indicates the rate work was performed (power output) from moment to moment during the cardiac cycle.

It should be made clear that the term "work" as used in these discussions pertains to mechanical work and not total work which also includes "physiologic" work. It is not yet possible to measure physiologic work or efficiency of the heart directly.

Thus, a method has been described by which the time course of work and power output during a cardiac cycle may be estimated indirectly. Using the principles outlined, studies were performed in which these parameters were determined for normal subjects and for patients with congestive heart failure exposed to various environmental conditions. The results of these studies and applications of the above calculations as well as clinical observations concerning cardiac function are described in the following chapter.

REFERENCES

1. Burch, G. E., Ray, C. T. and Cronvich, J. A.: The George Fahr Lecture; certain mechanical peculiarities of the human cardiac pump in normal and diseased states. *Circulation,* 5:504, 1952.
2. Wiggers, C. J.: *Physiology in Health and Disease.* Ed. 5. Philadelphia, W. B. Saunders Co., 1955.

XI

THE EFFECT OF THERMAL STRESS ON THE NORMAL AND DISEASED CARDIOVASCULAR SYSTEMS OF MAN

THE cardiovascular system of homeothermic man participates greatly in adjustments to variations in environmental conditions. The studies conducted in this laboratory on the influence of a hot and humid environment upon the heart have been divided into three phases for convenience of presentation. These include (1) clinical observations on subjects with a normal cardiovascular system, (2) clinical observations on subjects with various types of cardiovascular disease, and, (3) measurements of cardiac output, work and power in subjects with normal and diseased hearts.

OBSERVATIONS ON PATIENTS IN AIR-CONDITIONED AND NON-AIR-CONDITIONED HOSPITAL WARDS

These studies were obtained on patients in the wards of the Charity Hospital in New Orleans during the summers of 1957 and 1958 (1). Two wards immediately adjacent to each other were used. The types of patients admitted to these wards, as well as the quality of care received by the patients, were in every way comparable. However, one of the wards was air-conditioned, whereas the other ward was non-air-conditioned and open to the warm and humid summer weather.

The patients hospitalized in the two wards were examined at least twice daily between July 1 and August 15 of each of the two years. This period corresponds to the warmest and most uncomfortable time of the year in New Orleans. A total of 163 patients was observed, 88 in the air-conditioned ward and 75 in the non-air-conditioned ward. At each examination the blood pressure, pulse rate, respiration rate and body temperature were recorded (Table 9). The general appearance of the patients was noted, with special attention to restlessness, irritability, sweating and well-being.

Clinical Observations on Patients with a normal Cardiovascular System. By comparison with the non-air-conditioned ward, it was found that the patients in the air-conditioned ward enjoyed longer and more restful sleep. For example, in the cool ward at 7:00 a. m. most of the patients were still asleep, whereas at the same hour in the warm ward most of the patients were sitting near their beds or walking around. There was a general appearance of calm and quiet in the air-conditioned ward with outside noises reduced or eliminated. The patients slept frequently during the day. In the non-air-conditioned ward the patients appeared restless, irritable, sweaty, and sometimes agitated, annoying outside noises were readily heard, and only the more ill patients slept during the day.

Nursing care was more efficient in the cool atmosphere of the air-conditioned ward than in the warm and humid non-air-conditioned ward. The suppression of perspiration and objectionable odors provided comfort to the patients, nurses, and maids. Linen remained clean and unwrinkled longer, tending to prevent and improve the management of decubitus ulcer. Also, the amount of linen used was less in the air-conditioned ward than in the warm ward. Atopic patients were more satisfactorily managed in the air-conditioned than in the non-air-conditioned ward, probably due in part to the fact that allergens were filtered out of the environment as well as to the comfort and ease with which thermal balance was maintained. The attitude and morale of all personnel in contact with the patients were better in the air-conditioned than in the non-air-conditioned ward. An occasional patient who preferred hot weather experienced adverse effects in the cool ward. These complaints were not serious. They included nasal stuffiness, chilly sensations and arthralgia.

Clinical Observations on Patients with Cardiovascular Disease. In addition to the general beneficial effects of an air-conditioned ward already discussed, certain specific benefits were noted in patients with cardiovascular disease. The patients with congestive heart failure compensated more quickly in the cool, comfortable ward than in the warm and humid one. Particular care was taken to determine the presence or absence of dyspnea, orthopnea and gallop rhythm in the patients with congestive heart

TABLE 9

Mean Clinical Data Obtained in Air-Conditioned and Non-Air-Conditioned Wards During Warm and Humid Summers in New Orleans

Ward	*No. of Patients*	*No. of Determinations*	*Age Mean Yr.*	*Mean Blood Pressures* mm. Hg.	*Mean Pulse Rate Min.*	*Mean Respiratory Rate Min.*	*Mean Body Temperature* °F.	*Ward Temperature* *Day* *Mean* °F.	*Range* °F.	*Night* *Mean* °F.	*Range* °F.	*Mean Relative Humidity* %
Air-conditioned	88	7,680	48	130/77	83.5	21.5	98.4	76	(71–76)	75	(72–76)	65.7
Non-air-conditioned	75	6,444	43	135/76	89.5	21.5	98.4	87	(79–90)	84	(80–88)	83.8

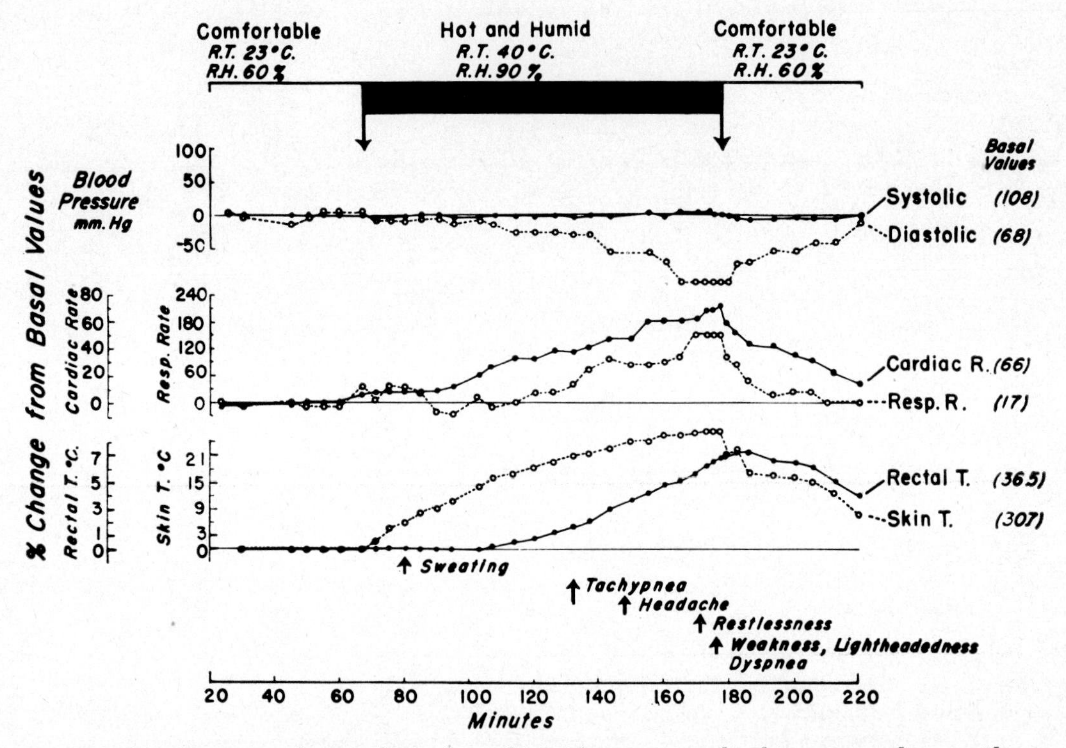

Fig. 98. Summary of physiologic data obtained on a normal subject exposed to rapid elevation in atmospheric temperature and humidity. It can be seen that the cardiovascular and pulmonary systems began to change about 40 minutes after exposure to the hot and humid atmosphere. As the duration of exposure to the environment progressed, the symptoms and signs of physiologic disturbances became intensified. (From *Am. J. M. Sc.*, 223:45, 1952.)

failure. Patients were observed for weeks in the warm and humid ward, who demonstrated little improvement in these signs despite adequate medical care. When a patient in the warm and humid ward no longer improved and the signs of congestive heart failure were still evident, the patient was transferred to the air-conditioned ward. Without exception, improvement in the clinical course of the disease developed and in some patients the improvement was dramatic. In one patient a protodiastolic gallop rhythm which had been present for ten days in the warm ward was no longer audible after twelve hours in the air-conditioned ward. Another patient with extreme orthopnea who exhibited little or no improvement while in the warm and humid ward despite intense medical therapy, including phlebotomy, was transferred to the air-conditioned ward and in less than 48 hours was able to lie comfortably on one pillow (1).

The management of patients with cerebrovascular accidents was also more satisfactory in the air-conditioned ward for several reasons. Patients with cerebrovascular accidents frequently have difficulty with thermal regulation even if the thermoregulatory center is not directly involved in the vascular disease. The hyperthermia in these patients may be transitory and is more easily managed in an air-conditioned ward. This is in contrast to the patient with midbrain damage and hyperthermia in whom survival almost never occurs. In the first type of patient a cool environment decreases water and electrolyte loss from the skin and makes temperature control physiologically easier. Comatose patients were observed in the warm ward, who were literally drenched in their own perspiration and in whom the rectal temperature was moderately elevated. When such a patient was removed to the cool ward, the skin became dry and the rectal temperature at times decreased two or three degrees Fahrenheit.

The blood pressure of hypertensive patients was more easily regulated in the cool ward than in the warm ward. They were less restless and irritable, obtained longer hours of bed rest and the more tranquil surroundings of the air-conditioned ward were conducive to relaxation.

OBSERVATIONS ON PATIENTS IN THE CLIMATIC ROOM

In order to study in a more systematic way the clinical response of patients with and without cardiovascular disease to a hot and humid environment, 25 subjects (13 controls and 12 with congestive heart failure) were subjected to a rapid elevation in atmospheric temperature and humidity in specially constructed climatic rooms (2). The subjects rested in bed for 60 to 90 minutes in the climatic room with a comfortable atmosphere (23° ± 1° C., 60% ± 10% R. H.) and the cardiac and respiratory rates, blood pressure, skin color, sweating, general clinical appearance and psychic changes of the subjects were noted. The atmosphere of the room was then changed to hot and humid (40° ± 2° C., 85% ± 15% R. H.) and the clinical observations repeated.

Effect of Thermal Stress on Normal Subjects. The typical response of a control subject is summarized by Figure 98. There was an increase in skin temperature followed shortly by a more gradual rise in rectal temperature. Tachycardia developed and respiratory activity increased. Tachypnea, hyperventilation, slight dyspnea and in some subjects the hyperventilation syndrome developed. Extreme peripheral vasodilatation in association with a marked increase in pulse pressure was observed. After prolonged exposure blanching and wrinkling of the skin of the extremities developed. Systolic blood pressure remained essentially unchanged, occasionally decreasing during the early period of exposure or increasing near the end of exposure in some subjects. The diastolic blood pressure decreased considerably and, as recorded at the fifth phase of the Korotkoff sounds, fell to zero. As exposure continued, the subjects became irritable and complained of weakness, faintness, and of being extremely hot. With continued exposure disturbances of the central nervous system developed, including headaches, visual disturbances, restlessness and muscular tremor. In none of the control subjects were gallop rhythm, pulmonary congestion or evidence of left ventricular failure observed even though the duration of exposure continued essentially to the voluntary limit of the subject.

The response of the venous pressure to a hot and humid environment was

TABLE 10

EFFECT OF HOT AND HUMID ENVIRONMENT ON VENOUS PRESSURE OF MAN

Subject Number	Vein*	*Venous Pressure* Comfortable Room mm. H_2O	Hot Room mm. H_2O	Increase mm. H_2O	Increase %	Time in Hot Room min.
1	dorsal vein of hand	200	235	35	12.5	30
	median basilic	120	145	25	20.8	
	median basilic	155	190	35	22.6	
2	dorsal vein of hand	195	240	45	23.1	40
	median basilic (R)	160	185	25	13.6	
	dorsal vein of hand (R)	205	270	65	31.2	
	median basilic	110	195	85	77.3	
3	dorsal vein of hand	155	200	45	29.0	30
	dorsal vein of foot	180	220	40	22.2	
	median basilic	100	120	20	20.0	
4	dorsal vein of hand	135	160	25	18.5	60
	dorsal vein of foot	145	185	40	27.6	
	median basilic	95	160	65	67.1	
5	dorsal vein of hand	165	205	40	23.6	30
	dorsal vein of foot	195	235	40	20.5	
6	median basilic	130	145	15	17.7	35
	dorsal vein of hand	165	205	40	23.6	
	median basilic	115	155	40	34.8	
7	dorsal vein of hand	145	205	60	41.4	30
	dorsal vein of foot	145	165	20	13.8	
	median basilic	115	210	95	82.5	
8	dorsal vein of hand	140	230	90	64.3	45
	dorsal vein of foot	170	220	50	29.4	
	median basilic	110	130	20	18.2	
9	dorsal vein of hand	140	175	35	25.0	35
	dorsal vein of foot	155	170	15	9.7	
	median basilic	95	120	25	26.4	
10	dorsal vein of hand	140	185	45	32.2	40
	dorsal vein of foot	160	205	45	28.1	

* All veins measured are on the left side unless otherwise indicated by (R) denoting right side.

Influence of Hot, Humid Atmosphere on Subject with Chronic Congestive Heart Failure

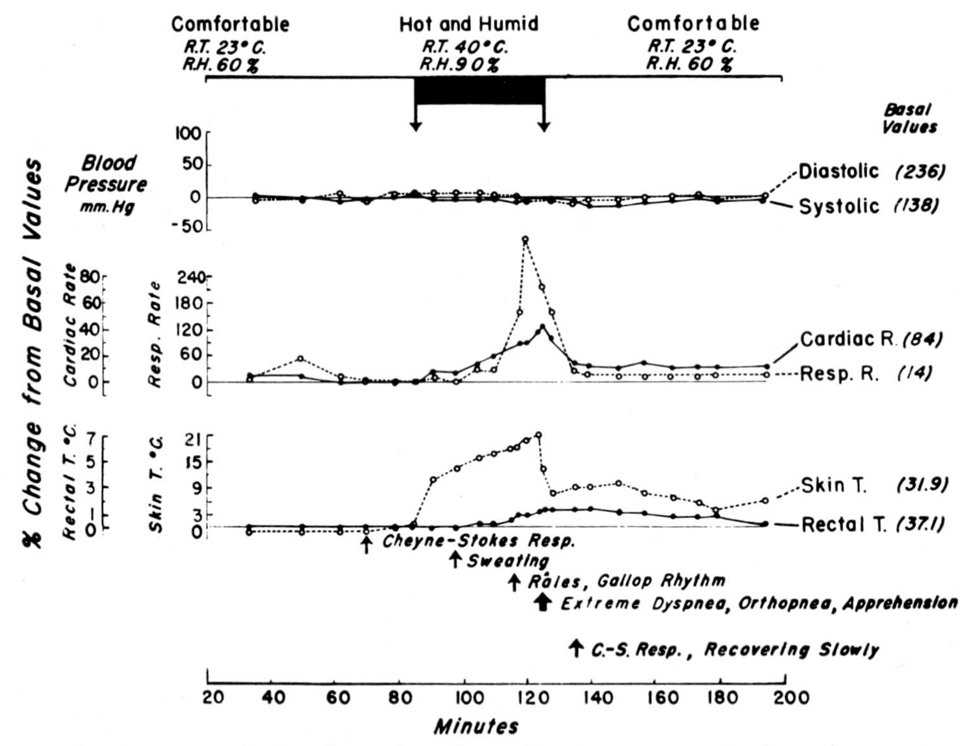

Fig. 99. Summary of physiologic data obtained on a patient with chronic congestive heart failure and hypertensive cardiovascular disease before, during, and after exposure to a hot and humid environment. The subject was without medication for two weeks prior to the study. Under the influence of a hot and humid atmosphere clinical manifestations of acute cardiac asthma developed, being characterized by extreme dyspnea and orthopnea, diffuse rales in the lungs and intensification of the gallop rhythm. (From *Am. J. M., Sc.*, 223:45, 1952.)

studied in ten subjects by first measuring the venous pressure with the subjects in a comfortable environment (25° C., 60% R. H.) and again after the subjects were exposed to a hot and humid environment (40° to 45° C., 100% R.H.) for 30 to 60 minutes (3). The venous pressure was measured in the dorsal vein of the hand or foot and the median basilic vein. In each subject a rise in venous pressure was noted (Table 10).

Effect of Thermal Stress on Patients with Congestive Heart Failure. The reactions manifested clinically by the subjects with chronic congestive heart failure were essentially similar to, but less predictable than, those of the control subjects. However, certain important differences were noted. The patients with congestive heart failure were not able to tolerate the hot and humid atmosphere as long as the control subjects. A typical response for a patient with chronic congestive heart failure is shown in Figure 99. Dyspnea and orthopnea were prominent symptoms. When a patient with congestive failure and a control subject were observed side by side

TABLE 11

SIGNS AND SYMPTOMS WHICH DEVELOPED IN THE HOT AND HUMID ATMOSPHERE

A. CARDIOVASCULAR SYSTEM
1. Increased cardiac activity
   a. Increase in cardiac rate
   b. Development or intensification of murmurs
2. Blood pressure changes
   a. Systolic—increase or decrease
   b. Diastolic—decrease
3. Gallop rhythm—development or intensification
4. Pulsus paradoxus
5. Pulsus alternans
6. Cardiac arrhythmias
7. Syncope (faintness)
8. Venous engorgement
9. Hemorrhagic phenomenon
10. Blanching and wrinkling of skin of extremities at end of exposure

B. RESPIRATORY SYSTEM
1. Increased respiratory activity
   a. Hyperventilation and hyperventilation syndrome
   b. Dyspnea and orthopnea
   c. Coughing
2. Rales
3. Cardiac and allergic type asthma

C. CENTRAL NERVOUS SYSTEM
1. Irritability and restlessness
2. Weakness and anxiety
3. Headache
4. Visual disturbances
5. Bladder incontinence
6. More advanced nervous disorders

in the same atmospheric surroundings, it was noted that the former developed severe dyspnea, orthopnea, apprehension and other evidences of "left ventricular" failure at the same time that the control subject was just beginning to sweat and exhibit an increase in cardiac rate. The patient with chronic congestive heart failure developed rales in the bases of both lungs, dyspnea, cervical venous engorgement and gallop rhythm as acute cardiac asthma developed. Gallop rhythm was accentuated or produced in two-thirds of the patients with chronic congestive heart failure. Murmurs were produced or intensified in both groups of patients. The patients with cardiac disease showed greater cardiac stress, as manifested by a bounding precordium and epigastric pulsations. Premature atrial and ventricular contractions were the only cardiac arrhythmias to develop during these studies. Premature beats, if present prior to exposure to the hot and humid atmosphere, usually became less frequent with the appearance of tachycardia and recurred when the cardiac rate decreased during recovery from the heat. The diastolic blood pressure tended to decrease less in the subjects with heart failure. However, the duration of exposure to a hot and humid environment was decidedly less than for the control subjects. Cheyne-Stokes respiration disappeared when dyspnea was precipitated by the hot and humid atmosphere only to reappear during the period of recovery. In general, the onset of the rise in body temperature occurred later in the control subjects, whereas the hyperthermia was more sustained in the patients with congestive heart failure after return to a comfortable environment. The patients with cardiac disease lost more weight in the hot and humid environment than did the control subjects who were being studied at the same time. The mean weight loss for the patients with chronic congestive heart failure and for the control subjects observed simultaneously was 0.43 kg./hr./m^2 and 0.24 kg./hr./m^2, respectively.

The return to the basal or pre-exposure physiologic state after thermal exposure was less rapid in the patients with congestive heart failure, as judged by the rate with which the cardiac rate decreased, dyspnea subsided and the patient returned to a state of well-being. In most instances all subjects returned to their respective previous basal states within one to two hours. The signs and symptoms which developed upon exposure to a hot and humid environment are summarized in Table 11.

CARDIAC OUTPUT, WORK AND POWER IN SUBJECTS WITH NORMAL AND DISEASED HEARTS EXPOSED TO A HOT AND HUMID ENVIRONMENT

These studies were conducted in two phases. The first group of studies was performed with the subjects resting in bed in the experimental climatic room (4). The room was first maintained at a neutral environment (73° F., 60% R.H.) and then made hot and humid (111° F., 86% R.H.). The second group of studies was performed in an air-conditioned and non-air-conditioned ward at the Charity Hospital during the warm and humid summer weather in New Orleans (5, 6). Half of the subjects in this latter group were studied first in the non-air-conditioned ward exposed to the hot and humid summer weather and then in an air-conditioned and comfortable ward. The other half was exposed first to the cool air-conditioned ward and then to the warm and humid atmosphere of the non-air-conditioned ward.

The following measurements were made for all subjects in both environments: (1) cardiac output, by right heart catheterization and the Fick principle, (2) right ventricular pressure, recorded directly and continuously by means of a strain gauge and electrocardiographic string galvanometer, (3) arterial blood pressure, directly, and (4)

TABLE 12

CARDIAC WORK

Subject Number	*Cardiac Output* (L/Min.)		*Stroke Volume* (cc.)		*Systemic Resistance* (Dyne-sec./cm.[5])		*Heat Produced* (Cal./Hr.)	
	Comf.	*Hot*	*Comf.*	*Hot*	*Comf.*	*Hot*	*Comf.*	*Hot*
CONTROL SERIES								
1	2.2	3.5	30.6	35.0	3199	1668	71.5	129.8
2	3.2	20.5	51.6	256.2	2199	359	34.3	214.2
3	9.6	36.6	112.9	332.7	825	247	82.2	231.1
Mean	5.0	20.2	65.0	208.0	2074	758	62.7	192.4
CONGESTIVE HEART FAILURE SERIES (CLINICALLY COMPENSATED)								
1	2.34	4.1	26.6	43.8	4477	2574	57.5	84.8
2	4.2	8.9	77.8	118.7	3180	1365	60.1	108.3
3	6.9	11.9	73.4	119.0	1403	645	76.6	124.8
4	7.1	15.0	95.0	115.0	1374	917	90.5	174.1
Mean	5.1	10.0	68.2	99.1	2609	1375	71.2	123.0

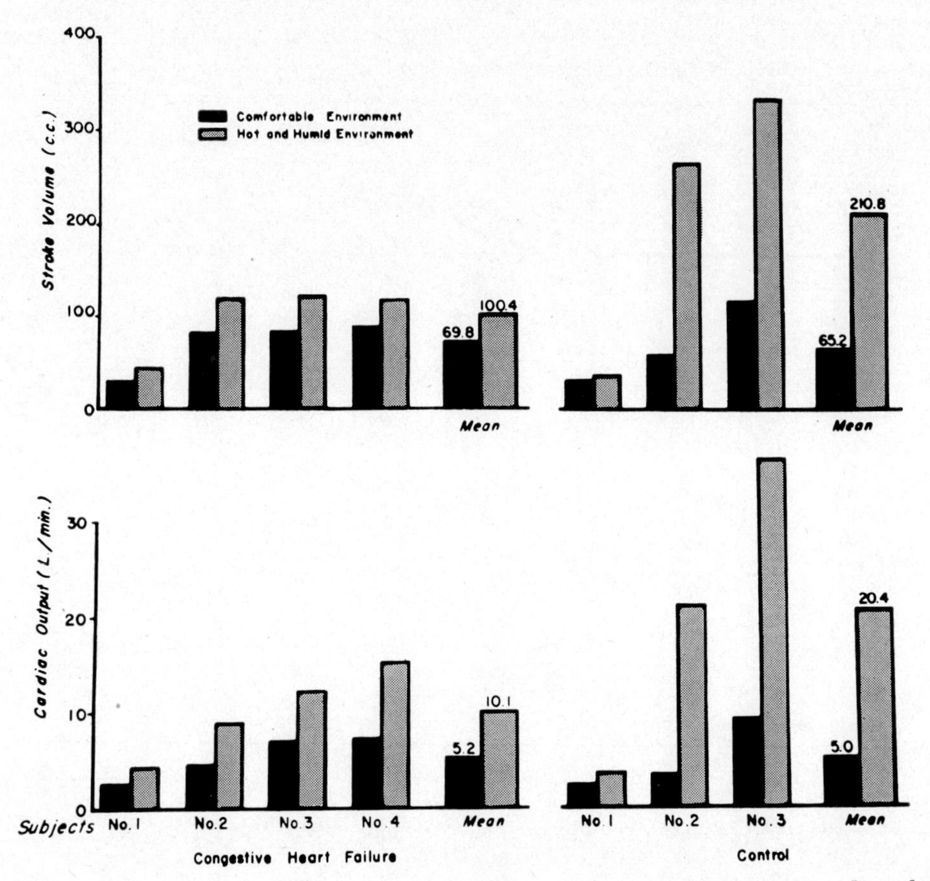

Fig. 100. Influence of a hot and humid environment on cardiac output and stroke volume of three control subjects and of four patients with congestive heart failure. No corrections were made for surface area because of the inaccuracy of the method. (From *Am. Heart J.*, 53:665, 1957.)

various respiratory parameters (Tables 12, 13). Using necessary assumptions, as described in Chapter 10, the following calculations were made for both ventricles: (1) time-course curves of volume and pressure, (2) volume-pressure diagrams, (3) time-course curves of accumulated work, and (4) time-course curves of power output.

Seven patients were studied in the climatic room, 3 of whom were control subjects without cardiovascular disease and 4 of whom were patients with chronic congestive heart failure. The subjects with cardiac disease were carefully selected on the basis of ability to tolerate the hot and humid environment despite mild to moderate heart failure, functional classes II to III. All were receiving conventional therapy, including digatalis.

The subjects were studied at least 3 hours postprandially. They first rested in the climatic room maintained at a comfortable atmosphere (73° F., 60% R.H.). When the patients appeared to be in a basal state, cardiac output and other measurements were obtained. The room atmosphere was then gradually changed to hot and humid (111° F., 86% R. H.) over a period of about one hour, since it was not known how well

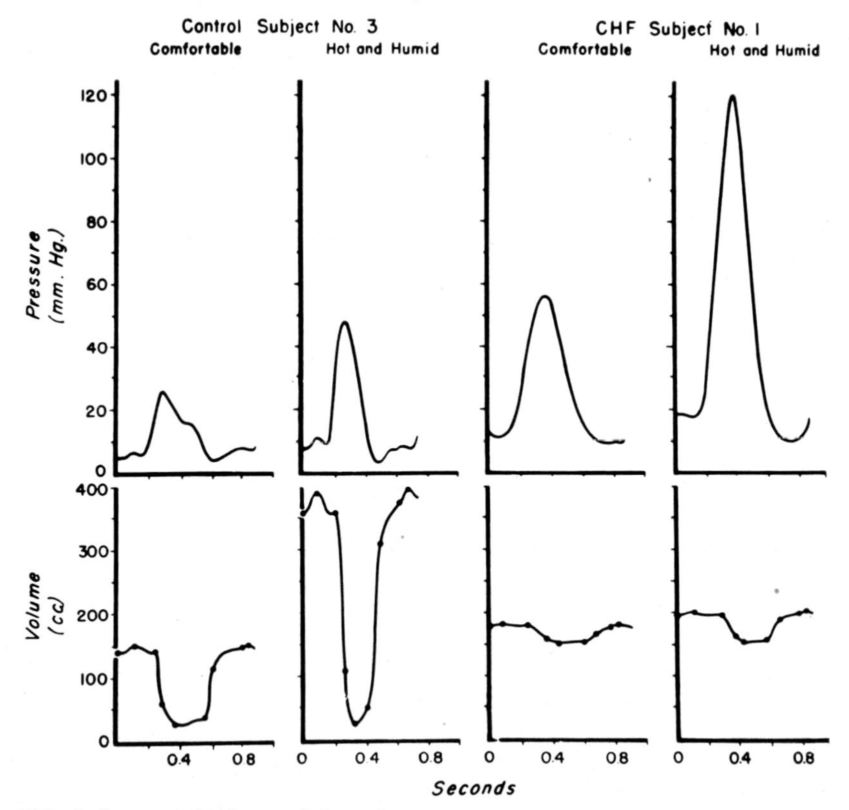

Fig. 101. Influence of a hot and humid environment on the simultaneous time courses of pressure and volume of the right ventricle for a representative control subject and a patient with chronic congestive failure. Considerably higher pressure was developed by the right ventricle of the subject with congestive heart failure to eject much less blood per cardiac stroke. (From *Am. Heart J.*, 53:665, 1957.)

the subjects with congestive heart failure would tolerate the environment and the necessary physiologic procedures. The measurements were repeated in the hot and humid atmosphere. The duration of exposure to the hot and humid environment was varied according to individual tolerance. After an ambient temperature of 111° F. was reached, the patients with congestive heart failure usually remained in the climatic room from 45 to 60 minutes, whereas the normal subjects remained from one to two hours.

Cardiac Output and Stroke Volume. The cardiac output and stroke volume increased in every subject upon exposure to the hot and humid environment (Table 12, Fig. 100). The mean cardiac output increased about four times in the control subjects and about two times in the subjects with congestive heart failure.

Time-Course Curves of Volume and Pressure. Time-course curves of volume and pressure for the right and left ventricles of a control subject and of a pa-

TABLE 13

MEASUREMENTS OF BLOOD PRESSURE

Subject Number	*Arterial Blood Pressure*				*Right Ventricular Pressure*				*Right Ventricular Rate*		*Pressure*			
	Systolic (mm. Hg)		*Diastolic* (mm. Hg)		*Systolic* (mm. Hg)		*Diastolic* (mm. Hg)				*Right Ventricle* (cm. H_2O)		*Right Atrium* (cm. H_2O)	
	Comf.	*Hot*	*Comf.*	*Hot*	*Comf.*	*Hot*	*Comf.*	*Hot*	*Comf.*	*Hot*	*Comf.*	*Hot*	*Comf.*	*Hot*
CONTROL SERIES														
1	118	128	74	34	17	38	5	11	72	100	17.3	16.5	10.0	11.5
2	118	130	74	70	25	33	6	8	62	80	18.5	20.0	8.5	10.0
3	144	174	70	68	26	42	3.4	8	85	110	22.0	21.0	10.0	8.0
Mean	127	144	73	57	23	38	4.8	9	73	97	19.3	19.2	9.5	9.8
CONGESTIVE HEART FAILURE SERIES (CLINICALLY COMPENSATED)														
1	168	160	110	120	56	94	11.2	13.5	88	96	29.0	....	....	....
2	220	190	130	130	24	72	7.1	24.0	54	75	....	....	....	....
3	168	132	90	76	34	52	13.0	20.0	94	100	15.5	18.8	5.6	9.0
4	174	232	86	128	41	58	8.8	11.0	75	130	29.5	43.0	5.0	16.5
Mean	183	179	104	114	39	69	10.5	17.1	78	100	24.7	30.9	5.3	12.7

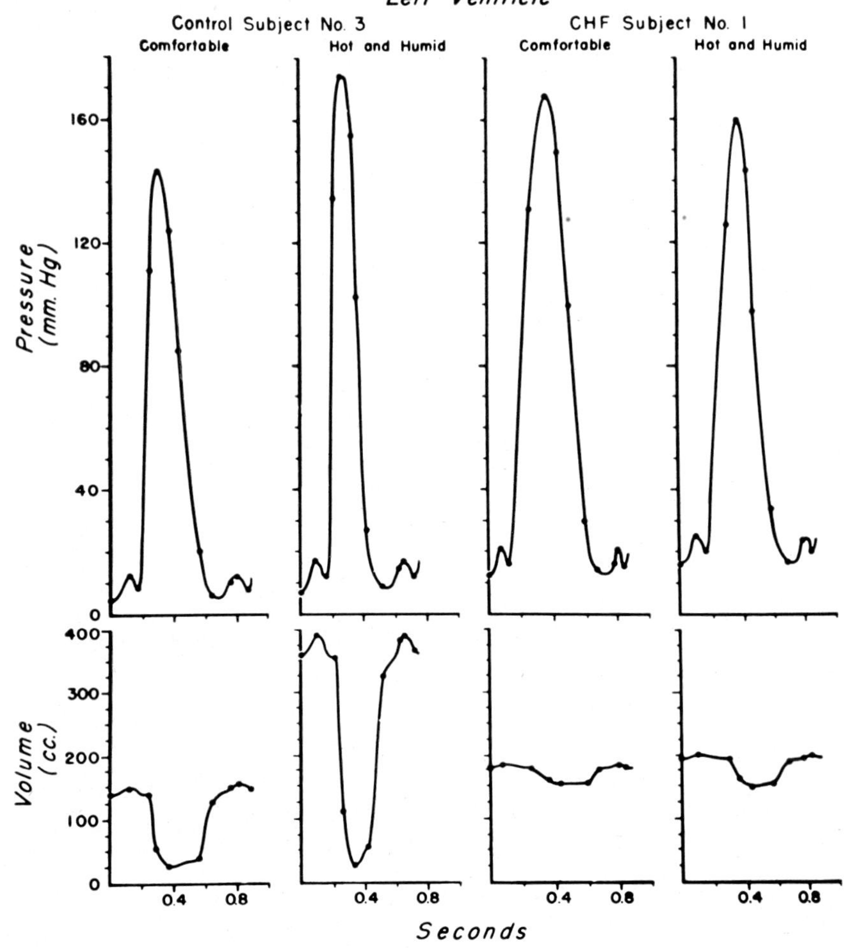

Fig. 102. Influence of a hot and humid environment on the time courses of pressure and volume of the left ventricle for the same cardiac cycles and same subjects shown in Figure 101. A relatively higher pressure was developed by the left ventricle of the patient with chronic congestive heart failure than that of the normal subject to eject much less blood. (From *Am. Heart J.*, *53*:665, 1957.)

tient with congestive heart failure are shown in Figures 101 and 102. Generally, higher pressure was developed by the hearts of the patients with congestive heart failure than by those of the control subjects in the hot and humid environment (Table 13).

Despite the development of a considerably higher ventricular pressure, the heart of the patient with congestive heart failure was unable to increase the volume of blood ejected to the same degree as the heart of the normal subject. In other words, a higher pressure was developed by the hearts of the patients with congestive heart failure than by those of the control subjects to eject less blood. This phenomenon is demonstrated by the pressure-volume diagrams shown in Figures 103 and 104.

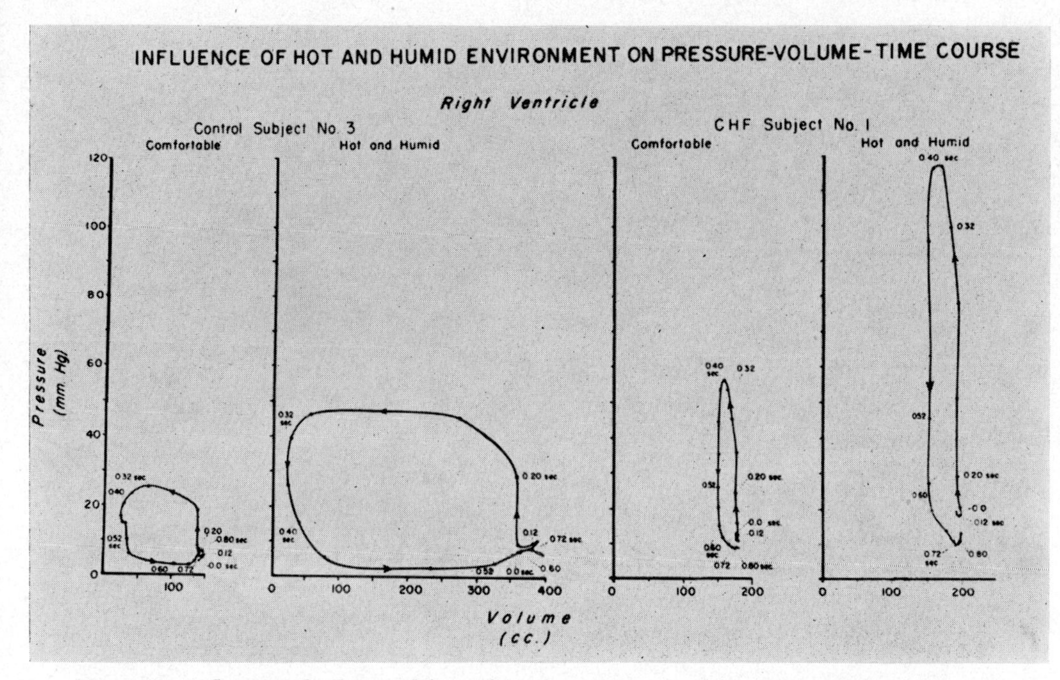

Fig. 103. Influence of a hot and humid environment on volume-pressure-time diagrams of the right ventricle for the representative control subject and the patient with chronic congestive heart failure shown in Figures 101 and 102. The more vertical loops for the patient with heart failure were characteristic for both ventricles of all patients with congestive heart failure. This vertical configuration of the loops is further evidence of the development of a relatively high pressure by the myocardium in order to eject a relatively small volume of blood per stroke. The area enclosed by these curves is an index of the work produced by the myocardium for that cardiac cycle. (From *Am. Heart J.*, *53*:665, 1957.)

Pressure-Volume Diagrams. The pressure-volume diagrams of patients with heart failure were characteristically more "vertical" than those of normal subjects (Figs. 103, 104). This vertical configuration of the pressure-volume loops is further evidence of the development of a relatively high pressure by the myocardium in order to eject a relatively small volume of blood per stroke. The area within the loop is an index of the manifested work of the heart per cardiac cycle.

Accumulated Mechanical Work. Integration of the pressure-volume diagram provides the time-course curve of accumulated mechanical work. The heart of the control subject was able to perform relatively more work at rest in a comfortable environment than that of the patient with congestive heart failure (Fig. 105). Although the cardiac work increased in all subjects studied when the environment was made hot and humid, the increase was much more pronounced in the control subjects. Since subjects with congestive heart failure become clinically worse in a hot and humid environment, it must be assumed that the increase in heart work was not adequate to maintain homeostasis. THE FAILURE TO ACHIEVE THE NECESSARY LEVELS OF CARDIAC OUTPUT AND WORK MAY BE THE

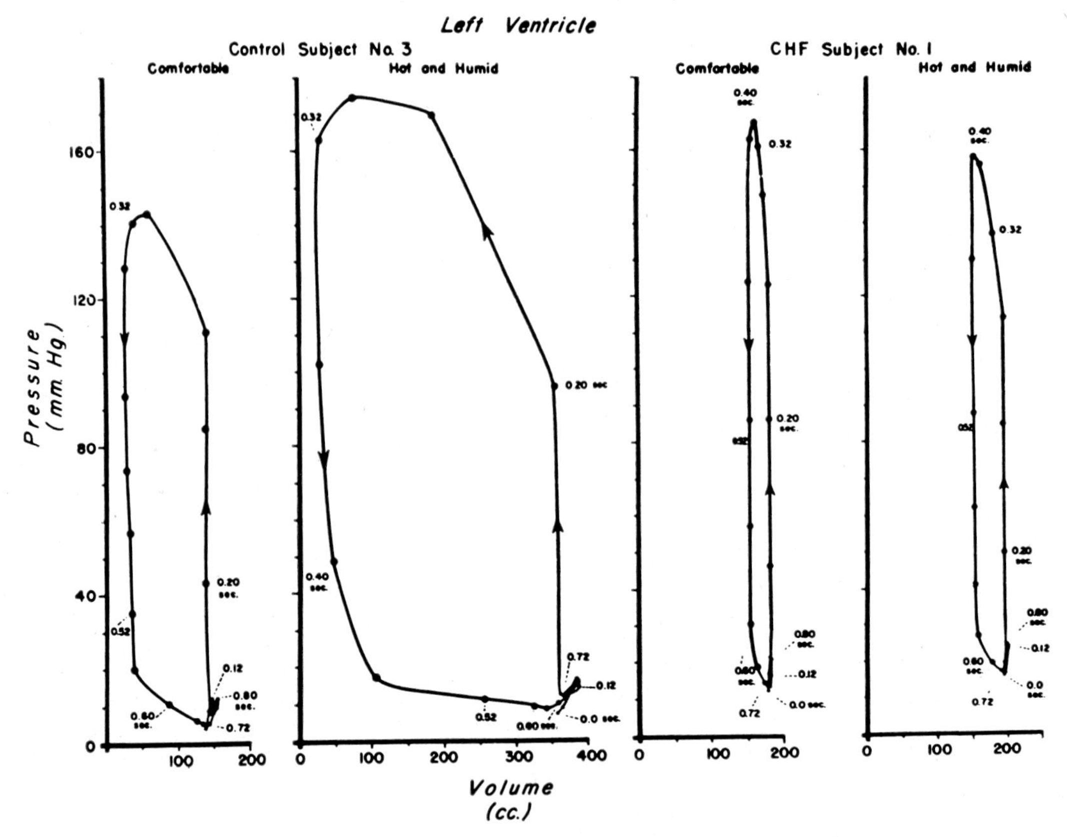

Fig. 104. Influence of a hot and humid environment on volume-pressure-time "loops" of the left ventricle for the same control subject and patient with chronic congestive heart failure shown in Figure 101. (From *Am. Heart J.*, 53:665, 1957.)

FUNDAMENTAL PHYSIOLOGIC EXPRESSION OF CONGESTIVE HEART FAILURE.

Alterations in Myocardial Tension. Tension of the wall of the ventricles may be expressed as:

$$T = \frac{RP}{2}, \quad (15)$$

where R is the radius of a spherical-shaped ventricle and P is the intraventricular pressure.

The time course of tension in dynes/cm² represents the tension developed by the walls of the ventricles during the cardiac cycle (Fig. 106). This assumption that the ventricles are spherical is obviously erroneous but convenient for these discussions. In most instances the time course of tension in the ventricular wall was greater for the patients with dilated hearts and heart failure than for the normal subjects (Fig. 106). With exposure to a hot and humid environment the tension developed by the walls of the ventricles increased in both groups of subjects but to a greater degree in the patients with chronic congestive heart failure. In congestive heart failure, because of cardiac dilatation and a residual or end-diastolic volume greater than normal, tension in the wall of the ventricles tended to be greater and the ventricles tended to be less efficient than in a normal-sized heart.

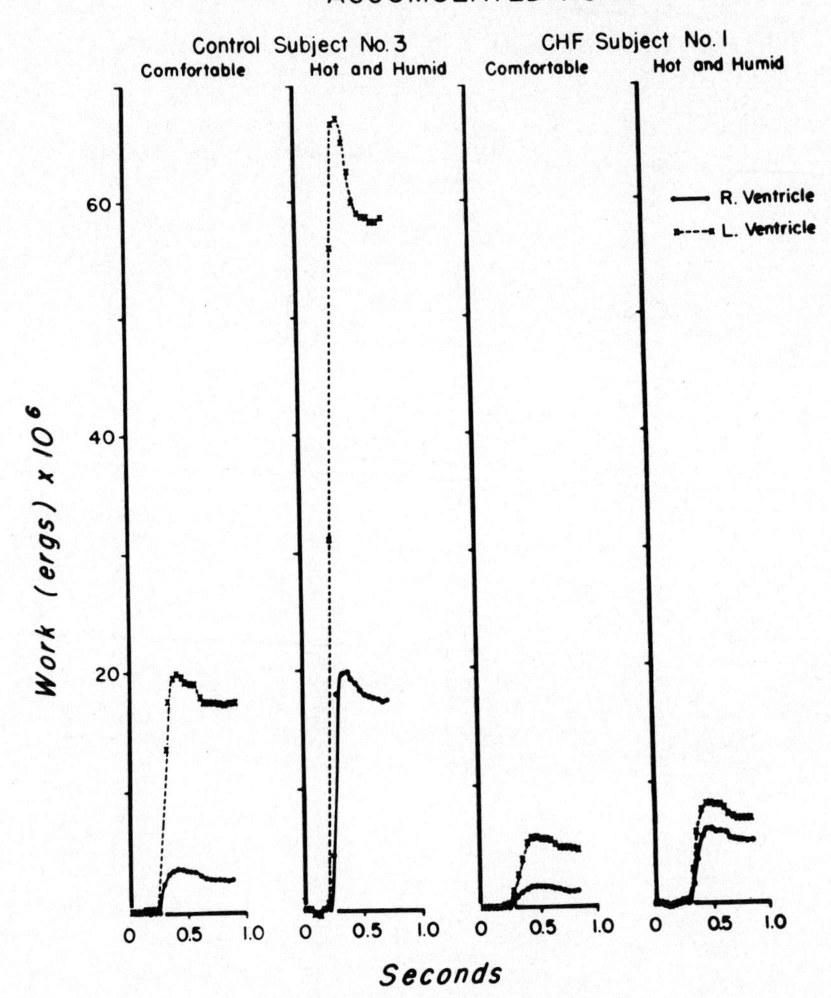

Fig. 105. Influence of a hot and humid environment on the time course of accumulated work for the right and left ventricles of the same subjects shown in Figures 103 and 104. (From *Am. Heart J.*, 53:665, 1957.)

CARDIAC OUTPUT, WORK AND POWER IN SUBJECTS EXPOSED TO WARM AND HUMID SUMMER WEATHER

The studies above were performed at extreme levels of atmospheric heat and humidity. However, it was also important to know if warm and humid weather, such as is encountered in the wards of the Charity Hospital in New Orleans during the hot summer months of July and August, produces a similar increase in cardiac output and work. To investigate this problem studies similar to those just described were performed on patients at rest in bed in the wards of the hospital during the tropical climate of midsummer. For contrast, the same patients were studied again in a cool and comfortable air-conditioned

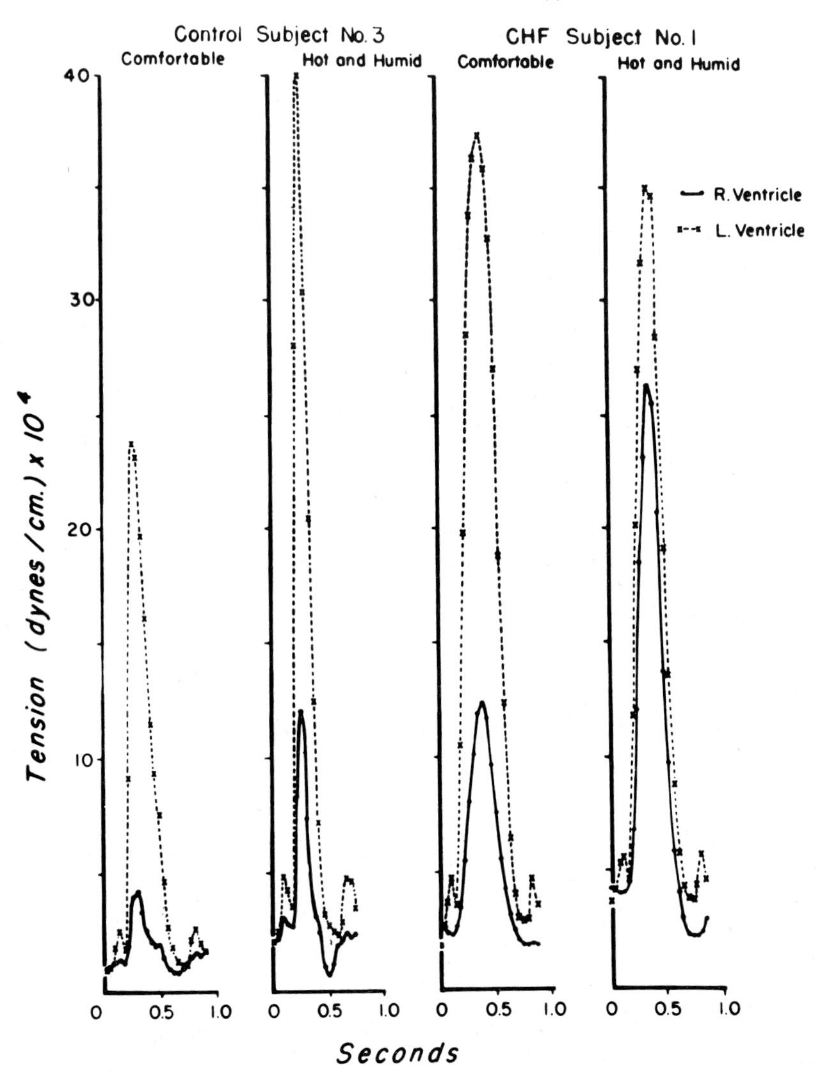

Fig. 106. Influence of a hot and humid environment on the time course of tension developed in the walls of both ventricles of the same subjects shown in Figure 105. In the patient with congestive heart failure, relatively more tension developed to eject less blood per stroke than in the control subject. (From *Am. Heart J.*, *53*:665, 1957.)

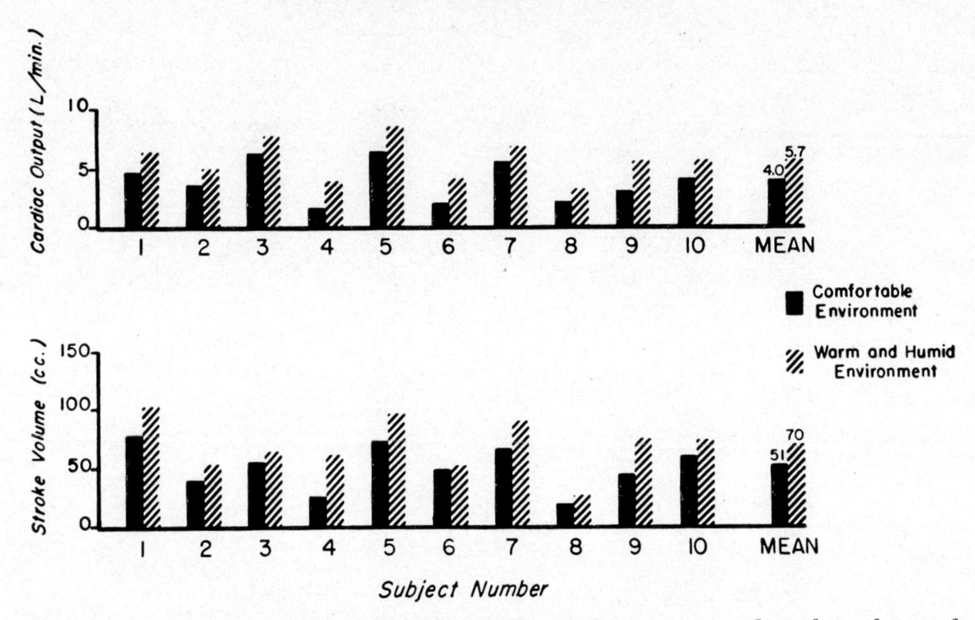

Fig. 107. Influence of tropical weather on the cardiac output and stroke volume of 10 subjects resting in bed in a comfortable air-conditioned ward and in a hot and humid ward open to the summer weather of New Orleans. (From *Arch. Int. Med.*, *104*:553, 1959.)

TABLE 14

INFLUENCE OF TROPICAL WEATHER ON CARDIAC OUTPUT OF 10 ADULT NEGRO PATIENTS AT REST IN HOSPITAL

Subject No.	*Cool Ward* L/Min.	*Cardiac Output Warm Ward* L/Min.	*Increase* %
1	4.7	6.4	36
2	3.6	5.0	39
3	6.4	7.8	22
4	1.6	3.9	144
5	6.5	8.6	32
6	2.0	4.1	105
7	5.6	6.8	21
8	2.2	3.2	45
9	3.0	5.6	87
10	4.1	5.7	39
Mean	4.0	5.7	57

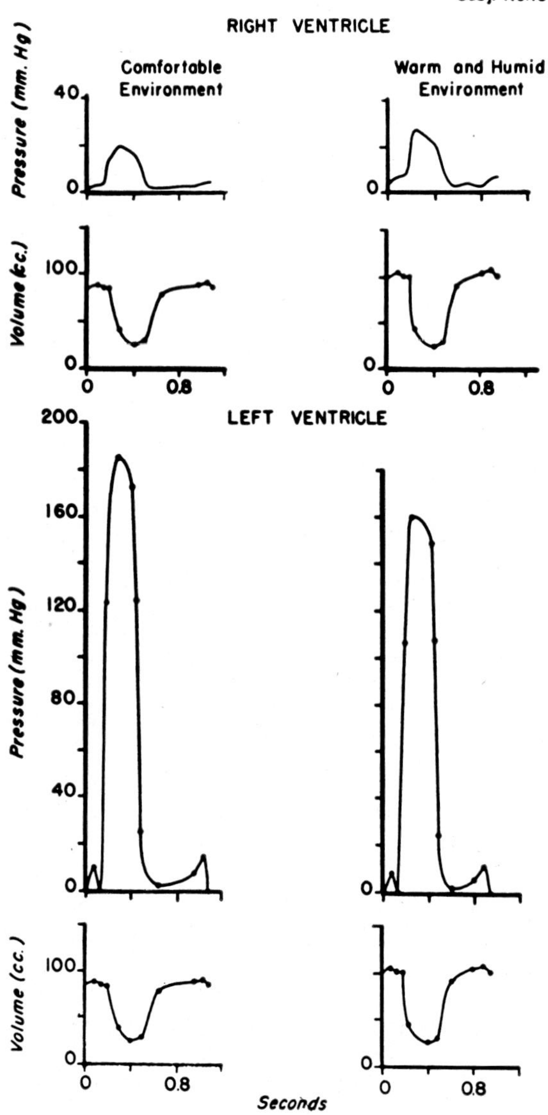

Fig. 108. Influence of tropical weather on the time courses of pressure and volume of both ventricles of a representative subject without cardiovascular disease. (From *Arch. Int. Med., 104*:553, 1959.)

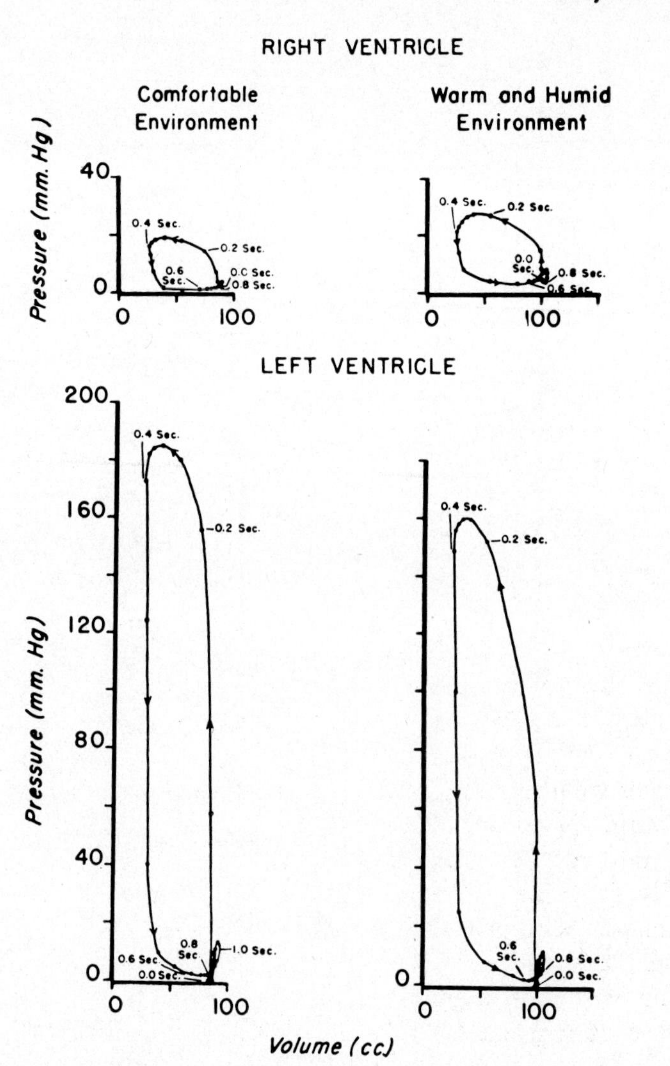

Fig. 109. Influence of tropical weather on the pressure-volume diagram of both ventricles for the same subject and under the same environmental conditions shown in Figure 108. (From *Arch. Int. Med.*, *104*:553, 1959.)

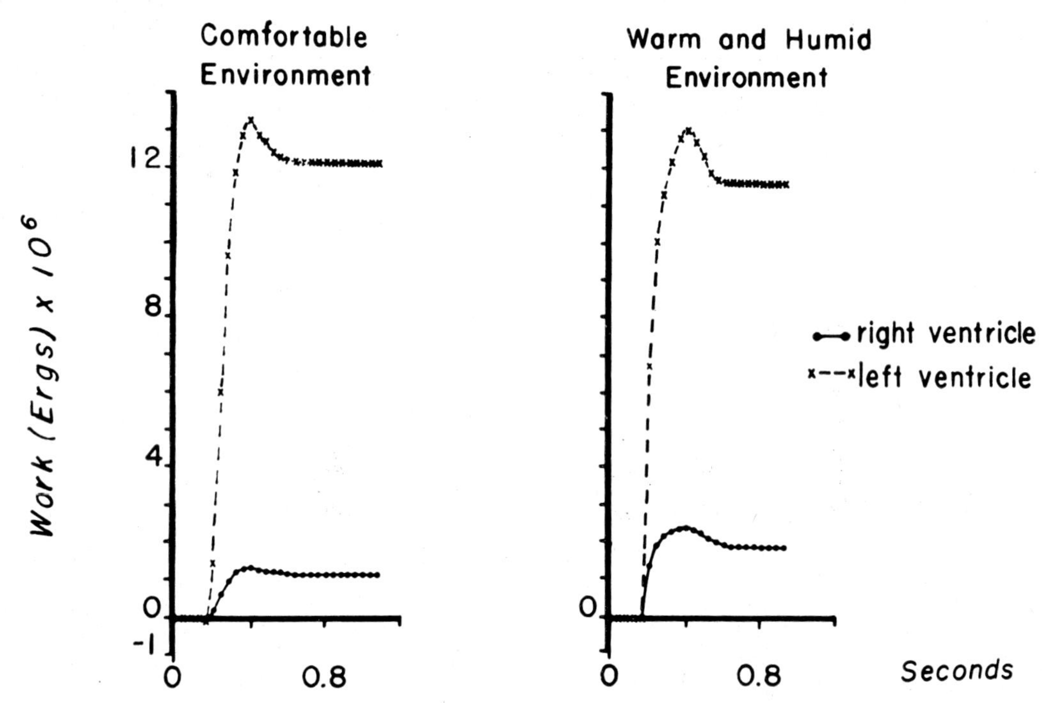

Fig. 110. Influence of tropical weather on the time course of accumulated work of both ventricles for the same subject and environmental conditions shown in Figures 108 and 109. (From *Arch. Int. Med.,* *104*:553, 1959.)

ward. Ten patients without evidence of congestive heart failure were studied.

The *mean cardiac output* was 57% greater in the warm and humid ward open to the summer weather than in the air-conditioned ward (Fig. 107, Table 14). The pulse rate for the group remained essentially the same in the non-air-conditioned and air-conditioned environments. Thus, the cardiac output was greater in the warm and humid environment because of a greater stroke volume.

The *pressure* developed by the myocardium of both ventricles was generally greater in the warm and humid environment than in the cool, air-conditioned one. In some instances the pressure in one ventricle increased, whereas that in the other remained the same or decreased (Fig. 108). When the ventricular pressure decreased, the increase in cardiac output was actually associated with a decrease in cardiac work. Thus, an increase in cardiac output is not necessarily associated with an increase in cardiac work. Furthermore, if pulmonary and systemic arterial pressures change discordantly, the work of one ventricle may increase while that of the other may remain the same or decrease. The pressure-volume diagrams (Fig. 109) and time-course curves of accumulated work (Fig. 110) and power (Fig. 111) showed an increase of these parameters in a warm and humid environment. They also demonstrated the benefits of air-conditioning on the heart inasmuch as a cool environment favored rest of the heart.

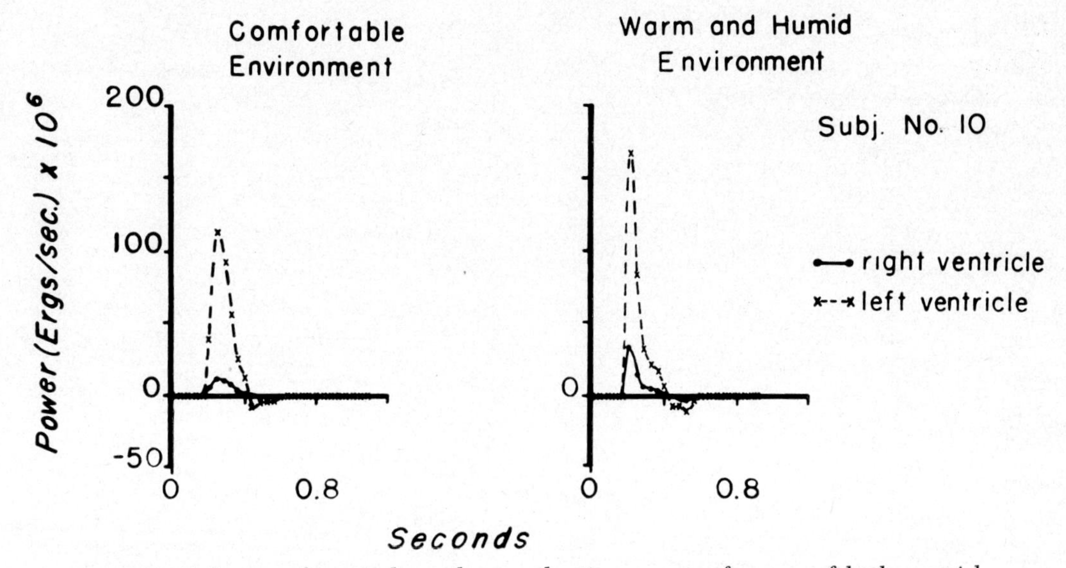

Fig. 111. Influence of tropical weather on the time course of power of both ventricles for the same subject and environmental conditions shown for Figure 110. (From *Arch. Int. Med.*, *104*:553, 1959.)

PATHOPHYSIOLOGIC INTERPRETATIONS

A hot and humid environment increases cardiac output, stroke volume, mechanical and physiologic cardiac work, and tension upon the walls of the ventricles. These changes are associated with thermal regulation. A subject lying supine in bed in a warm and humid environment may increase his cardiac work without exercise and without movement. If cardiac rest is indicated as a therapeutic measure, placing the patient at rest in a warm and humid environment (as, for example, a non-air-conditioned hospital ward in midsummer) may actually increase rather than decrease cardiac work. Thus, the paradox arises in which the body is at rest but the heart is performing an excessive amount of work.

One of the pathophysiologic expressions of the increase in cardiac work is the development of acute left ventricular failure in patients with cardiac disease in a hot and humid environment. Whenever elimination of body heat is impaired, vasodilatation of the vessels of the skin develops with increased cardiac rate, more rapid circulation, and greater cardiac output associated with an increase in cardiac work. Thermal stimulation in the presence of impaired cardiac reserve due to heart disease might be expected to produce a clinical syndrome of acute left ventricular failure. The increased burden of thermoregulation imposed by a hot and humid environment is in many ways analogous to a form of strenuous exercise. In addition, patients in congestive heart failure have lower rates of sweating than normal (Chapter 4). In this type of patient thermal stress results in a vicious cycle in which the cardiac output increases in order to eliminate heat, but the failure to sweat properly impairs heat loss and heat may actually be absorbed from the environment, which, in turn, results in a need for still greater cardiac work. Such a chain of events may kill the patient. On the other hand, relief from the thermal burden often results in a dramatic improvement in the clinical state of the patient. A patient awakened from sleep because of paroxysmal nocturnal dyspnea may gain relief from his symptoms by walking to an open window or a porch where the cool air permits heat loss to occur without stress upon the heart and circulation.

Theoretic considerations presented some years ago (7) provide an explanation for the difficulty with thermal regulation experienced by patients with dilated hearts. In the normal heart during systole the intraventricular pressure rises without an increase in the tension of the myocardial fibers. Thus, the normal-sized heart can reduce its tension during contraction as systole progresses and still maintain a normal level of blood pressure. On the other hand, the dilated heart with an increased end-diastolic volume must work progressively harder throughout systole because myocardial tension must be increased to increase pressure as systole progresses to maintain cardiac output (8). When it is necessary for the dilated heart to increase cardiac output, as, for example, upon exposure to thermal stress, the muscle fibers must contract with still greater tension, a definite work handicap which is not imposed upon the normal-sized heart.

Strenuous exercise or even moderate physical exertion, such as performing

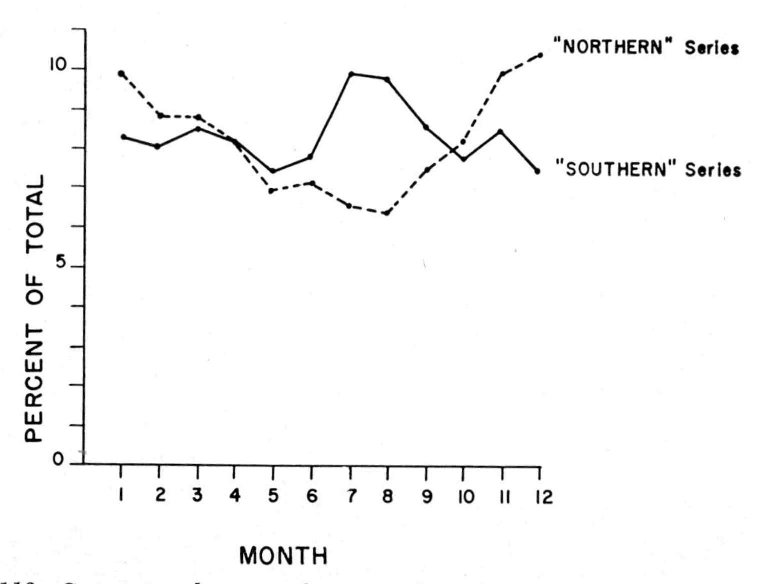

Fig. 112. Comparison between the seasonal incidence of coronary occlusion in nine northern cities ((Philadelphia (12, 13), Cincinnati (14), New York City (15), Kentuckiana Area (16), Boston (17), Los Angeles (18), Pittsburgh (19), Chicago (20) and Detroit (21))) and in two southern cities ((New Orleans (9) and Dallas (10))).

chores around the home or garden, results in more stress upon the cardiovascular system on hot and humid days than on cool ones. With acclimatization, however, man can perform more work with less physiologic disturbance than he can when he is not acclimatized. However, even acclimatized normal subjects often cannot establish a satisfactory steady physiologic state in a hot and humid environment.

Acute coronary occlusion is a partially meteorotropic disease. In the temperate regions of the United States the incidence of coronary occlusion is higher in winter than in summer (9). However, in the subtropical areas of this country where this problem has been studied, the incidence of coronary occlusion has been found to be higher in the summer than in the winter (Fig. 112) (9, 10). In New Orleans approximately 22% of the days each year have a maximal temperature of 90° F. or above, whereas only 0.2% of the days have a minimal temperature of 32° F. or below. Thus, the hot and humid summer weather of New Orleans constitutes climatic stress. The winters which are relatively mild do not impose an added burden on the heart.

In the northern United States the harsh winters are associated with greater climatic stress than the relatively mild summers. A high metabolic rate develops in cold climates in order to maintain body temperature. The increased metabolic rate, the high incidence of respiratory infections, and periods of increased physical exertion during the winter months combine to impose a burden on the heart. The demand placed on the heart of patients with cardiac disease may exceed the heart's ability to perform work and may result in the development of congestive heart failure or myocardial infarction. During the summer months sudden tropical inflows ("heat waves") may also result in cardiac stress, particularly if the metabolic rate is still high. During the first few days of a "heat wave" the number of patients admitted to hospital with myocardial infarction increases. Fortunately, "heat waves" are of relatively short duration. Also, during seasonal summer weather the cool nights provide relief from thermal stress. Thus, in the northern United States, except during sudden, severe and prolonged heat waves, the greatest climatic burden is placed on the cardiovascular system during the winter months.

There is, of course, a certain natural incidence of myocardial infarction; it is upon this "natural incidence" that climatic stress acts. Because the period of greatest climatic stress in New Orleans is the summer, it is in that season that the greatest number of acute coronary occlusions occur. In the northern areas of this country the period of greatest climatic stress is during the cold months of the year so that the greatest incidence of myocardial infarction is during the winter.

CINICAL APPLICATIONS

The patient with cardiac disease must be protected as much as possible from climatic stress. During periods of hot and humid weather the patient should be advised to avoid physical exertion. Air-conditioning of the home and work area is desirable. However, if this is impractical, at least the bedroom should be air-conditioned in order to eliminate the burden of heat dissipation during sleep and insure cardiac rest. As already indicated, during hot and humid weather the heart may be performing excessive work even with the body at complete rest.

A patient who sustains an acute insult to the cardiovascular system should be placed in a comfortable environment. If the hospital is not air-conditioned, an oxygen tent may be used for this purpose. A protodiastolic gallop rhythm may persist despite adequate digitalis, diuretic therapy and bed rest in a patient with congestive heart failure who is exposed to hot and humid weather. Moving the patient to a cool, comfortable environment may result in disappearance of the gallop rhythm and improvement in the clinical state. Also, simply moving a patient with congestive heart failure from a hot and humid environment to a cool and comfortable one may produce a diuretic response.

The frequency of anginal attacks may be increased by hot and humid weather, whereas it appears to be decreased by mildly warm (balmy) weather.

Cold weather is also stressful to the cardiovascular system. The demands placed on the heart for a greater cardiac output to maintain a high metabolic rate may not be tolerated by patients with cardiac disease. Physical exertion during exposure to cold weather may greatly increase cardiac work. The development of coronary thrombosis while shoveling snow is well known. Under such circumstances other mechanisms in addition to the cold weather may be responsible for the coronary occlusion. Among these is the possibility of the syndrome mentioned by Raab called "loafer's heart" (11). Since many people who shovel snow do not routinely perform heavy physical work, the unusual exertion may cause the release of excessive amounts of sympathetic amines into a system which is not prepared to detoxify these products at a rate rapid enough to prevent cardiovascular damage. Patients with heart disease should be advised against undue physical exertion during cold weather. The clothing should be warm but at the same time light. This can be accomplished by wearing several layers of light clothing. The air between each layer of clothing is an efficient insulator of body heat.

The greatest degree of cardiac stress is generally experienced during the first few days of either a tropical or polar inflow. The physiologic adjustments to the new weather conditions require increased cardiac work. Patients with heart disease should be taught the importance and dangers of these climatic influences. Since modern engineering makes it possible to maintain a stable microclimate, it is possible for patients with heart disease to avoid the harmful effects of sudden changes due to weather fronts. Because of the availability of accurate daily weather forecasts as well as long range weather forecasts, it is possible to plan necessary activities for periods during which weather conditions are stable. Socioeconomic factors determine in large measure how completely the adverse weather conditions can be avoided or modified. The patient with heart disease can be taught the importance of avoiding climatic stress. He should, through his own ingenuity, be able to modify his microclimate to avoid harmful climatic influences.

REFERENCES

1. Burch, G. E. and DePasquale, N.: Influence of air conditioning on hospitalized patients. *J.A.M.A.*, *170*:160, 1959.

2. Berenson, G. S. and Burch, G. E.: The response of patients with congestive heart failure to a rapid elevation in atmospheric temperature and humidity. *Am. J. M. Sc., 223:*45, 1952.

3. Threefoot, H. K.: The response of the venous pressure of man to a hot and humid environment. *Am. J. M. Sc., 224:*643, 1952.

4. Burch, G. E. and Hyman, A.: Influence of a hot and humid environment upon cardiac output and work in normal man and in patients with chronic congestive heart failure at rest. *Am. Heart J., 53:*665, 1957.

5. Burch, G. E. and Hyman, A.: A study of the influence of tropical weather on output of volume, work and power by the right and left ventricles of man at rest in bed. *Am. Heart J., 57:*247, 1959.

6. Burch, G. E., DePasquale, N., Hyman, A. and DeGraff, A. C.: Influence of tropical weather on cardiac output, work and power of right and left ventricles of man resting in hospital. *Arch. Int. Med., 104:*553, 1959.

7. Burch, G. E., Ray, C. T. and Cronvich, J. A.: The George Fahr Lecture; certain mechanical peculiarities of the human cardiac pump in normal and diseased states. *Circulation, 5:*504, 1952.

8. Burch, G. E.: Theoretic considerations of the time course of pressure developed and volume ejected by the normal and dilated left ventricle during systole. *Am. Heart J., 50:*352, 1955.

9. De Pasquale, N. P. and Burch, G. E.: The seasonal incidence of myocardial infarction in New Orleans. *Am. J. M. Sc., 242:*468, 1961.

10. Heyer, H. E., Teng, H. C. and Barris, W.: Increased frequency of acute myocardial infarction during summer months in warm climate; study of 1,386 cases from Dallas, Texas. *Am. Heart J., 45:*741, 1953.

11. Raab, W., Silva, P. de P. e and Starcheska, Y. K.: Adrenergic and cholinergic influences on the dynamic cycle of the normal human heart. *Cardiologia, 33:*350, 1958.

12. Wood, F. C. and Hedley, O. F.: The seasonal incidence of acute coronary occlusion in Philadelphia. *M. Clin. North America, 19:*151, 1935.

13. Hedley, O. F.: Five years' experience (1933-1937) with mortality from acute coronary occlusion in Philadelphia. *Ann. Int. Med., 13:*598, 1939.

14. Bean, W. B. and Mills, C. A.: Coronary occlusion, heart failure, and environmental temperatures. *Am. Heart J., 16:*701, 1938.

15. Master, A. M., Dack, S. and Jaffe, H. L.: Factors and events associated with onset of coronary artery thrombosis. *J.A.M.A., 109:*546, 1937.

16. Weiss, M. M.: Seasonal incidence of acute myocardial infarction in Kentuckiana area. *J. Kentucky M. A., 51:* 14, 1953.

17. Bean, W. B.: Infarction of heart; morphological and clinical appraisal of 300 cases; predisposing and precipitating conditions. *Am. Heart J., 14:*684, 1937.

18. Hoxie, H. J.: Seasonal incidence of coronary occlusion in mild climate; study based upon autopsy material. *Am. Heart J., 19:*475, 1940.

19. Mullins, W. L.: Age incidence and mortality in coronary occlusion; review of 400 cases. *Pennsylvania M. J., 39:*322, 1936.

20. Mintz, S. S. and Katz, L. N.: Recent myocardial infarction; analysis of 572 cases. *Arch. Int. Med., 80:*205, 1947.

21. Smith, F. J., Keyes, J. W. and Denham, R. M.: Myocardial infarction: study of acute phase in 920 patients. *Am. J. M. Sc., 221:*508, 1951.

XII

THE EFFECT OF THERMAL STRESS ON RENAL FUNCTION

THE kidneys contribute significantly to the maintenance of homeostasis in man exposed to a hot and stressful environment. The ability of the normal kidney to retain or excrete electrolytes and water according to body needs assures a healthy internal milieu in spite of thermal stress. Surprisingly little is known, however, concerning renal function in the adaptation to a hot and humid environment by normal man, and even less is known for diseased man. The influence of a comfortable and a warm and humid environment upon the rates of excretion of tritium (H^3), water (H_2O), chloride (Cl^{35}), radioisotopic chloride (Cl^{36}), sodium (Na^{23}), radiorubidium (Rb^{86}) and potassium (K^{39}) in normal subjects and in patients with congestive heart failure was studied in order to learn some of the effects of thermal stress on renal physiology.

These investigations were conducted on nine subjects under controlled metabolic conditions in an air-conditioned and a non-air-conditioned ward of the Charity Hospital in New Orleans during the midsummer of 1956. The dietary intake, serum concentration, space and mass and urinary excretion of H^3, Cl^{35}, Cl^{36}, Na^{23}, Rb^{86} and K^{39} were observed continuously over a 26-day period (1). The mean temperature and relative humidity of the air-conditioned ward were 74.4° F. (70.1° to 80.2° F) and 73.4% (60% to 90%), respectively, whereas the mean temperature and relative humidity of the non-air-conditioned ward were 83.4° F. (69.0° to 94.0° F.) and 80% (47% to 98%), respectively. A maximal daily temperature of 90° F. or greater was recorded for the warm and humid ward on 21 of the 26 days of the study. The subjects spent approximately equal time in both environments.

The daily dietary intake of sodium, potassium and chloride as well as the caloric intake was kept constant, whereas water intake was allowed as desired.

Five of the nine subjects were in congestive heart failure. All five subjects received digitalis daily and four of the five received mercurial diuretics from time to time (1). One of the four control subjects received 30 mg. of prednisone daily.

URINARY CLEARANCE RATES

Time-course curves of urinary clearance of K^{39}, Rb^{86}, H^3, Cl^{35}, Cl^{36} and Na^{23} are shown in Figure 113. The qualitative and quantitative similarities between clearance rates of Rb^{86} and K^{39} are evident. Potassium was excreted preferentially over Rb^{86}, but Rb^{86} traced K^{39} reasonably well, as shown previously

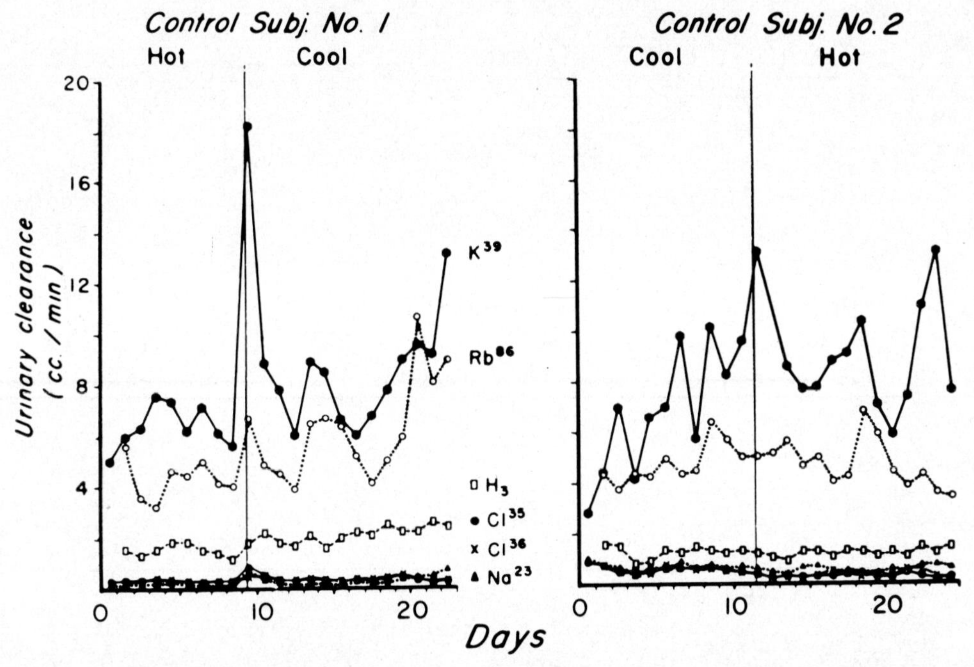

Fig. 113. Simultaneous time-course curves of urinary clearance of K^{39}, Rb^{86}, H^3, Cl^{35}, Cl^{36} and Na^{23} for two control subjects in a comfortable and in a hot and humid environment. (Modified from *J. Lab. & Clin. Med.*, 53:89, 1959.)

(2). The correlation coefficient was + 0.816 for these climatic studies.

Urinary Clearance of Rb^{86} and K^{39}. The average daily rates of clearance of potassium varied widely among the subjects and in the same subject from time to time, the minimal rate being about 4 ml. of plasma cleared per minute and the maximal rate 18 ml. per minute. The variations for the same subject were almost as great as the variations among the subjects. The mean rate of clearance of K^{39} and Rb^{86} was not influenced by the severity of the congestive heart failure nor by the environmental conditions (Figs. 114, 115). The administration of a mercurial diuretic had a variable effect upon the rates of clearance of K^{39} and Rb^{86}. The subject receiving prednisone had a negative potassium balance.

The absolute values of clearance of K^{39} reflected the variations in daily intake of potassium even though the day-to-day intake of potassium varied relatively little for any given subject. The minor variations in daily intake of K^{39} for any subject were insufficient to explain the marked differences in daily rates of clearance of potassium. Furthermore, the changes in intake and rate of clearance were not always directionally related. The progressive increase in the cumulative potassium balance noted in all except the subject receiving prednisone (Subject No. 6) is shown in Figure 116.

Urinary Clearance of Tritium. The rate of renal clearance of tritium varied directly with water intake and inversely with the rate of nonurinary water loss

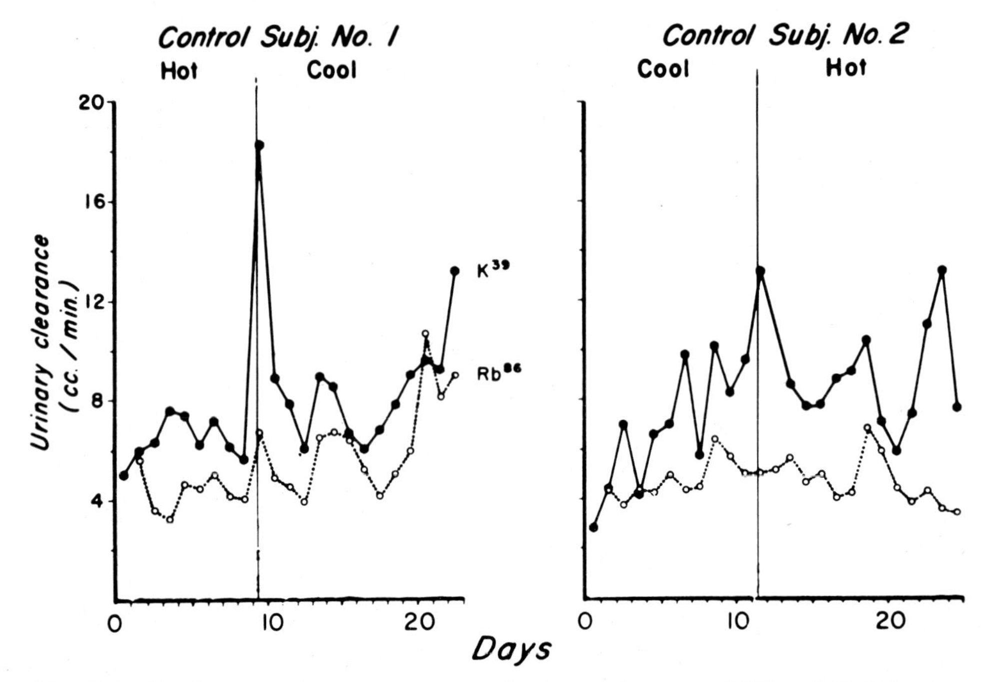

Fig. 114. Simultaneous time-course curves of urinary clearance of K^{39} and Rb^{86} for two normal subjects in a comfortable and a hot and humid environment. (Modified from *J. Lab. & Clin. Med.*, 53:89, 1959.)

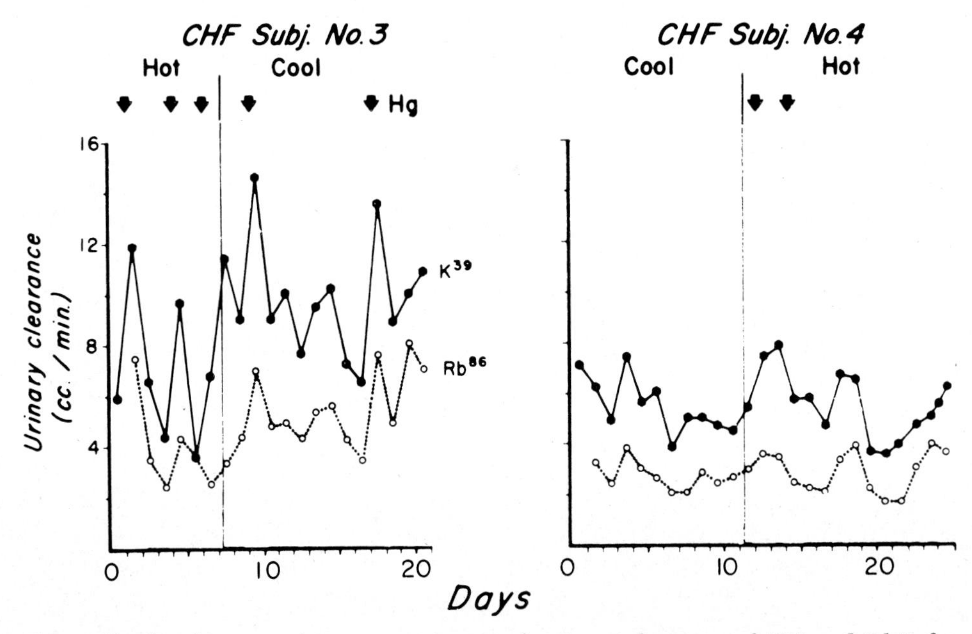

Fig. 115. Simultaneous time course curves of urinary clearance of K^{39} and Rb^{86} for two patients with congestive heart failure in comfortable and hot and humid environments. The arrows indicate administration of mercurial diuretics. (Modified from *J. Lab. & Clin. Med.*, 53:89, 1959.)

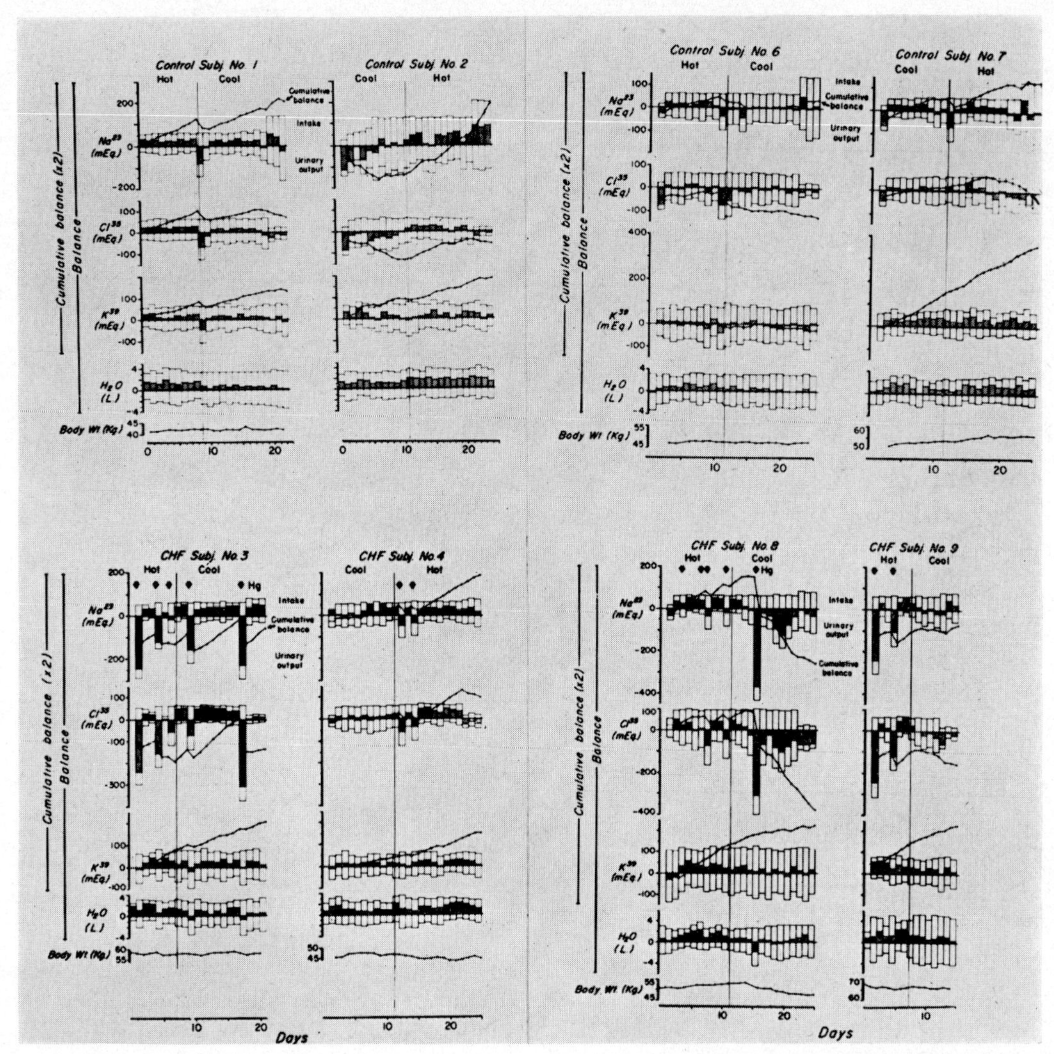

Fig. 116. Balance studies for Na^{23}, Cl^{35}, K^{39} and water in four normal subjects and four patients with congestive heart failure in comfortable and hot and humid environments. The ordinate values for cumulative balance are twice those shown for daily intake, urinary output and balance. (Modified from *J. Lab. & Clin. Med.*, *53*:89, 1959.)

(1). In two subjects (Subject Nos. 1 and 3) the rates of renal clearance of H^3 were slightly higher in the cool than in the warm environment (Fig. 117). Because there was little change in weight of the subjects, the rate of clearance of H^3 reflected the drinking habits of the individual. The subjects were allowed water as desired. They spontaneously drank sufficient quantities of water to maintain approximately the same rates of free water excretion for both the warm and humid and the cool environments. That H^3 is a suitable tracer of H^1 is indicated by the correlation coefficient of $+ 0.969$ for clearances of H^3 and H_2O. When mercurial diuretics or other factors increased the rates of clearance of Na^{23} and Cl^{35}, the clearance of H^3 also increased. Although the changes in the

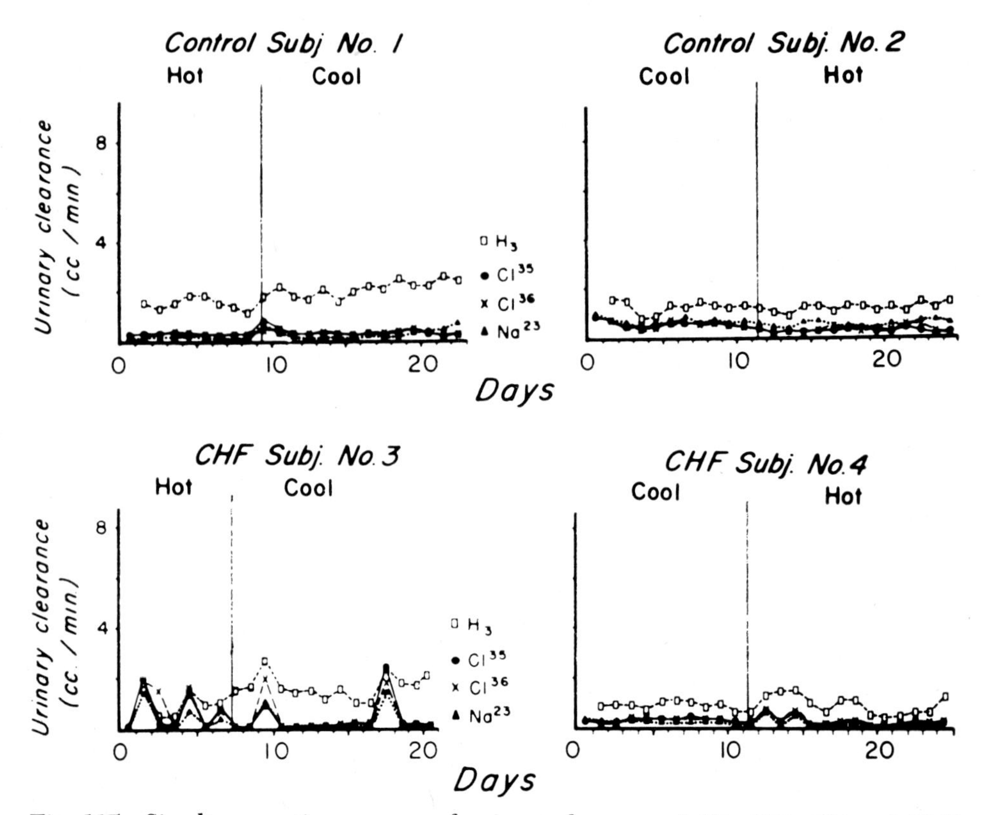

Fig. 117. Simultaneous time courses of urinary clearance of H^3, Cl^{35}, Cl^{36} and Na^{23} for two normal subjects and two patients with congestive heart failure in comfortable and hot and humid environments. (Modified from *J. Lab. & Clin. Med.*, *53*:89, 1959.)

clearance of Na^{23}, Cl^{35} and H^3 varied concordantly, they differed quantitatively.

Urinary Clearance of Cl^{36}, Cl^{35} and Na^{23}. The correlation coefficient for the rates of clearance of Cl^{35} and Cl^{36} was $+ 0.949$. This value should be unity, but the low level of counts of Cl^{36} in some specimens of urine was associated with errors in counting. The rates of clearance of Cl^{35} and Na^{23} were much lower than those of Rb^{86}, H^3 and K^{39} (Figs. 113, 117). The urinary clearance of chloride was generally greater than that of sodium. However, differences among subjects were related to dietary intake of these electrolytes as well as to the state of the congestive heart failure. There was no consistent effect of environment on the rates of urinary clearance of sodium or chloride. The effects of mercurial diuresis in some of the subjects made the effect of environment difficult to evaluate. The serum concentrations of chloride and sodium did not change significantly in any of the subjects.

The cumulative balances for Na^{23}, Cl^{35} and K^{39} for eight of the nine subjects studied are shown in Figure 116.

URINARY EXCRETION OF Cl^{35} AND K^{39} AS PERCENT OF CALCULATED MASS

The mass of Cl^{35} and of K^{39} was calculated from tracer dilution in four patients (two control subjects and two patients with congestive heart failure). The daily excretion was expressed as

TABLE 15

DAILY URINARY EXCRETION OF Cl^{35} AND K^{39} AS A PERCENT OF THE AVERAGE CALCULATED TOTAL MASS

	Cl^{35}			K^{39}*		
Subject Number	*Entire Study*	*Hot*	*Cold*	*Entire Study*	*Hot*	*Cold*
1	2.35	1.79	2.73	1.40	1.17	1.55
2	3.36	2.31	4.72	1.67	1.81	1.50
3†	4.29	6.48	3.19	1.96	1.48	2.20
4†	1.78	1.67	1.93	1.17	1.15	1.20

* Calculated from data on Rb^{86}.
† Congestive heart failure.

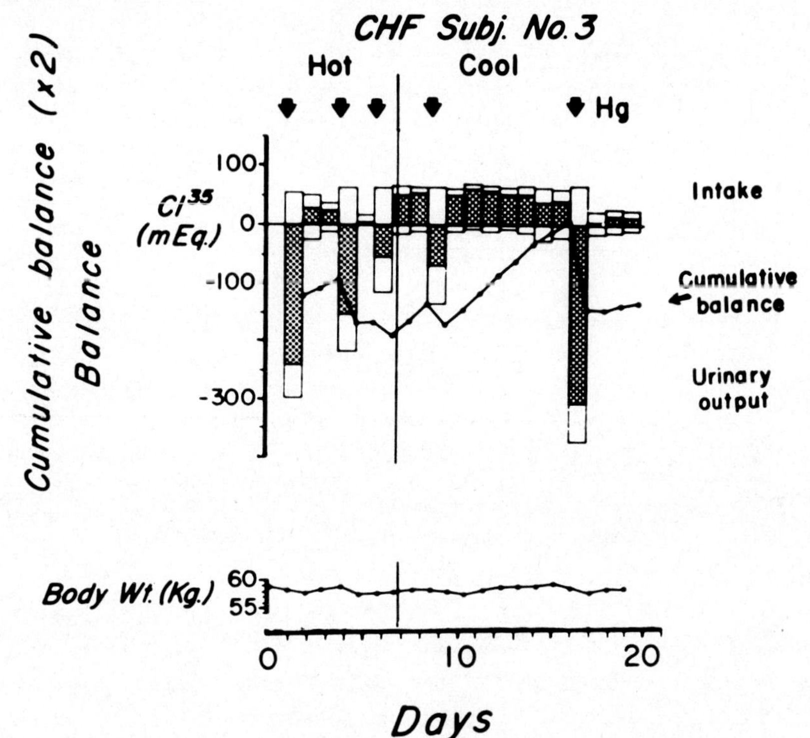

Fig. 118. Balance data for Cl^{35} in a patient with congestive heart failure in a comfortable and hot and humid environment receiving mercurial diuretics. See Figure 116 for explanation of ordinate values. (Modified from *J. Lab. & Clin. Med.*, 53:89, 1959.)

a percent of the "calculated" masses (Table 15). The excretion of chloride was expressed as a percent of the average daily M_t* (total body mass of stable electrolyte) for the entire study, whereas excretion of K^{39} was expressed as a percent of the estimated K^{39} mass during the period of days when this value was constant.

The excretion of Cl^{35} as a percent of calculated M_t for the two control subjects differed considerably (Table 15). Subject No. 1 excreted about 2% of her

*$M_t = S_t \times CM_t$ where M_t is calculated total chloride in grams, S_t is calculated chloride space in milliliter serum equivalents, and CM_t is serum concentration of Cl^{35} at time t, in grams per milliliter.

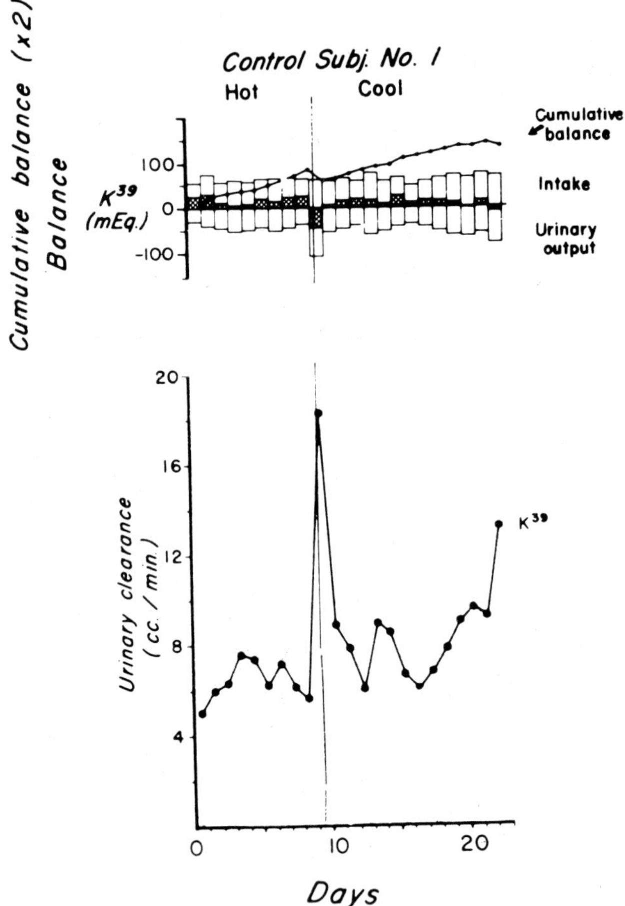

Fig. 119. Cumulative balance and urinary clearance of K^{39} for a normal subject in comfortable and hot and humid environments. (Modified from *J. Lab. & Clin. Med.,* 53:89, 1959.)

Cl^{35} mass daily with a peak rate noted on the day of transfer into the cool environment. Subject No. 2 excreted more chloride during exposure to the cool environment than during exposure to the hot and humid atmosphere. Subject No. 3 with congestive heart failure excreted slightly less than 1% of M_t on the days when she did not receive mercurial diuretics. The profound effect of mercurials on the excretion of chloride was demonstrated in this subject who excreted about 25% of the chloride calculated to be in her body during one day of mercurial diuresis (Fig. 118). The other patient with congestive heart failure (Subject No. 4) excreted about 2% of M_t daily while in the cool environment. In the hot and humid environment there was a decrease in the rate of excretion of Cl^{35} when a mercurial diuretic was not administered.

The time course of daily excretion of potassium expressed as a percent of the average calculated M_t varied directly with chloride on the days of mercurial diuresis. Environmental conditions had no effect on the rates of excretion of potassium except in Subject No. 1, who had a marked diuresis of K^{39} upon being transferred from the warm and humid to the air-conditioned ward (Fig. 119).

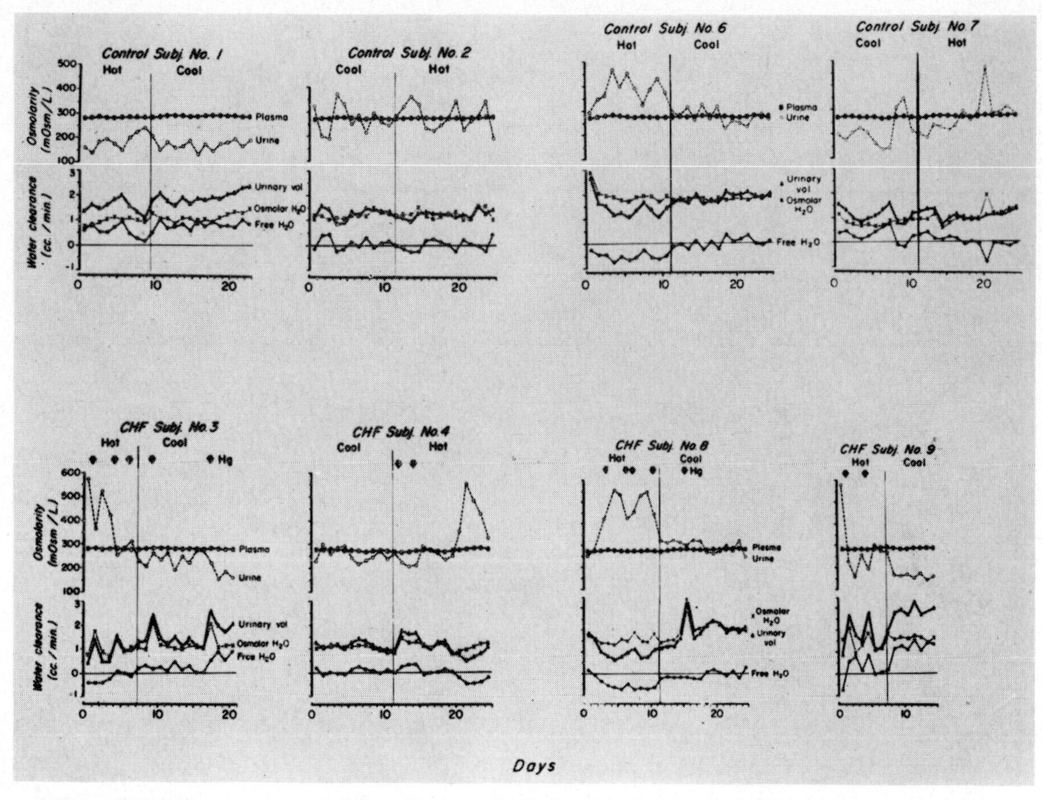

Fig. 120. Time courses of osmolarity of plasma and urine, urinary volumes, osmolar and free water clearances for the same subjects and environments shown in Figure 116. (Modified from *J. Lab. & Clin. Med.*, *53*:89, 1959.)

OSMOLAR EXCRETION AND GLOMERULAR FILTRATION

Osmolar Excretion. Plasma osmolarity changed very little throughout the entire period of the observations. This constancy was anticipated because of adequate water and electrolyte intake by all of the subjects. Urinary osmolarity, however, showed considerable variation among the subjects as well as for the same subject in the two environmental conditions (Fig. 120). The urinary osmolarity varied according to the electrolyte and water intake and was determined by the amount of electrolye and water that had to be excreted to maintain balance. In a hot and humid environment sweating would be expected to result in a rise in osmolarity of the urine. In all but two subjects (Subject Nos. 1 and 2) the urinary osmolarity was higher in the hot and humid environment than in the cool and comfortable one.

The time-course curves of average daily clearance rates of free water, osmolar water and total water expressed in milliliters per minute varied considerably (Fig. 120). The response to mercurial diuretics was not influenced by either a state of positive or negative free water clearance.

Free water, and thus total water excretion, reflected the difference between intake and nonurinary losses through the skin and respiratory tract. Since the subjects were allowed water as desired, free water excretion reflected drinking

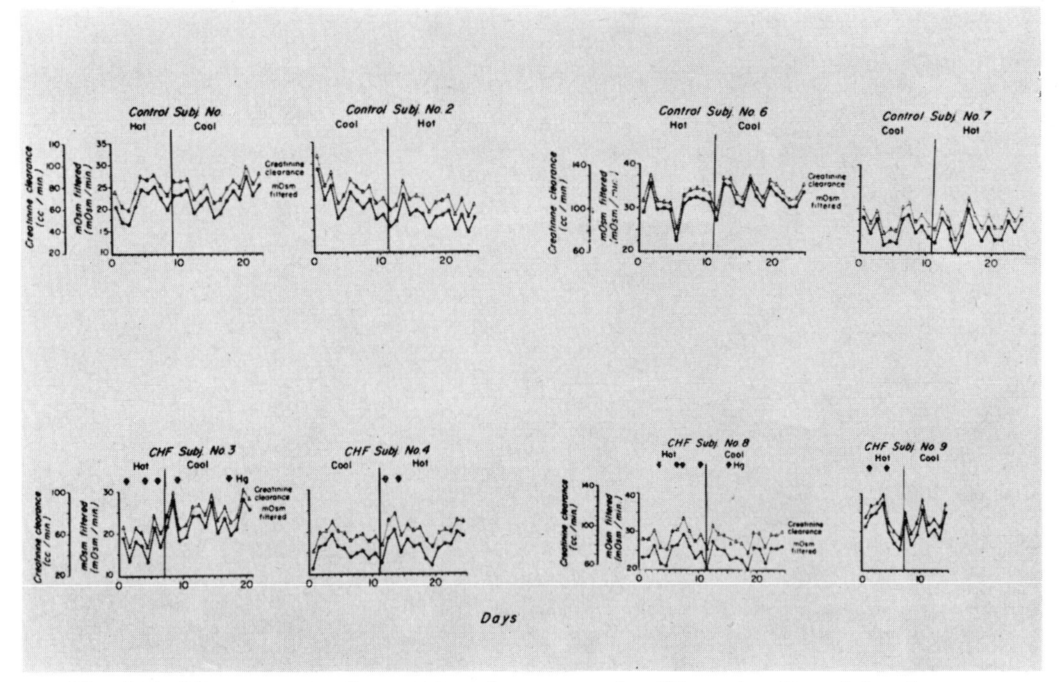

Fig. 121. Time courses of creatinine clearance and milliosmoles filtered for the same subjects and environments shown in Figures 116 and 120. (Modified from *J. Lab. & Clin. Med.*, 53:89, 1959.)

habits, which kept two of the subjects in a state of constant water diuresis even in a hot and humid environment.

Rate of Glomerular Filtration. The average daily glomerular filtration rate was measured by endogenous creatinine clearances. The time courses of glomerular filtration are shown in Figure 121. There were definite daily variations for the same subject. These variations were not influenced by osmolar load, the environment, nor mercurial or spontaneous diuresis; nor were they related to magnitude of osmolar, free or total water clearance rates. The average creatinine clearance was slightly higher in the cool environment (86.49 ml./min.) than in the warm and humid one (82.98 ml./min.). There were periods when the reverse was true in three of the subjects. The rates of creatinine clearance were as great in the patients with congestive heart failure as in the normal subjects. The patients with congestive heart failure showed less differences in glomerular filtration for the two environments than did the control subject.

PATHOPHYSIOLOGIC INTERPRETATIONS

The thermal stress involved in these studies was relatively mild. Nevertheless, certain differences in renal function were noted in the patients when they were in the air-conditioned and non-air-conditioned environments. Warm and humid summer weather resulted in an increase in the osmolarity of the urine and a tendency toward a negative free water clearance. Undoubtedly, these changes would have been greater if more intense thermal stimulation had been utilized or if the subjects had exerted themselves physically. Such a study was not practical since it would have required placing hospital patients in climatic rooms for long periods of time under metabolically controlled conditions.

Studies of renal function in natives of tropical regions would not provide much information concerning renal adaptation to heat because acclimatization would already exist. However, it is well known that when unacclimatized man is subjected to a hot and humid atmosphere there is an increase in the rate of sweating as well as a decrease in the chloride concentration in the sweat. Several days are required to reach a point of maximal conservation of chloride in sweat. This process apparently is mediated in part through the adrenal cortex. At the same time that the adrenal hormones are exerting their influence on the sweat glands to retain electrolytes, a similar influence is being exerted on the renal tubules.

The studies of Adolph on military personnel in the desert (3) provide information on renal function in acclimatized subjects. He found that the mean rate of urinary output was 935 cc./24 hr. for healthy males in the desert who were allowed all the water they wanted to drink. At the same time, the specific gravity of the urine averaged 1.027. This suggested that a small deficit of body water was necessary to stimulate drinking to compensate for the large quantities of water lost in the sweat or that the thirst mechanism and the electrolyte and water-controlling mechanism were adjusted to different levels. The urine flow of men living in the desert did not decrease proportionately with the body water deficit (3). Thus, under extreme deficits of body water Adolph found almost the same urine flow as under moderate deficits. Apparently, a certain amount of body water is obligated to solute excretion by the kidney so that little is gained in terms of water conservation by depriving the subject of water. Within limits the best method of saving water is to decrease solute excretion. This can be accomplished by a high carbohydrate diet. Such a diet spares protein catabolism which in turn decreases the amount of urea and ions the kidney must excrete. Reducing salt intake would also decrease urine solute excretion, but such a practice can be dangerous in a hot environment unless properly controlled.

Adolph found the concentration of chloride in the urine of men in the tropics to be the same as that of men in temperate climates (3). None of the individuals he studied had less than 34 mEq./L of chloride in the urine. There was no significant relationship between the specific gravity and the chloride content of the urine. Therefore, the specific gravity of urine is not a reliable index of salt depletion. Since the urine of men living in the desert is the most concentrated the body can produce, there is no advantage in drinking urine under conditions of water deprivation.

There is some evidence that acute renal colic caused by ureterolithiasis is more common during the hot months of the year than during the cool ones (4). This observation would seem consistent with the increase in urinary osmolarity found for the warm and humid environment.

The voluntary intake of water was of unusually large volume in some subjects acclimatized to the hot and humid environment (1). This increased intake of water continued for a few days after subjects were transferred to a cool evironment where extra requirements for water were not necessary. This "drinking habit" resulted in a large volume of dilute urine when the subjects were in the comfortably cool environment.

A diuresis is sometimes noted when patients are moved from a hot and humid environment to a cool, comfortable one. This is probably due in part to shifting of blood to the kidney. For example, studies in this laboratory on two normal subjects showed that renal blood flow measured by means of para-amino-hippuric acid decreased approximately 50% when the subjects were removed from a comfortable (25° C., 65% R.H.) to a hot and humid (42° C., 95% R.H.) environment. This reduction in renal flow apparently was due to a shift of blood from the viscera to the skin.

CLINICAL APPLICATIONS

A hot and humid environment produces a significant increase in extrarenal losses of water and electrolytes. This occurs even in patients at bed rest. The healthy kidney will conserve salt and water when extrarenal losses of these substances are excessive. On the other hand, the diseased kidney may not be able to conserve sodium, so that serious electrolyte difficulties may develop upon exposure to thermal stress. These considerations are particularly important in the patients receiving mercurial diuretics. For example, a patient who is being maintained on a low salt diet and frequent injections of a diuretic may become "salt-depleted" during the summer months when extrarenal losses of electrolytes are high. For this reason it is probably wise to allow this type of patient a moderate salt intake during the summer.

Patients with hypoadrenocorticism are unable to conserve electrolytes in the urine and may develop difficulty when sweating is profuse. These patients must be watched carefully during the summer months.

A patient with chronic renal disease and impaired renal function or renal insufficiency may experience no difficulty during the cool months of the year by maintaining a high fluid intake. However, in the summer, with large increases in extrarenal water loss, it may not be possible to maintain the fluid intake required to insure homeostasis by a kidney which has lost the ability to concentrate and dilute urine. It is not unusual to encounter such a problem during the warm and humid months of the summer. Placing such patients in an air-conditioned environment can be of great help toward re-establishing homeostasis and reducing the stresses on the physiologic mechanisms concerned with thermal regulation and water and electrolyte balance.

REFERENCES

1. Ray, C. T. and Burch, G. E.: Relationship of equilibrium of distribution, biologic decay rates, space and mass of H^3, Cl^{36} and Rb^{86} observed simultaneously in a comfortable and in a hot and humid environment in control subjects and in patients with congestive heart failure. *J. Lab. & Clin. Med.*, *53*:69, 1959.
2. Love, W. D. and Burch, G. E.: In vitro studies of aspects of the metabolism of sodium by human erythrocytes using $sodium^{22}$. *J. Lab. & Clin. Med.*, *41*:337, 1953.
3. Adolph, E. F.: *Physiology of Man in the Desert.* New York, Interscience Publishers, Inc., 1947.
4. Prince, C. L., Scardino, P. L. and Wolan, C. T.: Effect of temperature, humidity and dehydration on formation of renal calculi. *J. Urol.*, *75*:209, 1956.

XIII

GENERAL PHYSIOLOGIC RESPONSES TO THERMAL STIMULATION

As demonstrated in the preceding chapters, man maintains thermal equilibrium in spite of wide variations in environmental temperatures and humidities. The dermal, central and peripheral nervous, respiratory, cardiovascular and renal systems are among the many organ systems which participate in the physiologic adjustments necessary to maintain thermal balance. The endocrine and humoral and nervous systems integrate the many physiologic phenomena concerned with homeostasis. For example, sweating is initiated when the temperature of the blood reaching the hypothalamus exceeds a certain critical value (1). This critical temperature is undoubtedly involved in the process of acclimatization. The latent period required before a thermal stimulus will induce sweating is much shorter in subjects who are acclimatized to a hot environment than in those who are not (2). Also, by controlling the arteriovenous anastomoses in the skin the hypothalamus participates in the regulation of heat loss by radiation and convection. Again, the release of ACTH and other hormones in response to thermal stress prevents electrolyte depletion and insures the renal retention of sodium in thermally adapted man when sweating is excessive (3).

Physiologic adaptation to heat may fail in healthy man when he is exposed to too great a thermal stress or even when he is exposed to moderately hot environments for prolonged periods of time, especially if he is performing physical work. Illness, particularly chronic illness, reduces tolerance to thermal stress, so that adaptation fails sooner and at lower levels of environmental temperature in ill people than in healthy people.

The problem of thermal balance is simply a physical one in which heat gain must equal heat loss to maintain thermal balance. Man subjected to an extremely high environmental temperature and humidity, even for prolonged periods of time, would encounter no difficulty if heat loss could be maintained commensurate with heat production. Thermal difficulty arises when the process involved in maintaining heat loss fails.

To evaluate the clinical states of man related to thermal stress, the over-all physiologic reactions to increased body temperature must be known. This knowledge can then be applied to problems related to clinical, military, industrial and space medicine.

The experiments described in this chapter were designed to evaluate the general physiologic responses of man to

TABLE 16

ENVIRONMENTAL CONDITIONS NECESSARY TO INITIATE SWEATING IN NORMAL MAN RESTING QUIETLY IN A HOSPITAL TYPE BED*

				Before Sweating				*Sweating*			
Subject	*Age*	*Sex*	*Color*	*Temp.* (°C.)	*Relative Humidity* (%)	*Rate of Water Loss* mg. /cm.²/10 min. *Epigastrium*	*Forearm*	*Temp.* (°C.)	*Relative Humidity* (%)	*Rate of Water Loss* mg./cm.²/10 min. *Epigastrium*	*Forearm*
1	22	F	C	35	85	6.0	4.2	37.8	60	19.8	8.9
2	50	F	W	32.2	54	7.1	6.8	34.4	50	8.7	9.5
3	25	F	W	34.4	28	7.4	4.5	36.7	26	13.3	6.3
4	40	M	W	30.0	62	5.8	6.1	33.8	58	7.3	7.0
5	12	F	C	32.2	90	4.5	7.5	34.4	70	7.5	5.9
6	31	F	C	32.2	80	5.6	5.4	35.5	56	11.6	4.5
7	49	F	C	31.1	42	5.2	5.5	33.3	42	20.0	18.1
8	34	M	C	36.1	26	4.6	3.6	38.9	28	7.5	4.1
9	19	M	C	38.9	9.5	5.5	4.1	38.9	9	6.9	4.3
10	17	M	W	33.3	22	7.0	2.8	35.5	20	11.4	11.0
11	59	M	W	33.3	26	4.0	4.2	34.4	26	5.9	6.0
Mean				33.5	47.9	5.7	5.0	35.8	40.5	10.9	7.8
Max.				38.9	90	7.4	7.5	38.9	70	20.0	18.1
Min.				30.0	9.5	4.0	2.8	33.3	9	5.9	4.1

* The water lost before sweating is lost by diffusion. The onset of sweating in Subjects Nos. 5 and 6 showed local variations.

thermal stimulation and also to investigate some of the physical aspects of the relationship of heat loss to heat production. The studies show these responses to be merely a reaction to alterations in balance between heat production and heat loss.

THE INITIATION OF SWEATING

The most obvious reaction to exposure to a hot and humid environment is sweating. When ambient temperature exceeds body temperature, heat loss by radiation and convection can no longer occur; so heat must be lost by evaporation. The sweat provides for the loss of 0.59 Calorie for every gram of water vaporized. About 90% of the total heat lost by man subjected to high environmental temperatures is lost through the evaporation of sweat, and the remaining 10% is lost through the respiratory tract. The other avenues of heat loss already mentioned provide only negligible losses which can be ignored when calculating heat balance.

In order to learn the environmental temperature and relative humidity at which sweating is initiated in man, 11 normal subjects were studied in the experimental climatic room (Table 16) (4). After the subjects rested quietly for at least 60 minutes under comfortable environmental conditions (21° C., 50% R.H.), clothed only in a cotton gown, the rates of water loss from the skin of the epigastrium and volar surface of the right forearm were determined. The room temperature was then elevated 3° C. at a time and the relative humidity was changed in a variable fashion. After the subjects had been exposed to the new room conditions for 15 minutes, the rates of water loss were again measured. This procedure was continued until an environment was reached which was associated with a definite increase in the rates of water loss. Occasionally, as a check, the room temperature or humidity or both were lowered and the rates of water loss measured again. Then the temperature or humidity or both were raised again and another measurement of the rates of water loss obtained.

This method used to determine the moment at which sweating began was far more sensitive than merely observing the subjects for gross evidence of perspiration. Sweating was found, by direct collection, to be initiated at a lower temperature than that noted when the determinations depended upon the visible appearance of sweat on the skin.

The Sweating Threshold. The threshold level for sweating in normal man resting in bed was a temperature of 34.4° C. and a relative humidity of about 50%. Increased exercise and increased rate of heat production were accompanied by a proportionate lowering of the threshold. Generally, the onset of sweating coincided simultaneously for several skin areas. It is known that if sweating is induced by the application of a thermal stimulus to a localized area, the sweating will take place over the entire body surface. This indicates the reflex nature of sweating which depends in large part upon activation of the hypothalamic sweat center by warm blood. The time lag between the elevation in environmental temperature and the onset of sweating represents the latent period required to "arouse" the sweat center. Acclimatization to heat is accompanied by a shortening of this latent period.

The lower the relative humidity, the higher the air temperature required to initiate sweating. Thus, sweating was initiated by a temperature of about 36° C. when the relative humidity was 40% and 39° C. when the relative humidity was as low as 9%. This difference was probably due to the slight cooling effect of insensible water loss.

Cyclic Sweating. In one of the patients studied sweating was cyclic, i. e., it alternately occurred and ceased for about 15-minute periods, even though the room conditions remained unchanged. This suggests that sweating cooled the subject sufficiently to abolish the need for sweating for a certain period of time. The subject then accumulated heat and when a proper thermal threshold was reached sweating began again, the body was cooled, and then sweating stopped again. Such cyclic sweating conserves water and electrolytes and may represent ideal sweating.

REGIONAL VARIATIONS IN THE RATES OF SWEATING

The eccrine glands are distributed over the entire body except for the lips, glans penis, clitoris and prepuce. However, the number of glands as well as the secretory activity of the glands varies in different regions of the body (cf. Chapter 6).

The eccrine glands of the palms and soles and the apocrine glands of the axillae are usually not activated by heat but are readily stimulated by emotional disturbances. On the other hand, eccrine glands over the remainder of the body surface are stimulated by heat after a latent period but little by emotional stimuli. It is important to recognize these differences in order to understand regional variations of water loss.

Regional Variations in a Comfortable Environment. In a comfortable environment the areas of the body with the highest rates of water loss are, in descending order, soles of the feet, palms of the hands, finger tip (2RF), lateral surface of the arm, face, forehead, axilla, leg and epigastrium (Chapter 4, Fig. 11) (5). It should be noted that the palms and soles have the highest rates of water loss in a *comfortable* environment. Thus, sweating from these areas is not dependent upon thermal stimulation. Keeping the palms and soles moist serves a useful purpose in helping man to perform delicate tactile procedures as well as in grasping.

Regional Variations in a Hot and Humid Environment. In a *hot* and *humid* environment the highest rates of water loss, in descending order, were from the axilla, forehead, lateral surface of the arm, finger tip (2RF), palms of the hands, soles of the feet, legs and face (cheek) (Chapter 4, Fig. 11). It should be understood that the high rate of sweating from the axilla represents thermal activation of the eccrine and not the apocrine glands of that region. Also, the increase in the rate of water loss noted from the palms and soles does not necessarily indicate that the eccrine glands in these areas were activated entirely by heat since exposure to intense thermal stimulation is quite capable of producing an emotional stimulus strong enough to activate these glands. Nevertheless, it is evident from these experiments that palmar and plantar dermal sweating can be thermal in origin.

Although the rates of sweating were higher in the summer than in the winter, when water loss was measured during the winter or summer months under controlled laboratory conditions no definite differences in sweating rates were found for the same experimental environmental conditions of the climatic room.

PHYSIOLOGIC RESPONSES TO THERMAL STIMULATION

Upon thermal stimulation the physiologic alterations observed included a rise in skin temperature followed by a rise in rectal temperature, tachycardia, tachypnea, hyperventilation, peripheral vasodilatation, increase in pulse pressure, increase in venous pressure, irritability and restlessness, weakness, headaches, visual disturbances, muscular tremor, blanching and wrinkling of the skin of the extremities and syncope (Chapter 11, Fig. 98) (6).

EFFECT OF COOLING LOCALIZED AREAS OF BODY SURFACE ON THE PHYSIOLOGIC RESPONSES TO THERMAL STIMULATION

As discussed above, man should be able theoretically to tolerate exposure to hot and humid environments indefinitely and with no deleterious effects if heat balance is maintained. Since heat balance depends merely upon the physical problem of removing a quantity of heat equal to that produced, measures designed to permit thermal balance should inhibit most if not all of the general physiologic responses to a hot and humid environment. Under conditions of high environmental temperature and humidity, heat accumulated from the environment as well as the heat produced by the body must be removed. In order to test this hypothesis subjects were studied in a hot and humid environment with larger and larger areas of the body surface being cooled until the physiologic responses to thermal stimulation were completely inhibited.

Method of Study. Normal subjects rested for 30 minutes in a comfortable environment, after which the temperature and relative humidity of the cli-

Fig. 122. Photograph of the water-cooled chair.

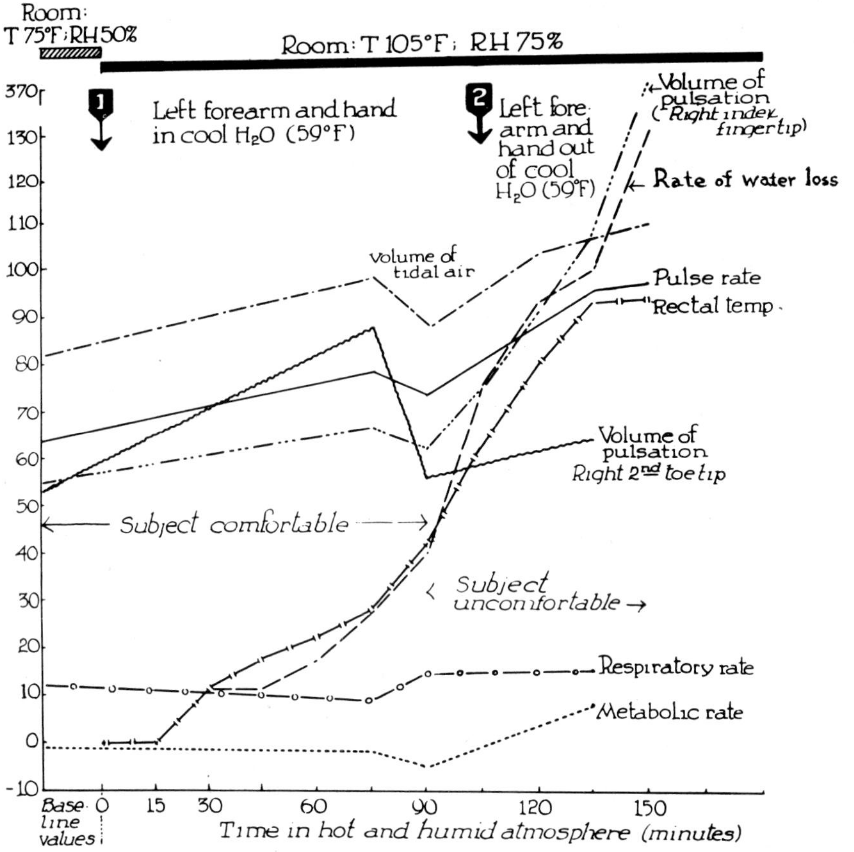

Fig. 123. The influence of cooling the forearm and hand on various physiologic phenomena in 5 young normal adult subjects resting quietly in a hot and humid room. The units of measurement indicated on the ordinate are water loss through sweating, mg./5 cm.² of surface area/ 5 min.; change in rectal temperature, 0.01° C.; volume of pulsations, mm.³/5 cc. part; pulse rate, beats/min.; respiratory rate, number/min.; volume of tidal air, in 100 cc. units; metabolic rate, percent of normal basal metabolic rate. (From *Proc. Soc. Exper. Biol. & Med.*, 55:190, 1944.)

matic room were raised to 105° F. and 75%, respectively (7). The rate of water loss from the right finger tip, right forearm and midepigastrium, the oral and rectal temperatures, pulse volume of the right index finger tip (2RF) and the right second toe tip (2RT), metabolic rate, tidal air, respiration rate and pulse rate were measured prior to and after cooling a localized area of the body surface.

Two groups of studies were performed. In the first group, after obtaining the above measurements for the comfortable and the hot and humid environments, the subject's left forearm and hand were placed in a water bath maintained at 59° F. and the measurements repeated (7). In the second group of studies, a larger area of body surface was cooled by means of a specially constructed water-cooled chair also maintained at 59° F. (Fig. 122) (7).

Effect of Cooling a Small Area of Body Surface. In the first group of experiments when the temperature was

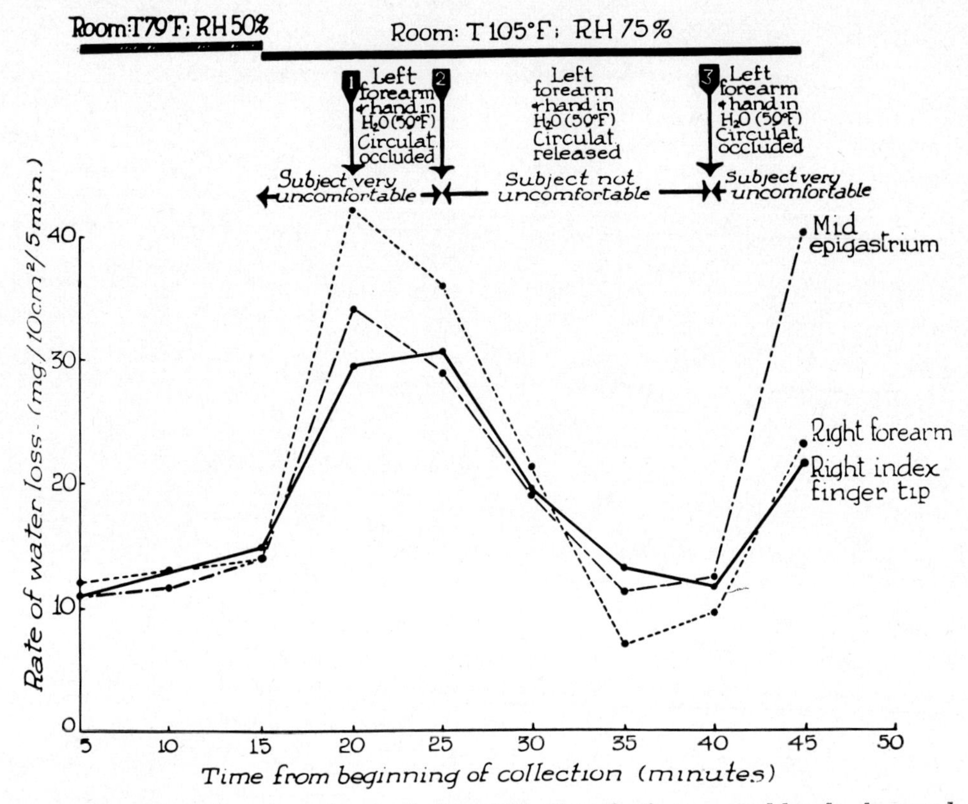

Fig. 124. The influence of the circulation of blood in the forearm and hand submerged in cool water (59° F.) upon the rate of water loss from the skin of 3 areas in a representative normal subject at rest in a hot and humid environment. (From *Proc. Soc. Exper. Biol. & Med.*, 55:190, 1944.)

made hot and humid the subjects complained of discomfort from the heat, the pulse volume and rate increased, the metabolic rate either decreased or did not change, the volume of tidal air increased, sweating became profuse, the rectal temperature rose and digital blood flow increased (Fig. 123). These responses represent normal physiologic reactions to an elevation in environmental temperature, and their sole function is to promote heat loss from the body.

When the subject's left forearm and hand were placed in the water bath maintained at 59° F., the physiologic changes listed above were partially but not completely inhibited (Fig. 123). The subjects were able to remain in the hot and humid environment for long periods of time. The physiologic changes produced by a hot environment recurred whenever the forearm and hand were removed from the water bath. If the circulation to the arm submerged in the cool water bath was arrested by means of a pneumatic cuff, the partial inhibition of the physiologic changes to a hot and humid environment provided for by the localized cooling ceased (Fig. 124). When the circulation was released, the physiologic changes brought about by the hot and humid environment disappeared (Fig. 124). This intermittent re-

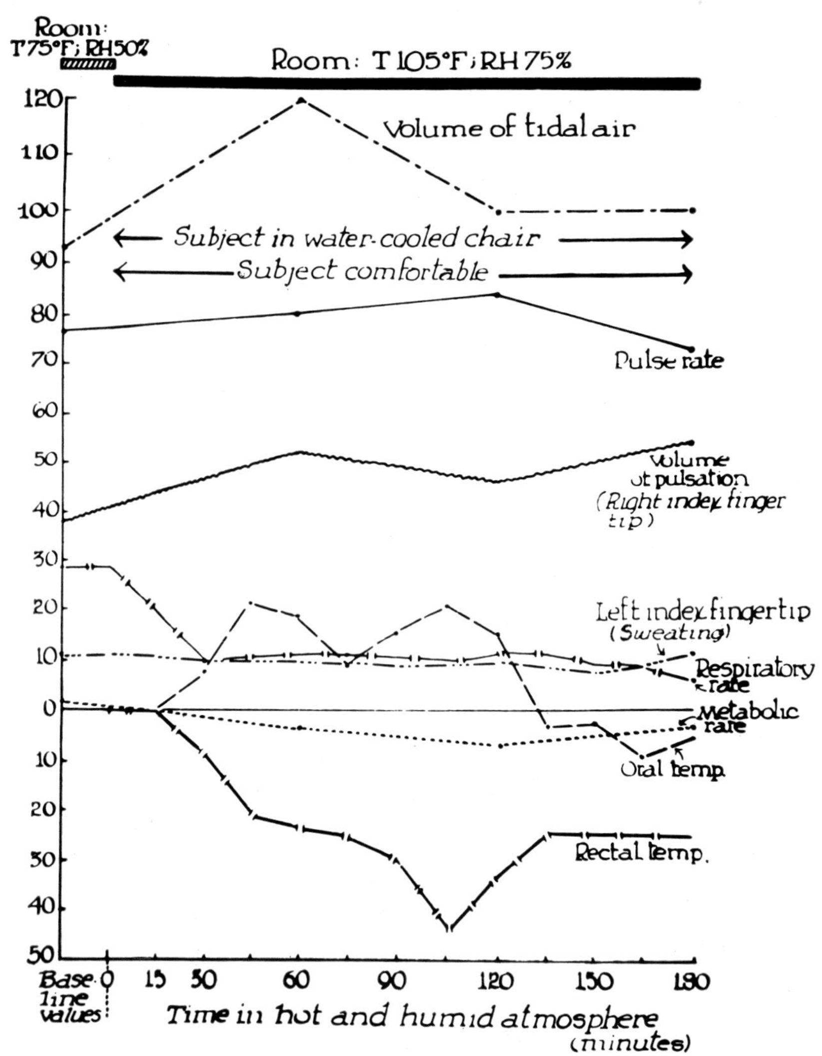

Fig. 125. The influence of cooling a large portion of the body in a water-cooled chair (Fig. 122) on various physiologic phenomena in 5 normal subjects. Consult Figure 123 for explanation of ordinate values. (From *Proc. Soc. Exper. Biol. & Med.*, 55:190, 1944.)

sponse could be produced by arresting and releasing the circulation to the arm and hand submerged in the cool water bath or by removing the arm and hand from the bath and resubmerging them after a period of time.

Effect of Cooling a Large Area of Body Surface. In a second group of subjects an area of body surface extending from the inferior angles of the scapulae to a line between the middle and lower thirds of the thighs was cooled in the water-cooled chair. The chair was cooled by circulating water at 59° F. through the seat, back and two sides of the chair (Fig. 122). When the large area of body surface was cooled, the physiologic changes in response to the hot and humid environment were almost completely inhibited (Fig. 125). The

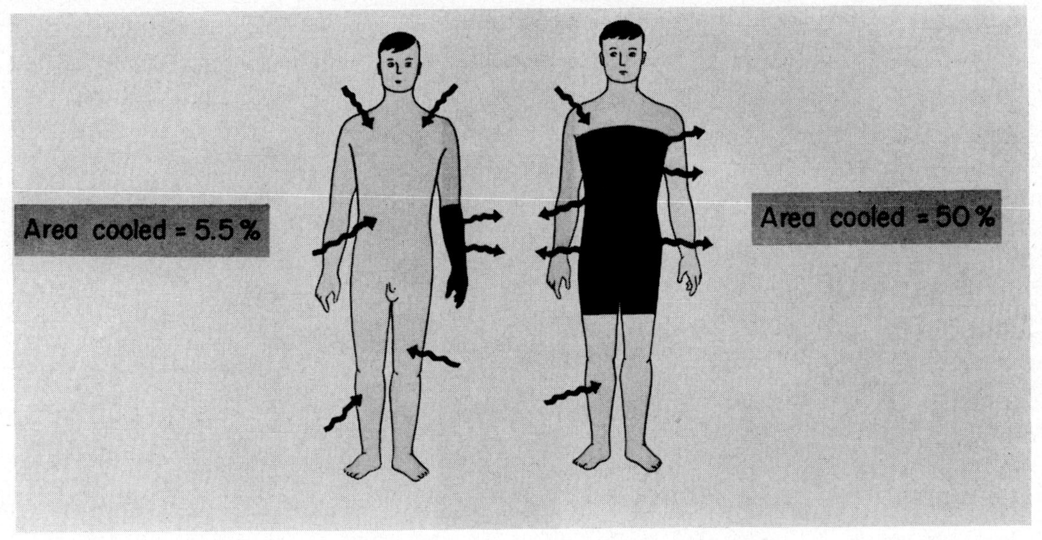

Fig. 126. Schematic representation of the size of the areas of the body cooled.

subjects were able to remain in the extremely hot and humid room without any discomfort for prolonged periods of time. Some of them sat comfortably in the hot and humid environment (105° F., 75% R.H.) and read. The observers experienced such discomfort in the same environment that they had to leave the room periodically. When larger areas of the body were cooled, the temperature in the room could be raised to 116° F. and 75% relative humidity with little discomfort to the subjects.

It is obvious that simply providing an avenue for heat loss commensurate with heat gain is all that is required to maintain thermal balance. If a portion of the body is cooled as a means of providing heat loss, the physiologic changes which are instituted by the organism to maintain thermal balance and which are associated with heat stress are unnecessary and do not occur. Local cooling by water to maintain thermal balance was more effective than the normal physiologic adjustments which only worsened the situation by actually increasing the rate of absorption of heat from the atmosphere. The normal physiologic responses were unable to maintain thermal balance in the two hot environments. Furthermore, the physiologic changes are unhealthful, stressful and hinder man's capacity to perform physical and mental work.

The extent of the area cooled not only determines the amount of heat lost from the body but also limits the area exposed to the hot environment where absorption of heat can occur. Obviously, the larger the area cooled, the hotter the environment that can be tolerated. With only a small portion of the body cooled, man could be exposed to a mild or moderately hot and humid atmosphere without physiologic disturbance. When the environment is extremely hot and humid, the area cooled to maintain a comfortable physiologic state must be proportionately larger. In these experiments the forearm and hand that were cooled represented 5.5% of the total body surface, whereas that part of the trunk and upper two-thirds of the thighs which were cooled represented 50% of the body surface (Fig. 126). The relatively great vascularity of the hand and fingers increases their capacity for heat transfer and thus tends to compensate for the smaller area cooled.

PATHOPHYSIOLOGIC INTERPRETATIONS

The pathophysiologic importance of the changes described in this chapter have, for the most part, already been discussed or are so evident that they need no further discussion.

However, it is important to remember that when the environmental temperature and relative humidity are too high to permit sufficient loss of heat through evaporation, cardiovascular changes develop in an effort to increase the rate of heat loss from the body. However, these changes are associated with an absorption rather than a loss of heat due to an increased peripheral (dermal) circulation. This produces an even more stressful situation and creates a potentially fatal vicious cycle, for, as heat is gained, further increases in cardiac work develop in an attempt to dissipate this additional heat. Providing for heat loss by means of special procedures or devices eliminates the necessity for physiologic alterations in order to maintain thermal equilibrium. Air-conditioning produces an artificial environment in which physiologic alterations are unnecessary to maintain homeostasis and, therefore, no stress is imposed on the cardiovascular system.

CLINICAL APPLICATIONS

The clinical problems related to thermal stress have been discussed in previous sections of this book. However, one aspect of these problems may be mentioned here. It is inevitable that man will some day travel beyond the earth's atmosphere. As a result of his explorations he will undoubtedly encounter a wide range of environmental temperatures. The effectiveness with which cooling isolated areas of skin can eliminate thermal stress may be used to advantage when high temperatures are encountered. The technique of cooling can be adapted to allow freedom of motion so that necessary tasks can be performed. In addition, cooling of local areas of man, himself, may be used in industry, farming, defense and other endeavors where it is physically or economically impossible to air-condition the entire environment.

REFERENCES

1. Amatruda, T. T., Jr. and Welt, L. G.: Secretion of electrolytes in thermal sweat. *J. Appl. Physiol.*, *5*:759, 1953.
2. Kuno, Y.: *Human Perspiration.* Springfield, Thomas, 1956.
3. Conn, J. W.: Electrolyte composition of sweat; clinical implication as an index of adrenal cortical function. *Arch. Int. Med.*, *83*:416, 1949.
4. Burch, G. E.: Environmental conditions which initiate sweating in resting man. *Proc. Soc. Exper. Biol. & Med.*, *67:* 521, 1948.
5. Burch, G. E. and Sodeman, W. A.: Regional relationships of rate of water loss in normal adults in a subtropical climate. *Am. J. Physiol.*, *138*:603, 1943.
6. Berenson, G. S. and Burch, G. E.: The response of patients with congestive heart failure to a rapid elevation in atmospheric temperature and humidity. *Am. J. M. Sc.*, *223*:45, 1952.
7. Burch, G. E. and Sodeman, W. A.: Effect of cooling isolated parts upon the comfort of man resting in hot humid environment. *Proc. Soc. Exper. Biol. & Med.*, *55:* 190, 1944.

XIV

CLINICAL SYNDROMES DUE TO EXCESSIVE EXPOSURE TO A HOT AND HUMID CLIMATE

Exposure to a hot and humid environment may result in four clinical syndromes which are associated with disturbances in the heat-regulating mechanism or in electrolyte balance or in both. These syndromes are:

(1) heat asthenia (calasthenia)
(2) heat cramps
(3) heat exhaustion
(4) heat stroke or heat pyrexia.

Although various aspects of these problems have been considered in previous chapters, these syndromes are considered in greater detail in this chapter. It should be remembered that these syndromes are not encountered exclusively in subtropical and tropical climatic zones but occur during the summer months in the temperate climatic zones as well as under various industrial working conditions. In fact, heat exhaustion and heat stroke tend to be more common in the temperate zones than in the tropical zone. This can be explained in part on the basis of the increased metabolic rate which accompanies acclimatization to cold. During a period of sudden tropical inflow (heat wave) a decrease in the metabolic rate as well as other physiologic adjustments may not occur rapidly enough to maintain thermal balance. The thermal regulating mechanisms may be taxed beyond their capacity so that they fail. In addition, improper housing and clothing habits and lack of adequate facilities for cooling, such as fans, air-conditioning and the like, may contribute to the failure to maintain thermal balance. On the other hand, natives of the tropics are protected in part from heat exhaustion and heat pyrexia because of a low metabolic rate which decreases the requirements for heat dissipation. They also have the proper housing, clothing habits, body build and necessary physiologic functional states to cope satisfactorily with a hot and humid environment even when working hard and long.

HEAT ASTHENIA (CALASTHENIA)

Man may escape the infectious and nutritional diseases of the tropics but he cannot completely escape the climate. Moreover, in almost any region of the world man will at times find himself in a stressful and uncomfortably hot and humid environment.

Heat asthenia refers to a syndrome which has probably been experienced at one time or another by all inhabitants of the temperate and tropical climatic zones. The manifestations of this syndrome are not distinctive and consist primarily of easy fatigue, headache, mental and physical inefficiency, decrease in appetite, dyspepsia, insomnia, restlessness, irritability, general asthenia and a disinterest in work. These symptoms are frequently associated with sweating, tachycardia and tachypnea. The development of this syndrome may not represent disease but the individual is certainly "ill at ease."

Although calasthenia reflects mild physiologic adjustments to a hot and humid environment, the psychic disturbances associated with this syndrome may themselves be incapacitating. Boredom and depression may lead to involutional behavior patterns, alcoholism and a variety of other social problems. In this respect natives of the tropics are less affected than immigrants to these regions. Thus, acclimatization to a hot and humid environment involves not only physiologic adjustments but psychic ones as well.

A special type of calasthenia develops when excessive sweating results in poral closure of the sweat ducts. Because of the functional anhidrosis which accompanies this phenomenon, the dissipation of body heat is inefficient. Serious thermal difficulty may occur if a large number of sweat glands are involved. In milder instances malaise, fatigue, pruritus and mental lassitude are present.

The constitutional symptoms associated with calasthenia are not accompanied by any measurable abnormalities in body chemistry and may themselves represent somatic manifestations of the psychic disturbances. However, in patients who are ill the burden of thermal regulation may overload the cardiovascular system sufficiently to produce mild symptoms of circulatory stress such as irritability, easy fatigue, loss of appetite, cough and paroxysmal nocturnal dyspnea. In this type of patient it is especially important to recognize the early signs of calasthenia because of the increased susceptibility to heat exhaustion and heat stroke.

Because the symptoms of calasthenia are the most common of all the reactions to a hot and humid environment, air-conditioning has become a large and important industry. It is obvious that most of the signs and symptoms of this syndrome can be avoided by providing a comfortably cool air-conditioned environment. However, if the psychic manifestations predominate, a temporary visit to a cooler climate may be necessary. In this respect personnel from temperate climates assigned to jobs in the tropics should obtain long vacations at least every two years. The monotony of tropical weather contributes to the mental lassitude and inefficiency. Vacationing in a region with turbulent weather and wide daily fluctuations in temperature restores physical and mental vitality.

HEAT CRAMPS

Heat cramps are associated with painful muscle spasms following muscular activity in a hot environment (1). Synonyms for this syndrome include stoker's cramps, mill cramps, canecutter's cramps, miner's cramps and fireman's cramps. Heat cramps represents the most common of the three syndromes considered to be true diseased states associated with hot and humid climate.

Incidence. People living in tropical climates have learned to reduce their muscular activity during the hot periods of the day. This results in decreased heat production at the time when heat elimination is most difficult. However, in certain instances such as in mines, in soldiers during forced marches, in particular industries (foundry work) or because of thoughtlessness, heat production may continue at a high rate in an environment in which the dissipation of heat is difficult. The syndrome is more common in the young and vigorous than in the elderly or debilitated because strenuous physical activity is usually necessary to produce heat cramps. This is in contrast to heat exhaustion and heat stroke which are more frequent among elderly or debilitated and ill people.

Organic disease, alcoholism, acute gastrointestinal disturbances, poor hygiene, fatigue and malnutrition increase individual susceptibility to heat cramps. These should be considered when evaluating people for situations which may require exposure to environments that are likely to produce excessive sweating. Repeated and recent attacks of heat cramps as well as lack of acclimatization predispose to other and more severe episodes of heat cramps.

Pathogenesis. When the environmental temperature exceeds body temperature, body heat can no longer be lost by radiation and convection and heat loss must take place through the evaporation of sweat. If the subject is performing heavy physical work, the load placed upon vaporization of sweat to remove body heat is greatly increased. However, if the relative humidity is high, the evaporation of sweat is impaired, thus reducing the efficiency of heat loss by sweating. If physical work is prolonged under such conditions, the rate of sweating increases markedly and the loss of sodium and chloride ions in the sweat can be considerable resulting in a decrease in the concentration of these electrolytes in the blood and tissues. When critically low levels of concentration are reached, heat cramps develop. Since water as well as electrolytes is lost, the concentrations of sodium and chloride in the serum are not usually reduced until large amounts of water are drunk without replacing salt. The reduction in the concentration of sodium and chloride ions precipitates heat cramps.

Clinical Observations. The physical examination is usually not remarkable except for spasm of voluntary muscles. Early in the disease there are gradual involuntary spasmodic contractions of the skeletal muscles with the flexor muscles of the fingers usually being the first to be affected. The cramp occurs every few minutes. In some individuals the larger muscles such as those of the limbs and the abdominal wall are involved instead of the smaller muscle groups. When the abdominal muscles are involved, the condition may resemble that of acute abdominal disease. The muscles remain contracted for a variable length of time but usually not for more than three minutes. The affected muscles exhibit fibrillary twitchings and are stony hard during contraction. The contractions are associated with severe pain which increases as the contractions increase to reach a peak and then gradually subside with relief of pain. The mechanism of the pain is unknown but is probably related to local effects within the muscles secondary to the electrolyte disturbances. The contractions and pain at times may be quite mild so that the individual continues to work without seeking medical attention. Sudden movement, jarring or palpation of the muscles may precipitate an episode of spasm. The Chvostek and Trousseau signs are absent. However, the neurologic examination is normal. With each muscle spasm the pupils dilate. The patient may be sweating profusely and the skin is cold and clammy. The pulse may be rapid but is usually normal as are the other vital signs. The mortality rate is nil if proper therapy is instituted. However, if concomitant disease exists or if the patient is neglected, the illness may be fatal.

Laboratory Data. The hemoglobin and hematocrit are increased due to dehydration. The white blood cell count is increased, probably as a result of the muscular activity and dehydration.

The urine output is reduced slightly in quantity but there usually is no marked oliguria. The pH of the urine is usually about 5.0. Increased quantity of albumin may be present in the urine. An increased urinary excretion of phosphate and creatinine suggests phosphocreatine breakdown. There may also be a negative nitrogen balance. The urinary concentration of chloride is low. During the first few days of therapy with salt and water administration there is relatively little sodium and chloride excreted in the urine.

The serum levels of sodium and chloride are characteristically lowered. The serum chloride is usually below 100 mEq./L and may decline to as low as 54 mEq./L. The serum sodium is usually below 140 mEq./L. Only the inorganic base is lowered in heat cramps. The serum potassium may be increased. These changes result in an alteration of the ratio of sodium to potassium, a possible contributing factor to the muscle spasm. The calcium level of the blood is never decreased but may be increased. The serum magnesium is not changed and blood sugar is normal. Also, the inorganic phosphate may be slightly increased.

The serum proteins are elevated and may reach a value of 12.7 gm. percent due primarily to an increase in the globulin fraction. The albumin fraction may be depressed. Hydration usually restores the albumin-to-globulin ratio to normal. The increased protein concentration of the blood is responsible, at least in part, for the elevated total serum calcium sometimes found in heat cramps.

The acid-base balance may be moderately disturbed. The concentrations of all ions are altered in the same direction except that of the bicarbonate ion which may be increased, decreased or normal. The pH of the blood is usually below 7.40 and may be as low as 7.08. The acidosis is due to a depletion of base rather than an accumulation of organic acids. Lactic acid is usually normal. The non-protein nitrogen content of the serum is usually elevated.

Pathology. Because of the essential benignity of the disease autopsy studies on patients dying from heat cramps are rare. However, vascular congestion of the lungs and gastric mucosa have been described.

Differential Diagnosis. Painful muscular spasms may occur in a number of diseases including hypoparathyroidism, black widow spider bite, acute abdominal disease, nocturnal cramps, gastric crises of tabes dorsalis, epilepsy, trichinosis, hysteria, uremia and malaria. The diagnosis of heat cramps depends upon a history of strenuous muscular exercise in a hot environment associated with profuse sweating. The fact that the spasms are intermittent helps differentiate heat cramps from acute abdominal disease. The absence of Chvostek and Trousseau signs in patients with heat cramps separates this entity from those diseases associated with a low serum calcium and tetany such as hypoparathyroidism and uremia. The postictal stage of grand mal epilepsy easily identifies that disease. In gastric crisis of tabes dorsalis deep, intermittent, intense abdominal pain may be present. The pain is due to gastric spasm. Fluoroscopic examination during periods of pain shows the stomach to be contracted. This disease is not usually associated with skeletal muscle spasms, a useful differentiating point. Muscle spasm and pain in trichinosis is usually associated with larval migration. During this stage of the infection patients are too ill to perform the amount of physical exertion usually required before heat cramps develop. Furthermore, the patients usually have a high body temperature and show signs of periorbital edema as well as edema of the involved muscles. Painful abdominal spasm, when it occurs in malaria, usually is associated with severe infestation. Hepatosplenomegaly, jaundice, debilitation and delirium present a clinical picture quite unlike that of heat cramps. Black widow spider bite (Latrodectus mactans) is often followed by severe, painful spasm of the abdominal muscles. The diagnosis is best made by locating the site of the bite which is usually red and swollen. The onset of the spasm is gradual rather than sudden as in heat cramps.

Treatment. Therapy should be directed primarily toward removing the patient to a cool environment and replacing sodium, chloride and other electrolytes and water. If possible the salt should be given orally. In an adult the oral administration of 15 to 20 gm. of NaCl daily in the form of tablets (not enteric-coated) and sufficient water to maintain a daily urine volume of 1,500 cc. is adequate in most instances. If the patient cannot take oral fluids because of gastrointestinal disturbances or profound weakness, physiologic saline should be administered intravenously.

The pain which is a result of the muscle spasms usually does not respond to sedatives or analgesics including morphine. In most instances the pain subsides rapidly following adequate salt and water replacement. After recovery the patients should rest in a cool environment for several days.

Preventive measures should be instituted before the patient returns to strenuous activity to avoid recurrence of heat cramps. These should include daily supplementation of the salt intake either by salt tablets or by salting the drinking water and instructing the patient of the prodromal signs and symptoms of heat cramps. Since high salt intake is undesirable in patients with cardiovascular-renal disease, such persons should be advised to avoid any activity that may produce this syndrome.

HEAT EXHAUSTION

Heat exhaustion or heat collapse is characterized by profuse sweating, weakness, vertigo, syncope, pallor, low blood pressure, a thready rapid pulse, a subnormal, normal or slightly elevated temperature and the general findings of peripheral circulatory collapse. Heat cramps may be associated with heat exhaustion.

Incidence. Heat exhaustion is associated with prolonged periods of hot weather and is precipitated by excessive exposure to sun and physical exertion or both. Poor health, salt restriction and lack of acclimatization are predisposing factors (2). Recent immigrants to the tropics from cooler climatic areas may develop the syndrome of heat exhaustion if they fail to take the proper precautions of obtaining adequate rest, wearing suitable clothing and avoiding excessive food intake. In military establishments located in subtropical and tropical areas heat exhaustion is one of the most common causes for hospitalization of military personnel.

Pathogenesis. The pathogenesis of heat exhaustion is similar to that of heat cramps in that prolonged physical exertion in a hot and humid environment is responsible for the syndrome. In extremely hot climates, such as in deserts, the syndrome may develop even if physical exertion is only moderate. An inadequate intake of salt and water is an important factor in the development of heat exhaustion. Unlike heat pyrexia or heat stroke (vide infra) and like heat cramps, there is no collapse of the thermal regulating mechanisms. Instead, there appears to be a failure of vasomotor control over the blood vessels. The blood vessels of the skin dilate and blood is shunted from the vital areas of the body to the skin. The loss of vasomotor control appears to be related to failure of the vasomotor center in the medulla oblongata. Whether this is due to failure of the "pressor" center or complete dominance by the "depressor" center is unknown. Pantothenic acid deficiency may also be a factor in heat exhaustion since animals exposed to excessive heat develop adrenal hemorrhages and experimental pantothenic acid deficiency produces adrenal congestion and hemorrhage (3). Although the relationship of these findings to heat exhaustion is unknown, the clinical picture of heat exhaustion resembles that of adrenal insufficiency.

Clinical Observations. Heat exhaustion is not difficult to identify. Prodromal symptoms include weakness, malaise, profuse perspiration, nervousness, lassitude, giddiness, insomnia, vertigo, headache and restlessness. These symptoms precede the development of the syndromes by one or two days. If therapy is not instituted, the symptoms increase in severity and, in addition, syncope, nausea, vomiting, cramps, dyspnea and temporary blindness develop. Finally, there is exhaustion and collapse. The patient appears to be in circulatory shock. The skin is pale, cool and clammy. A rapid, thready pulse is associated with a low arterial blood pressure. The body temperature is usually subnormal but may be normal or elevated. Should the patient fail to stop the physical exertion and enter a cool environment, unconsciousness and death may occur, or he may develop the highly fatal state of heat stroke.

A single attack of heat exhaustion predisposes to subsequent attacks. Furthermore, in subjects who have experienced an attack of heat exhaustion the prodromal symptoms may develop at only moderately elevated temperatures and with little physical exertion.

Laboratory Data. With some exceptions the laboratory findings are essentially similar to those of heat cramps. The dehydration which is usually present results in hemoconcentration and an elevation in the hematocrit and erythrocyte count. The blood urea nitrogen levels may be elevated. The blood chloride level is usually normal. The output of urine is normal but may be reduced in volume and concentrated. A trace of albumin, casts and erythrocytes may be found in the urine of some patients. In severe cases there is a tendency toward acidosis with a definite reduction in the alkaline reserve, evidenced by a reduced carbon dioxide combining power.

Pathology. Since heat exhaustion usually progresses into heat stroke before death, the pathologic changes which occur in heat exhaustion are not adequately known. In patients dying of heat exhaustion the pathologic findings are not specific but resemble those described for circulatory shock, including vascular congestion of the viscera with petechial hemorrhages and signs of early degeneration of the parenchymal cells.

Differential Diagnosis. Heat exhaustion must be differentiated from all states which produce circulatory shock. The history of a prodromal period of weakness, malaise and profuse sweating in a previously healthy person who has been exposed to a hot environment for prolonged periods of time usually establishes the diagnosis. Other possibilities such as insulin shock, myocardial infarction, acute pancreatitis and ruptured viscera can be eliminated by the history and/or the physical examination. The response to therapy is usually fairly rapid and complete. However, if response to therapy is inadequate, underlying diseases such as those mentioned above should be considered.

Treatment. Therapy should be directed toward restoring the body temperature to normal and re-establishing vasomotor tone. It is important to remove the patient to a cool environment. Hypertonic solutions of sodium chloride may be administered and are probably of value even in patients who are not salt depleted. It is usually not necessary to administer the sodium chloride intravenously. In severe cases pressor agents and whole blood administration may be necessary to combat shock. The question of digitalization is controversial. Patients with severe heat exhaustion have small hearts (probably due to hypovolemia) and it is difficult to understand why digitalis should be of any benefit. Hydrocortisone may be of value in severe cases not only because of the possibility of adrenal insufficiency but also because the drug may restore the capacity of the arterioles to constrict or sensitize the arterioles to pressor agents. There is some theoretic evidence to support the therapeutic use of pantothenic acid and thiamin in patients with the heat exhaustion syndrome.

HEAT STROKE

Heat stroke (sunstroke, heat collapse, thermic fever, heat hyperpyrexia) is characterized by extremely high fever and profound coma. It may be preceded by the symptoms of heat exhaustion.

Incidence. Heat stroke occurs primarily in people 60 years of age or older or in people with chronic debilitating illnesses. The disease may actually be more common in the temperate zone than in the tropics. The inhabitants of cities such as Boston and Cincinnati are accustomed to and physiologically adjusted for cool weather. They have relatively high metabolic rates. During severe and prolonged heat waves the difficulty of heat elimination combined with physical exertion and a high metabolic rate creates a situation in which a breakdown in the thermal regulatory mechanisms is likely to occur in susceptible persons. Heat stroke is also seen among persons working in a hot and humid environment in which there is no air movement, such as mines, the boiler rooms of factories and large ships and foundries.

Pathogenesis. As in heat cramps and heat exhaustion, when the environmental temperature exceeds body temperature heat must be lost by the evaporation of sweat. A high relative humidity impedes the vaporization of sweat and the body temperature rises with an increase in the rate of sweating. Somewhere in this vicious cycle the sweat glands cease to function and the body temperature rises to alarming levels due to the absorption of heat from the environment and the patient lapses into coma. The reason for the sudden failure of thermal regulation is unknown. Also unknown is the mechanism whereby some patients die as a result of heat exhaustion while still actively sweating, whereas others cease to sweat and die as a result of heat stroke. However, elderly persons and patients with such diseases as hypertension, arteriosclerosis and diabetes mellitus are predisposed to the development of this syndrome.

Clinical Observations. The prodromal symptoms consist of weakness, vertigo, nausea, syncope, headache, feeling of excessive warmth, abdominal pain typical of heat cramps and the symptoms and signs described previously for mild heat exhaustion. Most patients experience a cessation of sweating shortly before the onset of the heat stroke. Prior to the cessation of sweating the patients sweat profusely.

The acute phase of this disease is characterized by a markedly elevated body temperature and coma. The body temperature is usually above 106° F. and may reach 112°F. There is no evidence of sweating and the skin is hot, dry and flushed. The systolic blood pressure and the pulse pressure are elevated early in the disease, but with prolonged hyperpyrexia the blood pressure falls and circulatory collapse develops. A maculopapular eruption may be evident over the trunk. The tendon reflexes may be diminished and the muscles flaccid. Incontinence of feces usually indicates severe depression of the central nervous system. Cerebellar dysfunction is not uncommon in heat stroke. Evidence of cerebellar damage may persist even after complete recovery from heat stroke. Thus, instances of permanent ataxia, dysarthria and tremor have been recorded (4). The respiration is usually not labored but is rapid and strenuous. Patients who are not in coma show signs of mental confusion.

Congestive heart failure usually is not present except in patients with previous heart disease and myocardial insufficiency. There may be coarse rales and at times fine rales in the lungs. Pulmonary edema may develop. The pulse may be full and bounding but later becomes weak and feeble.

Death is usually due to one of several complications. Acute renal tubular necrosis is not uncommon in patients with severe hyperpyrexia or prolonged shock. Death is usually due to hyperkalemia as a result of widespread breakdown of body tissue. The urine of patients with acute renal failure and heat stroke usually has a specific gravity of less than 1.020. Albuminuria and pyuria are also frequently present. Because of the oliguria, care must be taken not to overhydrate such patients. The great tendency to give saline solutions to patients with heat stroke has resulted in overhydration of many such patients with associated renal failure. Convulsive seizures may develop as a result of the electrolyte disturbances which follow the renal failure.

In a minority of patients with heat stroke there may be damage to the myocardium. Subendocardial hemorrhage is probably the most common cardiac complication (5). There is a peculiar but unexplained predilection for these hemorrhages to involve the left side of the interventricular septum. Acute myocardial infarction has been reported in heat stroke in the absence of coronary artery disease.

The venous pressure is usually not elevated in heat stroke. However, the over-zealous administration of intravenous fluids may precipitate pulmonary edema, especially in elderly patients with poor cardiac reserve.

Some degree of hepatocellular damage is frequent, if not universal, in heat stroke, and patients with this syndrome may die in hepatic coma (5). Jaundice may be present even in mild instances of heat stroke. In some instances the fulminating nature of the hepatic insufficiency has suggested viral hepatitis (6).

A decrease in the red blood cell survival time has been demonstrated in heat stroke. Thrombocytopenia may also be present. Because of the hemolysis, reticulocytosis is usually present. When these hematologic abnormalities exist, anemia and/or various hemorrhagic manifestations such as petechial hemorrhages and gastrointestinal bleeding may be present. Also, capillary damage secondary to anoxia may contribute to the hemorrhagic complications (7).

Laboratory Data. Leukocytosis is usually present in heat stroke. However, the blood count may be normal. Eosinophilia is frequent during the early stages of the disease. Because there is little dehydration there is no evidence of hemoconcentration. The urine is concentrated, yields an acid reaction and contains albumin, casts and erythrocytes. The chloride content of the urine is reduced.

The serum proteins and the albumin-to-globulin ratio are normal. The serum sodium and chloride are also usually normal. The serum potassium is usually lowered in the early stages of the disease.

Hyperbilirubinemia may be present in heat stroke and may be accompanied by bromsulphalein retention, hypoprothrombinemia, and an elevated serum transaminase.

The acid-base balance is altered and a mild acidosis may develop. The carbon dioxide content of the blood is definitely lowered. The high temperature, muscular activity with oxygen debt and the accumulation of lactic acid are probably responsible for the altered acid-base balance. It has been suggested that the low serum potassium and CO_2 may be due to respiratory alkalosis secondary to the hyperventilation of hyperpyrexia. However, the process of acclimatization is associated with a functional hyperadrenalism so that there is a decrease in the loss of sodium and chloride in the sweat and urine, whereas there is an increase in the loss of potassium through these channels. The negative nitrogen balance which is associated with acclimatization also contributes to the potassium depletion. If renal failure develops, hyperkalemia replaces the hypokalemia (5).

Pathology. Necropsy studies on patients with heat stroke have demonstrated generalized vascular congestion particularly in the brain, lungs and abdominal viscera (8). Subendocardial hemorrhage, rupture of myocardial muscle fibers and myocardial infarction have been described for the heart. The kidneys may show acute tubular necrosis. Liver biopsy in heat stroke has shown fatty metamorphoses and focal infiltrates with lymphocytes. In fatal cases centrolobular necrosis of the liver has been found. In the brain cerebral edema, neuronal degeneration and gliosis have been described. Degenerative changes in the caudate nucleus, putamen and corpus striatum may be present. The damage to nervous tissue appears to be most extensive in the cerebellum with edema of the Purkinje layer and an absolute decrease in the number of Purkinje cells (4).

Differential Diagnosis. There are few clinical states which resemble heat stroke. Dry, hot, flushed skin with marked elevation in body temperature is sometimes seen in severe infections such as meningitis, septicemia, pneumonitis and malaria. Care must be taken to exclude the presence of such diseases. However, it should be remembered that because of pulmonary congestion a secondary pneumonitis may develop in heat stroke. Atropine poisoning may produce hot, flushed, dry skin. Because the eccrine sweat glands have cholinergic innervation the sweating is inhibited by atropine. The failure to sweat results in an increase in the body temperature of patients with febrile illnesses or in persons exposed to hot and humid environments. This problem is particularly important in infants. Aplasia of the sweat glands produces heat intolerance. Exposure to a hot and humid environment will cause the body temperature to increase because of absorption of radiant energy from the sun in the absence of an effective means of heat elimination. These conditions are essentially similar to heat stroke. Their differentiation from the latter depends upon history and subsequent clinical observation.

Treatment. Heat stroke is a medical emergency, and once the diagnosis is made treatment must not be delayed even momentarily. Since the syndrome is a result of the breakdown of the thermoregulatory mechanisms, treatment is directed primarily toward reducing the body temperature. This is best accomplished by placing the patient in a tub of iced water (35° F.). Wet sheets and fanning are poor substitutes for immersion in iced water and should be used only if a tub is not available. The rectal temperature should be recorded frequently, and when it falls to 102° F. the patient should be removed from the tub. After removal of the patient from the iced bath the body temperature should be watched carefully, and if a recrudescence of fever develops the patient should again be immersed in iced water. The return of sweating within 24 hours usually indicates that the patient will survive. Massaging the muscles while the patient is in the iced water bath promotes the delivery of cool blood from the periphery to the viscera and brain. If the patient can take fluids orally, salty broth and sweetened tea should be prescribed for the first few days. In those who cannot take fluids orally the intravenous administration of 10% glucose in saline may be recommended. Intravenous fluids should be administered cautiously in elderly or debilitated patients. It should be remembered that many patients with heat stroke are hyperkalemic. After recovery patients should be kept at bed rest for several days to several weeks depending upon the severity of the disease and associated illnesses. In elderly patients the longer period of bed rest is advisable because of the possibility of a diminished cardiac reserve. Furthermore, the possibility of exaggerating subclinical myocardial, hepatic, central nervous system and renal damage by not allowing sufficient time for recuperation warrants the empirical use of prolonged bed rest with good nursing and nutrition in a cool or air-conditioned environment.

The treatment of heat stroke which has become complicated requires a great deal of vigilance and skill. If renal failure and oliguria are present, fluids must be administered according to urinary output and insensible water loss. Since heat stroke is a catabolic disease, daily weights may be misleading in that the patient may be accumulating fluid without a proportionate increase in weight. Hyperkalemia should be treated with glucose and insulin. Daily electrocardiograms and blood chemistries when possible should be utilized to follow the course of the hyperkalemia. If uremia develops or if the hyperkalemia is uncontrolled, extracorporeal dialysis should be considered.

The treatment of circulatory shock in patients with heat stroke presents an extremely difficult problem. The administration of intravenous fluids may precipitate pulmonary edema due to direct myocardial damage or to pre-existing myocardial disease. Furthermore, the pulmonary capillaries are usually already engorged due to heat damage. Whole blood transfusions present similar problems. The use of dextran should probably be avoided since dextran has an inhibitory effect on platelet function. As already discussed, patients with heat stroke may have thrombocytopenia, in which case dextran may precipitate uncontrollable bleeding. Vasopressors such as norepinephrine constrict the dermal blood vessels and interfere with the transfer of heat from the core to the skin. Consideration of these factors should guide the treatment of circulatory shock. The use of norepinephrine combined with vigorous efforts to assist in the removal of body heat is probably the surest means of combating shock. Hydrocortisone has been recommended (9) but should only be administered with the norepinephrine if signs of adrenal insufficiency are present. Hydrocortisone renders the arterioles more susceptible to the action of norepinephrine, a fact which may cause excessive vasoconstriction and ischemia in vital vascular beds. Anuria may occur as a result of such therapy.

Recently, the treatment of heat stroke has been criticized as being unphysiologic (10) since it does nothing to alter heat production. It has been recommended that heat stroke be treated by the intravenous administration of a combination of phenothiazine compounds. The use of these drugs is based on their ability to decrease the metabolic rate, reduce body temperature and prevent hemorrhagic shock. Combination therapy is recommended because these compounds are synergistic. This type of therapy is particularly applicable to military medicine since heat stroke may occur under circumstances in which sufficient quantities of ice for immersion of the patient may not be available.

DIFFERENTIATING CHARACTERISTICS OF HEAT CRAMPS, HEAT EXHAUSTION AND HEAT STROKE (TABLE 17)

Heat cramps is the mildest of the definite syndromes associated with excessive exposure to a hot and humid environment. The cardiovascular and thermoregulatory systems are intact. The patient has an essentially normal blood pressure and sweats profusely, the skin

TABLE 17

Differentiating Characteristics of Heat Cramps, Heat Exhaustion and Heat Stroke

	Heat Cramps	*Heat Exhaustion*	*Heat Stroke*
Cardiovascular System	Intact	Collapse	Intact early, collapse with continued hyperpyrexia
Thermoregulatory System	Intact	Intact	Collapse
Body Temperature	Normal	Subnormal usually, but may be normal or elevated	Marked elevation
Blood Pressure	Normal	Lowered	Elevated
Mechanism	Salt depletion	Loss of vasomotor control of the blood vessels	Cessation of sweating due to failure of the thermoregulatory mechanism
Main Symptom Complex	Severe muscle cramps	Circulatory collapse	High fever, delirium, stupor, coma
Skin	Warm, moist	Pale, cold and clammy	Flushed, hot, dry
Main Therapeutic Measures	Cool environment, rest, NaCl and water bath	Cool environment, NaCl, water and rest, pressor agents if necessary, ? hydrocortisone, thiamin, pantothenic acid	Iced water bath or wet sheets and fanning, prolonged rest, pressor agents and hydrocortisone only if necessary, phenothiazine drugs
Prognosis	Excellent	Good	Very poor, probably greater than 50% mortality rate
Incidence	Fairly common	Common	Relatively uncommon
Age	Any age, usually younger age groups	Any age, more common in elderly subjects	Usually in elderly or debilitated individuals

being warm and moist. The body temperature is only slightly elevated or is normal. In *heat exhaustion* there is a loss of vasomotor control of the blood vessels and circulatory shock. The skin is pale and cold. Since the patient sweats, the skin is moist (cold and clammy). The pulse is thready and the blood pressure is low. The body temperature is subnormal or normal. In *heat stroke* there is a loss of thermoregulatory control and sweating ceases. The skin is flushed, hot and dry, the pulse is bounding and full, and the blood pressure is elevated. The body temperature is markedly elevated. Delirium or coma is present.

REFERENCES

1. Burch, G. E.: The normal and abnormal physiologic effects of tropical climate. *New Orleans M. & S. J., 98*:14, 1945.
2. Ferris, E. B., Jr., Blankenhorn, M. A., Robinson, H. W. and Cullen, G. E.: Heat stroke: clinical and chemical observations on 44 cases. *J. Clin. Invest., 17*:249, 1938.
3. Mills, C. A.: Climatic Factors in Health and Disease. In *Medical Physics,* O. Glasser ed. Chicago, Ill., The Yearbook Publishers, 1943.
4. Stewart, R. M.: On the occurrence of cerebellar syndrome following heat stroke. *Rev. Neurol. Psychiat., 16*:78, 1918.
5. Knochel, J. P., Beisel, W. R., Herndon, E. G., Jr., Gerard, E. S. and Barry, K. G.: The renal, cardiovascular, hematologic and serum electrolyte abnormalities of heat stroke. *Am. J. Med., 30*:299, 1961.
6. Herman, R. H. and Sullivan, B. H., Jr.; Heatstroke and jaundice. *Am. J. Med., 27*:154, 1959.
7. Halden, E. R.: Hematological studies in heat stroke: anemia of heat stroke with emphasis on hemolytic component. *Am. J. Med., 19*:141, 1955.
8. Malamund, N., Haymaker, W. and Custer, P. R.: Heatstroke: a clinicopathologic study of 125 fatal cases. *Mil. Surgeon, 99*:397, 1946.
9. Waugh, W. H.: Cortisone and the treatment of heat stroke. *Ann. Int. Med., 41*:841, 1954.
10. Hoagland, R. J. and Bishop, R. H.: A physiologic treatment of heat stroke. *Am. J. M. Sc., 241*:415, 1961.

INDEX

A

Acclimatization, 71, 72, 130, 167
  adrenal gland in, 73
  cardiovascular system in, 130
  definition of, 71
  renal function in, 167
  sweat and rate of, 72
    composition of, 72, 73, 167
  to heat, 72, 73
Adolph, E. F., 167
Air-conditioning, 147, 152, 155, 156, 178
  effect on allergy, 127
  effect on cardiovascular system,
    normal, 133, 147, 152
    diseased, 134-136
  effect on renal function, 158-168
  effect on sweating, 73
  effect on water loss, 37, 38
  in dermatophytosis, 74
  in heat asthenia, 180
  in hospital wards, 133-136
  in oxygen tents, 128, 156
Allen's rule, 6
Allergy, cold, 99
  effect of air-conditioning on, 127
  meteorotropism of, 126
Alpha deflection, description of, 85
  in cold environment, 91
  in hot environment, 88
  in vasoconstriction, 85
Apocrine sweat glands, distribution of, 58
  function of, 58
Arteriovenous anastomoses, digital blood flow and, 91
  hypothalamus and, 9
  thermal regulation and, 9, 91, 92
Atrophic sweat glands, 27

B

Basal pulsatile flow, definition of, 83
Benedict, C. G., 23
Benedict, F. G., 23
Bergmenn's rule, 6
Beta deflection, description of, 85
  in cold environment, 91
  in hot environment, 88
  in vasoconstriction, 85
Bioclimatology, definition of, 3
Blister, cantharides, 41. *See also* Cantharides blister
Blood pressure, arterial, effect of hot and humid environment on, 136
Burns, electrolyte transfer in, 56
Burton, A. C., 7

C

Cadavers, water loss in, 24
Cantharides blister, electrolyte transfer through base of, 49-56
  formation of, 41
  water loss through base of, 41
  water loss through top of, 42
Cardiac output, effect of air-conditioning on, 147, 152
  effect of intense thermal stimulation on, 142
  relation to climate, 147, 152
Cardiac work, determination of, 130, 132
  effect of air-conditioning on, 152
  effect of intense thermal stimulation on, 140, 145
  relation to climate, 147, 152
Cardiovascular system, acclimatization of, 130
  cardiac output, 142, 147, 152
  cardiac work, 130, 132, 140, 145, 147, 152
  diseases of, 36, 99, 100, 114-116, 119, 121, 122, 124, 135, 136, 155, 158-168
  effect of air-conditioning on, 133-136, 147, 152
  in congestive heart failure, digital blood flow in, 98
    effect of air-conditioning on, 134
      clinical observations, 134
    effect of hot and humid environment on, 140, 153
      cardiac output, 140, 142
      cardiac work, 145
      clinical observations, 134, 138
      myocardial tension, 146
      stroke volume, 142, 145, 153
      ventricular pressure, 142, 145
      ventricular volume, 142, 145
  in heat exhaustion, 183
  in heat stroke, 185
  in myocardial infarction, 155
  in thermal regulation, 178
  normal, digital blood flow in, 85
    effect of air-conditioning on, 133
      cardiac output, 147, 152
      cardiac work, 152
      clinical observations, 133
      power output of heart, 152
      ventricular pressure, 152
      ventricular volume, 152
    effect of hot and humid environment on, 140, 147, 152
      cardiac output, 142, 152
      cardiac work, 145, 152
      clinical observations, 133, 136
      myocardial tension, 146
      power output of heart, 152
      stroke volume, 142, 153
      ventricular pressure, 142, 145, 152
      ventricular volume, 142, 145, 152
Climate, acclimatization, 71, 72, 130, 167
  adaptation to, 4
  Allen's rule, relation to, 6
  Bergmenn's rule, relation to, 6
  clothing and, 7
    clo unit, 7
  definition of, 4
  effect on composition of sweat, 65

effect on heart, volume output of, 147, 152
power output of, 147, 152
work of, 147, 152
Gloger's rule, relation to, 6
heat waves and, 7
ideal, 7
microclimate and, 5, 156
pulsations of, 5
relation to accidents, 4
Climatic rooms, 60, 61, 87, 91, 112-124, 136, 138, 140
Clo unit, 7
Cold injury, 98
Congestive heart failure, digital blood flow in, 98
effect of air-conditioning on, 134
effect of thermal stress on, 99, 134, 138, 140, 142, 145, 146, 158-168
electrolyte transfer in, 50, 55
heat intolerance in, 125
heat loss in, from lungs, 119, 121, 122
from skin, 36
heat production in, 124
renal function in, 158-168
water loss from lungs in, 114, 115
Countercurrent blood flow, 9, 96
Cyclic sweating, 31, 171

D

Dermal blood flow. *See* Digital blood flow
Diet, effect on composition of sweat, 64
Digital blood flow, 76
alpha deflections, description of, 85
effect of environment on, 87, 91, 92
arteriovenous anastomoses and, 9, 91, 92
basal pulsatile flow, 83
beta deflections, description of, 85
effect of environment on, 88, 91
complemental pulsatile flow, 83
determination of, rheoplethysmography, 77
effect of environment on, cold, 91, 92, 96, 99
hot and humid, 87, 91, 98, 99, 100
gamma deflections, description of, 85
hunting phenomenon and, 96
in diseased states, 98-100
congestive heart failure, 98
Raynaud's disease, 99, 100
pulse waves, 85
regional variations in, 98
respiratory waves, 85
skin temperature and, 92
venous, in cold environment 92
in hot and humid environment, 91
di Sant'Agnese, P. A., 71

E

Eccrine sweat glands, distribution of, 58
function of, 58
Ectodermal dysplasia, 69
Electrolyte, balance, 37
concentration, in sweat, 60, 61, 63, 67, 69, 70, 71
effect of acclimatization on, 72, 167
effect of climate on, 65
effect of diet on, 64
effect of ischemia on, 65
in urine, 61, 158, 159, 162, 165, 168
transfer through denuded living skin, 50-56
determination of, 49
effect of histamine on, 53
effect of norepinephrine on, 55
in congestive heart failure, 51, 55
in exfoliative dermatitis, 56
Environment, cold, allergy to, 99
effect on digital blood flow, 91, 92, 96, 99
effect on heat loss from lungs, 121, 122, 124
effect on water loss from lungs, 112-115
injury due to, 98
hot and humid, effect on blood pressure, arterial, 136
venous, 138
effect on digital blood flow, 87, 91, 98-100
effect on heat loss, from lungs, 102 121, 122, 124
from skin, 10, 31, 36, 76
effect on heat production, 124
effect on renal function, 158-168
effect on sweating, 172
effect on water loss, from lungs, 112-115
from skin, 10, 25, 33-36, 170, 172
Exfoliative dermatitis, 56

F

Fibrocystic disease, 70, 73

G

Galeotti, G., 23
Gloger's rule, 6
Glomus bodies, 9

H

Heart, diseases of, 99, 134, 138, 155
effect of air-conditioning on, 100, 133-136, 147-152
effect of thermal stress on, 136, 138, 140, 142, 145, 146, 153
power output of, 132, 147
volume output of, 140, 142, 147, 152
work of, 130, 132, 140, 145, 147
Heat asthenia, 179
Heat cramps, 72, 179, 180
clinical observations in, 181
differential diagnosis of, 182, 189
incidence of, 180
laboratory data in, 182
pathogenesis of, 181
pathology of, 182
preventive measures for, 183
treatment of, 183
Heat exhaustion, 72, 179, 183
clinical observations in, 184
differential diagnosis of, 185
incidence of, 183
laboratory data in, 184
pathogenesis of, 184
pathology of, 185
treatment of, 185
Heat intolerance, atropine, cause of, 74
effect on water loss, 34
in congestive heart failure, 125
Heat loss, in congestive heart failure, from lungs, 121, 122
from skin, 36
from lungs, 102, 120
by convection, 109, 110, 120, 122
by decomposition of H_2CO_3, 109, 110, 120, 122

by evaporation, 109, 110, 120
calculation of, 110, 111
determination of, 108
relation to total body heat production, 124
total, 102, 110, 120, 124
from skin, 102
by conduction, 76
by convection, 76
by evaporation, 10, 33, 76
by radiation, 76
effect of local cooling on, 172, 174, 176
regional variations in, 77
thermal balance and, 177, 178
Heat stroke, 72, 179, 185
clinical observations in, 186
differential diagnosis of, 188
incidence of, 185
laboratory data in, 187
pathogenesis of, 185
pathology of, 187
treatment of, 188
Heat wave, 7
Hippocrates, 3
Human balance, 12-15
calibration of, 15
mechanism of, 12
photographic recorder of, 12
use of, 14
Hunting phenomenon, 96
Hyperhidrosis, 69
Hypohidrosis, 69
Hypothalamus, 9, 96
Hypothyroidism, 34

I

Insensible perspiration, 5, 10, 24, 27, 42, 44, 46
definition of, 10, 30
equation for, 31
Ischemia, effect on sweating, 65, 71

K

Kidney, blood flow to, 168
function of, 158-168
effect of acclimatization on, 167
effect of thermal stress on urine formation, 61
electrolyte excretion, 61, 158-165, 168
urine osmolarity, 165

L

Lewis, T., 96
Lungs, heat loss from, 102, 120
by convection, 109, 110, 120, 122
by decomposition of H_2CO_3, 109, 110, 120, 122
by evaporation, 109, 110, 120
calculation of, 110, 111
determination of, 108
relation to total body heat production, 124
total, 102, 110, 120, 124
relative humidity of expired air from, 119
surface area of, 102, 124
temperature of expired air from, 116
water loss from, 10, 22, 102, 112-116
as percent of total body water loss, 22, 23, 24, 102
determination of, 15, 103
effect of exercise on, 112, 115
in congestive heart failure, 114
relation to irrigation, 115, 116
relation to respiration, 112, 115, 116
seasonal variations in, 112

M

Meteorotropism, 4, 126
of crime rates, 4
of myocardial infarction, 155
of suicide, 4
Microclimate, 5, 156
Miliaria, 70
Mills, C. A., 6
Myocardial infarction, 155

O

Occult sweating, 10, 30
Oxygen tent, 128, 156

P

Peripheral blood flow. *See* Digital blood flow
Perspiration, insensible, 10, 22-38, 46, 47
occult, 10, 30
sensible, 5, 10, 25, 30, 34, 35, 36, 62, 65, 72, 167, 170, 171

R

Raab, W., 156
Raynaud's disease, 99, 100
Rheoplethysmography, concept of, 80-85
digital blood flow, measurement of, 77
method of, 77

S

Scleroderma, 35
Shapley, H., 5
Skin, as thermal barrier, 9
as water barrier, 10, 39, 44, 45
electrolyte transfer through, 50-56
determination of, 49
heat loss from, 102
by conduction, 76
by convection, 10, 76
by evaporation, 10, 33, 76
by radiation, 76
effect of local cooling on, 172, 174, 176
regional variations in, 77
surface area of, 102
temperature, reflexes, 95, 100
regional variations in, 95
relation to digital blood flow, 92
water loss from, 39
determination of, 12-21, 39-41, 49
effect of infrared radiation on, 47
effect of ischemia on, 35, 65, 71
effect of temperature on, 46
effect of ultraviolet radiation on, 47
effect of vapor pressure on, 47
insensible, through dead skin, 18, 24, 27, 41-48
through living skin, 16, 17, 22, 23, 25, 28, 34, 35, 36, 44
regional variations in, 25, 34, 35, 36, 171, 172
seasonal variations in, 22, 25
sensible 5, 17, 25, 28, 34, 35, 36, 62, 65, 72, 167, 170, 171
Sulzberger, M. B., 74
Sweat, collection of, 59
electrolyte concentration of, effect of acclimatization on, 72, 73, 167
effect of climate on, 65
effect of diet on, 64
effect of ischemia on, 65
normal, 63, 70
time course of, 60-64, 67-69
retention syndrome, 74

Sweat glands, apocrine, 58
  atrophic, 27
  distribution of, 58
  eccrine, 58
Sweat retention syndrome, 74
Sweating, and acclimatization, 72, 73, 167
  cyclic, 31, 171
  definition of, 10, 30
  effect of local cooling on, 172, 174, 176
  electrolyte excretion, 60, 61, 63-73, 167
    kinetics of, 67-69
  in dermatophytosis, 74
  in ectodermal dysplasia, 69
  in fibrocystic disease, 70
  in heat stroke, 186
  in hyperhidrosis, 69
  in hypohidrosis, 69
  in ischemia, 65, 71
  in miliaria, 70
  initiation of, 170, 171
  occult, definition of, 10, 30
  rate of, 60, 67, 69
    determination of, 17
    effect of air-conditioning on, 73
    effect of ischemia on, 71
    effect of sex on, 61, 64
    regional variations in, 25, 34, 35, 36, 62, 171, 172
      in comfortable environment, 171
      in hot and humid environment, 172
  threshold, 171

T

Thermal barrier, 9
Thermal countercurrent flow, 96
Thermal regulation, 76
  a-v anastomoses, role in, 9, 91
  countercurrent flow in, 9, 96
  effect of local cooling on, 172, 174, 176
  heat loss in, 177
  hypothalamus, role in, 9, 91, 96
  peripheral circulation, role in, 76
  venae comites, role in, 97, 98

U

Urey, H., 5

W

Water barrier, 10, 39, 44, 45
Water-cooled chair, 176
Water loss, and electrolyte balance, 37, 72, 73
  effect of acclimatization on, 72
  effect of air-conditioning on, 37, 38
  methods of measuring, 12-21
    from lungs, gravimetric with aluminum coils, 103-108
      human balance, 12-17
      tank, 16
    from skin, brass chamber, 17, 19
      brass cylinder, 19
      human balance, 12-16
  through feces, 10
  through lactation, 10
  through lungs, 10, 22, 102, 112-116
    as percent of total body water loss, 22, 23, 102
    determination of, 15, 103
    effect of environment on, 112-115
    effect of exercise on, 112, 115
    effect of metabolic rate on, 119
    effect of race on, 112
    effect of rate of irrigation on, 115
    effect of sex on, 112
    effect of type of breathing on, 112, 115, 116
    in congestive heart failure, 114
  through saliva, 10
  through skin, 10
    atrophic sweat glands and, 27
    in acromegaly, 35
    in congestive heart failure, 36
    in heat intolerance, 34
    in hypothyroidism, 34
    in nervous sweating, 34
    in occlusive vascular disease, 35
    in scleroderma, 35
  insensible, 16, 17, 22-31, 34, 35, 36, 39, 41-48
    as percent of total body water loss, 22 23
    calculation of, 31
    definition of, 10, 30
    determination of, 12-21, 42
    effect of abrasion on, 44
    effect of infrared radiation on, 47
    effect of keratin on, 45
    effect of lipids on, 44
    effect of protein on, 31
    effect of race on, 23, 27, 46
    effect of temperature on, 46
    effect of ultraviolet radiation on, 47
    effect of vapor pressure on, 47
    inhibiting layer to, 9, 39-44
    regional variations in, 25, 34, 35, 36
    seasonal variations in, 22, 25
    through cantharides blister, 42
    through dead skin, 24, 27, 41-48
    through denuded skin, 41, 44
    through living skin, 22, 23, 25, 28, 34, 35, 36
  occult, 10, 30
  sensible, 5, 18, 25, 34, 35, 36, 60-67, 170-178
    definition of, 10, 30
    determination of, 17
    effect of local cooling on, 172, 174, 176
    regional variations in, 25, 34, 35, 36, 62, 171-178
  through urine, 10
  total body, 22
    determination of, 12

Weather, definition of, 4

Wiggers, C. 130